D0938545

THE SUNNY SOUTH;

OR,

THE SOUTHERNER AT HOME,

EMBRACING

FIVE YEARS' EXPERIENCE OF A NORTHERN GOVERNESS

IN THE

LAND OF THE SUGAR AND THE COTTON.

EDITED BY

PROFESSOR J. H. INGRAHAM,

OF MISSISSIPPI.

"Stern winter smiles on that auspicious clime,
The fields are florid with unfading prime;
From the bleak pole no winds inclement blow,
Mold the round hail, or flake the fleecy snow;
But from the breezy deep the land inhales
The fragrant murmurs of the western gales."

NEGRO UNIVERSITIES PRESS
NEW YORK

Originally published in 1860 by G. G. Evans

Reprinted in 1968
by Negro Universities Press
A DIVISION OF GREENWOOD PUBLISHING CORP.
New York

Library of Congress Catalogue Card Number: 68-58061

Printed in the United States of America

EDITORIAL LETTER TO THIS VOLUME.

To GEORGE G. EVANS, ESQ.

SIR:—This manuscript of "Letters from the South," which I send you for your perusal, has been, as you will see, very carefully and plainly written out for the press, by a young Governess of this State, who diffidently declines to give her name in connection with the work.

It is true that the authorship of what has been composed from materials mainly by another hand, cannot be wholly claimed by either party: the work, therefore, if published by you, must go unaccredited and upon its own intrinsic merits.

Thirty years' residence at the South, chiefly at Natchez, Nashville, and Mobile, enables me to form, perhaps, a correct estimate of the accuracy of a work professing to relate the experiences of a stranger from the North, sojourning in the land of " tobacco, cotton, and sugar."

The writer has chosen to give the materials collected from experience and observation in the attractive form of familiar letters, addressed, by request, to an intelligent literary gentleman and editor in the North.

While presenting accurate pictures of " homes in the Sunny South," there is skillfully interwoven, an interesting narrative embodying the most romantic features of Southern rural life

(3)

on the tobacco, cotton, and sugar estates: the three forms under which true Southern Life presents itself.

The tone of the Book is strictly conservative and national; presenting the impartial view which an intelligent, unprejudiced, and highly cultivated Northern lady would take of the South, her temporary and agreeable home; and the presentation of such a work, though neither profound nor political, (but adapted for light, summer-perusal, when one covets pacific and pleasant reading,) at the present time, will, without doubt, be an acceptable gift to the reading public; especially, when hitherto so much in relation to our people and institutions is misunderstood and misinterpreted by those who have no personal knowledge either of Southerners or of Southern life.

This work has not been penned merely to meet any recent events. The letters composing it were commenced seven years ago, and leisurely produced in a period of three years, the last one having been completed in 1856; and were not written with any intention of ever taking a book form. Some of them appeared in 1853-4, in the Saturday Courier, a popular paper once published in your city, bearing the nom de plume of "Miss Kate Conyngham."

In consenting to commend them to your attention, I feel that I am contributing towards the publication of a work which will render more familiar "Southern Life at Home" to Northern minds, while its scenes, incidents, and characters will agreeably interest the reader.

If the publication of this letter will be of any service to the work, and contribute towards your favorable decision, I cheerfully give you permission to append it to the volume.

Very truly yours,
J. H. INGRAHAM.

Rose Cottage, near Natchez, Mississippi

PREFACE.

As most of the Letters embraced in this volume were written for the Editor of the late American Courier, and appeared therein, from time to time, the writer thereof has not seen fit to alter the local allusions, the style of address in the Letters, or the appellation of "Needles," by which they were originally designated. As these Letters were commenced, and many of them published before Mrs. Stowe's Uncle Tom was written, its pictures of South-western life have no reference to that work nor were influenced by it. These epistles are not replies to any attacks on the South, but a simple representation of Southern life, as viewed by an intelligent Northerner, whose opinions are frankly and fearlessly given.

The object of this work is to do justice to the Southern planter, and, at the same time, afford information in an agreeable form to the Northerner; and if these objects are obtained in any degree, the writer, in consenting to its publication as a volume, will be fully rewarded. One important fact ought not to be overlooked, which is, that ninety-nine out of every hundred of the governesses, tutors, professional men, and others, who flock to the South, "ten thousand a year," for the improvement of their fortunes, remain, (the young ladies, if they can obtain "Southern husbands,") and identify themselves fully with the Southern Institutions.

CONTENTS.

LETTER VI.

LETTER VII.

LETTER VIII.

LETTER IX.

LETTER X.

LETTER XI.

LETTER XII.

LETTER XIII.

LETTER XXV.

LETTER XXVI.

LETTER XXVII.

LETTER XXVIII.

LETTER XXIX.

LETTER XXX.

LETTER XLIII.

LETTER XLIV.

LETTER XLV.

LETTER XLVI.

LETTER XLVII.

LETTER XLVIII.

16 CONTENTS.

18   CONTENTS.

LETTER LXIX.

THE SUNNY SOUTH;

OR,

THE SOUTHERNER AT HOME.

LETTER I.

DEAR MR. ———:

NOT that you are very "dear" to me, for I never saw you in all my life, but then one must begin their epistles, and as everybody says *dear*, and don't mean any thing by it, I say dear too, and don't mean any thing by it, so don't flatter yourself in the least; for, if it were the fashion, and the whim hit my fancy, I should just as likely have written "Bear." You editors *presume* so much, you need to be put down.

I was going to begin my letter by saying why I call my letters "needles." Not, you may rest assured, because they are likely to be sharp and keen, for I have no doubt that they will be vastly *dull*, but one must have a *title*, and what must one do for one? Simple *"Letters"* would never tempt the eye. The pill must be gilt. You would, no doubt, laugh very good-humoredly if I should confess to you that I have been

(19)

bothering my poor little head for three hours to-day
for a title. A celebrated author once told me,—for I
have seen such lions in my day, and talked and flirted
with these lords of the quill, too,—that he thought more
of his "titles" than of the matter of his books, and
that was no slight matter either! He said he had
sometimes written out on a long paper, (like a subscrip-
tion list, I suppose,) a score of names, and then carefully
studied them, fancied how they would take the eye of
the lounger in the book-stores, or the passer-by, who
should glance at the big poster: he even used to go so
far as to set the title up in type, an amateur fount of
which he kept by him for this purpose, before he fully
fixed upon his "*clap-trap.*"

Now, I can imagine all this to be very necessary, and
I give this author credit for no inconsiderable knowledge
of human nature. Half the novels are bought by their
titles by half the world. I used to buy them so.
When I took this weighty fact into consideration, I was
sore perplexed. "Letters" I was resolved *not* to have.
"Epistles" looked like the New Testament, and I felt it
too sacred a word for me to make light use of; for I was
very properly brought up to reverence any thing about
the Scriptures. I thought of "Pen and Ink" sketches—
a nice title, but Mr. Willis had invented and used it:
happy gentleman with a gift for happy titles! for his
"Pencillings by the Way" is another that came into my
head, and I tried every way to parody it, but I couldn't
manage it at all, and gave it up. I thought of "Dots
and Lines," but somebody had got it before me, and nothing seemed left but *Dot* and go One; when, in my
troubles I pricked my finger with a needle that was

in my needle-book, which I was turning and turning
in my fingers while I was cogitating about my title. Instantly the idea flashed upon me, and the words, "Needles from my Needle-Book!" I seemed to read in the air
before my eyes. For fear I should forget the happy
combination, I scribbled it down on the spot, and determined to adopt it.

No doubt you will expect to find something short
and shrewd, ascetic and attic in my articles, but I promise you that you must look for nothing of the kind;
for it only takes *great* authors to write books that have
nothing to do with their titles, nor their titles with them.
The only defence I can make of my caption is that it is
very appropriate to my sex, being a fair weapon either
of offence or defence, as well as the glittering shuttle
of female industry. Would you believe it, sir, my pupil,
a wicked rogue of a beauty of sixteen, (for you must
know I am a governess, and but nineteen and a little
over, myself,) she has seen my title, and says I had better put, "Scissors" to it? Scissors and Needles! *Dear*
us, Mr. ——! what *would* you have thought to have
opened my package, and had *this* title met your asto-
nished editorial eyes?

"SCISSORS AND NEEDLES:"

"BY A YANKEE GIRL."

You have had in this specimen a touch of my South-
western pupil's mischief, and you shall know more of
her by-and-by, perhaps, if you print this letter and don't
say any thing saucy about it; for editors, who have lady
correspondents, ought to be exceedingly well-behaved and
mannerly, and appreciate the honor done them. Now.

having introduced my title to you, how shall I introduce myself and all the subjects I intend to let my pen run on about? I shall not give you my name, nor give you any clue to it, if you should be never so curious to find it out; for *men* have *so* much curiosity! even where there will be, as in my case, nothing worth the trouble of finding out, for I am not so vain as to fancy I shall ever be worth asking after. It will take more ink and paper than I shall ever destroy, to make a lady who would be "literary" singled out of the *troupes* of *bas bleu* that fill the land like the golden-winged butterflies in May. But I will do what I can to please, for my poor, innocent pen has got to travel a weary length, and I long to make happy more than one dear heart in this world. Authorship is not woman's sphere by nature, but by circumstances only. Oh, how many a gentle lady has the needle of poverty pricked on to seize, with trembling fingers, the awe-inspiring pen! and dip it into her heart, to write out its life for bread! Weary, oh! weary is the path to woman's little feet—the path furrowed deep by the ploughshare of penury. In the furrows she drops the seeds of hope, and waters them with tears. It is a rough way this path amid types, and in the hustle for popularity and pennies, the sex is not spared by the ruder ones, and the critic's iron point, that maddens the strong man, pierces to the heart the timid woman! Yet, once started, she must write or die; or, worse still, be dependent; and *this*, to a proud woman, is the *first* death of this world's deaths.

Do not think I am going to charge my palette with sombre tints, from these few sentences foregoing, or that I am in tears because I am for the first time taking up the fearful pen to write for coins of silver. I am young and full of hope, and my heart bounds with cheerful thoughts. I do not speak in allusion to myself, therefore, when I say that it is a sad lot for a woman to be *compelled* to toil with pen and ink for her bread; for the prospect before me is a pleasing one. The very idea that probably I shall see in *print* what I am writing, (if it please your pleasure, sir, to print it, though little worth it, I fear,) fills my bosom with an indefinable sensation of joy, slightly mingled with a timid apprehension. I am dying to see myself in type; not in the place where marriages are noticed; don't naughtily misconceive my meaning, sir; for I am not going to be married till I enjoy myself sensibly as a "young woman," a little longer yet. My situation here is a happy one, and if I only lived for myself I should not put pen to paper; for I am blessed with all I require to make me contented and grateful. The timid apprehension, I feel when I look forward, arises from a creeping doubt which once in a while coils itself around the tree of hope in my heart, touching the acceptance of my communications; for this doubt insinuates, with very serpent-like wickedness, that I shall not be proved to be clever enough to write any thing worth the printing. But "hope, and hope on," is the motto of my adoption, and I shall not despair: I never *could* despair. It seems to me that if I stood alone, the last one alive, upon a burning wreck in the mid Mediterranean, I should not despair, but believe that rescue would come.

This letter is only an introductory needle, a sort of autorial probe, to feel the way; or rather like the first needle placed in an electrical battery, to be increased afterwards in number, as the patient will bear.

Your correspondent,

KATE.

DATED FROM OVERTON PARK, BEYOND THE ALLEGHANIES.

P. S. In my next, I will tell you something about our Manor-house, and how this West-south land strikes the eye of one, cradled as I have been, among the Granite Mountains of the Pilgrim Land.

LETTER II.

It would no doubt please you, Mr. ——, to learn
something about us here at Overton Lodge—for this is
the name of the fine old Western Homestead for which
I have exchanged my cold, yet warm-hearted northern
clime. Overton Lodge, then, please to know, is a large,
commodious mansion of brick, square and stately, with a
double storied portico in front, from the upper gallery
of which is one of the finest landscape views a painter's
eye—even the eye of the deathless Cole—would care to
banquet on. In Tennessee? you will say, with a quizzi-
cal movement of the under lip, and an incredulous dropping of the outward corner of the nether eyelid. Yes,
in Tennessee, sir, for Overton Park is in this Western
Empire State. But, to my sketch—and don't interrupt
me sir, for any doubts about the verity of my writings,
for I never romance; ladies can write something besides
romances, sir!

From this upper portico the view stretches for miles
and leagues away, to a blue range of boldly beautiful
hills, that, when the atmosphere is a little hazed, seem
to be the blue sky itself bending down to repose upon
the undulating sea of forests, at their base. Between
these azure walls that bound our horizon westward, and
the mansion, lie belts of noble woodland, intermingled
with green intervals, through which wind transparent,

rock-channeled rivulets, (they would call them rivers in England,) bordered by fringes of maple, sycamore, and oak trees, opulent with verdure.

Nearer the house, comprising the first breadth of view, a mile and a half in width, stretch right and left the rich cotton and tobacco fields, like, in the distant *coup d'œil*, lakes of blue and green water, slightly ruffled by the breeze; while their level surface is relieved at pretty intervals by islands of trees—half acre clumps grouped in groves, and left by the overseer for shade, where slaves can retire in the fervid noon, to eat their coarse but abundant dinnèr, doubtless to *them* savory as Parisian cuisinerie. The picturesque aspect of these grove-islands is enhanced by the white walls of a negro-shelter-hut, which is built upon columns to afford protection from the rain.

The "Lodge," being placed with an eye to the capabilities of the surrounding prospect, upon a gently rising eminence, which is clothed with gardens to its foot, has a very imposing appearance, as it is approached along a winding carriage-way, that leads to it from the stage road. This is at least a league off, and its place can be indicated on dusty days from the house, by clouds of reddish brown dust rolled into the air and curling along the hedges, disturbed by the heavy wheels of the mail coach, or the lighter progress of some planter's carriage on its way from town.

It seemed to me when I first came in sight of the mansion, that was to be (I don't know how long) my home, that I was approaching the mansion of some English Baronet, at least; and the scenery of this part of Tennessee, I am told, bears a striking resemblance to that in the best part of England; and I can bear testimony that the neighboring gentlemen are vying in taste and wealth with each other, to make this country one of the most lovely in the land. For you must know that this is an opulent district, and the planters here count their estates rather by miles than acres.

I have described only the view in front of this stately edifice, from which I am writing you. From a little balcony that opens from my chamber window south, I get a view of a vale and upland, dotted with sheep and cattle, tended by a blind negro boy, who whistles all day, and I have no doubt sleeps soundly all night; who, with his dog, complete a very nice picture of its kind. The crest of the upland is topped by a wood, out of which, just where the acclivity dips eastward, stares a huge, bald, gray rock, in shape as much like a lion's head, as either of the heads of those lions on your Exchange steps in Philadelphia, for which I am credibly informed that a famous dog, belonging to a Monsieur Gardel, a talented gentleman of your city, sat; and very good lions they are—very like lions! If I recollect right, this dog, who sat as a model for a *pair* of lions, was called "Neptune."

I remember once seeing him at West Point, and falling in love with him, (with "Nep," not Monsieur G.,) when I was about—about—let me see—thirteen.

But let me finish my scenery. This lion's-head rock hangs over a deep *tarn*, where at mid-day, the water is black and polished as glass ebon; and near the tarn, not five yards from its margin, rises thirty feet in height, a green pyramid, one of the sepulchral mounds of the noble,

brave, mysterious Indians, now wasted, as McLellan, one
of the New England poets, says,

> " Like April snows
>   In the warm noon,"

before the burning radiance of the sun of civilization.
On the east side of the mansion, there is quite a different
view from either I have described. First, the eye rests
on a vast vegetable and fruit garden, a score of good
roods broad, crossed by wide graveled walks, dotted
with hot-houses, and enclosed by a white paling, half-
concealed in a luxuriant hedge of the thorny and beautiful
Cherokee rose. At two corners of the garden erected
on high places, is perched a monstrous pigeon house, to
and fro, above and about which its soft winged tenants
are flying in clouds at all times, like the scriptural doves
to their windows.

Of all birds, I love the dove, the home dove, with its
blue and brown breast, its affectionate, trustful glance,
and its musical, happy *coo*. I have loved them in the
streets of my native town from a child, and stopped and
watched them till I forgot school hour, and dinner hour,
as they fluttered, hopped, sidled, and pranced about the
fallen oats under the farmer's cart, or crowded about the
shop doors.

I never failed to have my pocket filled with grain and
crumbs for them, and I cannot now but smile at the recollection of myself, at twelve years old, seated on a
curb-stone, surrounded, and lit upon, and run over, and
almost had my eyes put out by their wings, as they
eagerly shared my bounty out of my hands and lap.
Many a black mark at school for tardiness, and many a

scolding at home have I to lay to the account of the blue
doves. Yet I love them still; and ere long they will find
out—these in the dove-cotes—that they have a friend
near; and I dare say in my little balcony, ere I have
been here a month, will be enacted the street scenes of
my girlish days.

Beyond the garden is a large pond or lake, and on the
declivity of the opposite shore appears, half hid in the
trees of its pretty streets, one of the most novel and
striking towns I ever beheld. It is the " Quartier" or
African village of the estate, the Negropolis of the slave
population. It is composed of some thirty dwellings,
white-washed, one story high, arranged on two streets
that follow the margin of the pond. Each cottage is
neat and comfortable, with a small garden patch behind
it ; and in front are rows of shade trees for the whole
length of the street, growing near enough to each house
to afford shade to the roofs. The streets themselves are
green sward, intersected by well-trodden footpaths which
lead from door to door.

Overlooking them all, and a little higher up the gentle
ascent, is a house of more pretension, built of brick, with
a belfry at one end, containing a bell as loud as a
church bell, which I hear rung every morning at day-
break, and at noon, and at nine o'clock at night. This
house belongs to, or rather is occupied by, the overseer, or
manager, as these gentlemen prefer being designated.
Over this house rises a majestic range of mountainous
heights, of great beauty, from the summit of one of
which, three miles off, and which is designated by a
single scathed tree rising from a bosom of foliage, a view

can be obtained, with a good glass, of the city, six
leagues or thereabouts to the north; and also of one of
the shining windings of the romantic Cumberland, as
it, for a mile or two, leaves its embracing cliffs to roll
gloriously along in the cloudless sunlight.

LETTER III.

You will have formed some idea, Mr. ——, from the descriptions in my last, of the characteristics of the place from which I write these communications. You will perceive that I am domiciliated in one of those fine old mansions of the West where the lordly proprietors live more like feudal nobles than simple farmers. In the bosom of this beautiful scenery which I have endeavored to picture to you, and within the walls of this hospitable abode, I hope to make my home, at least for two years to come.

Perhaps you would like to know something about me before I came here to assume, at the age of nineteen, the grave and responsible position of governess. I am quite willing to gratify your curiosity. But first let me describe to you what is now passing beneath my window, for I write within full sight of the lawn. There I can see Colonel Peyton, the father of my pupil, seated upon a finely formed bay nag, a rifle laid carelessly across his saddle, and two fine deer-dogs standing by his horse's forelegs and looking up wistfully into their master's face. He has upon his head a broad-brimmed, white beaver, turned up in front, something after the fashion of the ancient cocked hat, a manner of wearing it that lends him, with his manly features and silver gray locks, a decided military air. Over a brown linen hunting frock is slung a leather belt, appended to which is his powder-horn and shot-bag; and with his boots drawn *á la Hussar*, over his trowsers, and armed with silver spurs, he sits accoutred for the field, a handsome specimen of an American Western gentleman preparing for a hunt. Standing just in front of his stirrup is a negro fifty years of age, (about his master's,) his old straw hat in his hand and his head bent forward in an attitude at once respectful and attentive, listening to orders from his master.

" You hear, Pete, that as soon as the young gentlemen arrive, you are to mount the filly and bring them to the wood."

" Yiss, massa !" and Peter bowed like a thorough-bred gentleman, so courteous was the air with which he bent his head.

" You will find me either at the Crow's Pine, or else about the Salt Lick.   See that they bring their guns."

" Yiss, massa !"

"And don't let that noisy whelp of yours," here the colonel cracked his whip-lash at a wretched, shaggy monster of a dog that crouched, as if fully conscious of his bad reputation, behind the legs of the negro; "don't let him come into the forest again; if he does, I'll hang him.   He spoiled our sport last Thursday."

"I know he did, mass'.   He berry ignorum dog, some-time; he nebber hab much telligencts like odder gemmen dogs, massa; but Injun shan't come *dis* time."

The colonel now pointed with the end of his riding whip to a gate, which Peter hastened to open; standing bare-headed till his master rode through it; and then closing it he returned to the house, the villainous-looking dog Injun capering about him, as much overjoyed at being released from the awe of the colonel's eye, as a roguish school-boy when the "master" steps out.

"You mighty grad, Injun, aint you?" I overhear Peter say to his companion, "but you better keep quiet and min' you' business at home, or sure 'nuff massa 'll hab you hang'd. You a'n't fit hunt deer like de gemmen's genteel dog, you nigger you; all you do is frighten 'em away from de stan', and keep massa and oder gemmen from gettin' shot at 'em, you scar'crow! Massa sarve you right he shoot you, Injun!"

Peter's voice was lost as he went with a limping shuffle around the house. I can see the noble form of the colonel as his horse bears him along the avenue, and so out across the green dell at an easy pace. Now he stops to speak to the poor blind shepherd boy, who raises his cap, and seems happy to be noticed. The sheep start and bound away before the horse's feet, and the lazy kine slowly give him the path. Now he winds about the base of the lion's head cliff, and is now lost to sight in the dark grove of elm and maple that half conceals the tarn. Above his head wheels the black-winged vulture in approaching circles, as if he well knew that there was always blood to be found in the hunter's path.

I will return to my room, and resume—myself! But I am again interrupted. The ajar door of my elegant apartment opens, and a negress of sixteen enters with a silver cup of water, upon a silver salver. She is barefooted, and her head is bound with a gay handkerchief tastefully and uniquely twisted into a sort of oriental turban; for the taste of these daughters of Africa is instinctively Eastern. A blue cotton gown completes her simple attire, save a pair of bright brass ear-rings, and a couple of brass and one silver ring upon her shapely fingers; for her hands, and fingers, and finger nails, though the former are brown as a chestnut, are exquisitely shaped. Ugly hands seem to belong to the Anglo Saxons, I think, especially to those of cold climates; for the farther we go south, the more elegant the female hand.

The name of the African maid is Eda, which is, I suppose, a corruption of Edith. She was given to my charge as my waiting-woman, on the first evening of my arrival here; and by night she sleeps on a rug at the door of my chamber. At first, I was shocked and alarmed to have a negress sleep in the chamber with me; but now, I am so accustomed to her presence, and she is so willing, so watchful, so attentive, so useful, that I am quite reconciled to having her. "Missis, glass water, please?" she said, curtseying, and dropping her large lustrous eyes with habitual submission, as she presented the salver.

I had not asked for water, but I find that it is the custom for some one of the servants to go over the house several times a day to every person, wherever they happen to be, whether on the portico walking, or in the library reading, or even pursuing them into the garden to offer them water. This is a hospitable, and in the hot weather of this climate, a refreshing custom. Southerners are all great water drinkers. At evening, when we are seated on the piazza, enjoying the beauty of the western skies, sherbet, water, fruit, and even ice creams have been brought out to us. Indeed, there seems to be some useful person continually engaged in some mysterious corner of this large house, preparing luxuries to dispense through the day to the inmates, and to chance visitors, of which there are not a few.

When I first arrived here, and it has been scarcely a month—I was amazed at the number of servants. There are no less than seven in the house, and full as many more connected with the gardens, stables, and for out-door domestic duty, beside the two hundred plantation hands that work always in the field as agriculturists; for the domestic slaves and the field slaves are two distinct classes on an estate like this, and never interchange labor, save indeed, when a refractory house servant is sometimes sent into the field, to toil under the hot sun as punishment, for a week or so. And the difference is not merely in employment, but in character and appearance. The field servant is heavy, loutish, and slow; his features scarce elevated in expression above the mule, which is his co-laborer. The domestic servant is more sprightly, better clad, more intelligent and animated, apes polite manners, and imitates the polished airs of the well-bred "white folk." By contact constantly with the family, they use better language, have their faculties sharpened, and, in a dozen ways, show their superiority to the less favored helots of the plough. This superiority they love to exhibit, and I have been amused at their assumption of hauteur when they had occasion to hold intercourse with any of the "field hands," sent to the house on an errand.

Altogether the house servants are very different creatures. Four of them have intelligent faces, are excellent pastry-cooks, laundresses, dairywomen, and seamstresses, and seem, really, to take as much part and lively interest in household matters as the matron, their mistress.

"Can you read, Eda?" I asked of my little Timbuctoo maid, as I replaced the silver tumbler on the waiter. "No, Missis," and her large velvet-black eyes danced in their wide pearly spheres, as if she thought it would be a fine thing to know how.

"I know spell my name, missis. Missy Bel teach me dat!"

In my next you shall, certainly, have a little account of myself; but I feel myself of so little importance, that the least thing tempts my pen away from the egotistical theme.

Yours respectfully,
KATE C.

LETTER IV.

JUST as I was about to drop my pen into my ink-stand to commence this epistle, the clear, startling cry of a hunter's horn in the forest drew me to the window, which overlooked the south, and the cliff called the Lion's head. Just emerging from the wood was a caval-cade, that reminded me of something of a similar de-scription Scott has in one of his romances. First, there rode the colonel, our "lord of the manor," bare-headed, his gun laid across his saddle-bow, and his hunting skirt open at the collar, and thrown negligently back over his shoulders. By his side were some half dozen dogs, trotting along with their red tongues lolling out and look-ing, for all the world, thoroughly beat out with the day's chase. Behind the colonel came a negro, mounted, with a wounded dog laid across the neck of his horse. Be-hind the negro, riding on elegantly shaped horses, cantered two young men, one of them very handsome, but dressed in a frock coat, and gaiters of blue cottonade. His rifle was slung at his back; he was belted, and a knife and a powder flask were in his girdle. His companion was more fashionably dressed, and instead of a rifle carried only a light bird gun. In the rear followed two negro men on foot, bearing between them a slain deer, slung by the fetlocks to a newly-cut branch. Two or three African boys, and some half dozen more dogs completed

the cortêge.   One of the young men (the handsome one
in the kerseys) carried a horn, which, ever and anon, he
wound cheerily to give notice at the Lodge of their approach.   So I will leave them to make their way to the
house, and fulfil the promise made in my last, to let you
understand why a Yankee girl finds herself a dweller in
the far South-west.

Shall I begin in the true romantic vein, Mr. ——, or
in the style biographique?   I think I will, for the sake
of trying my forte that way, assume the manner of the
tale-writers; for perhaps one of these days, who knows?
I may get to the dignity of being a story-writer to the
Ledger or magazines, a distinction (all things being equal
—that is, the *quid* being equal to the *quo* as my brother
used to say) I should feel highly honored, I confess, to
arrive at.   Now to my own story:

Once upon a time there stood in a New England
village, not far from Portland in Maine, a little cottage,
white, with a portico trellised by honeysuckles, and a
little gate in the paling in-the front of it.   The cottage
stood upon a quiet street, near the outskirts of the
village, and was so near the river-bank, that I, who was
one of the "cottagers," could toss pebbles into its lucid
bosom from my window.   It was a quiet spot, this village
with its garden-buried houses, its one tin-plated spire,
shining in the sun like a silver "extinguisher," its green
river shores, and pleasant woodlands where the boys had
famous bird's-nesting of Saturday afternoons.

My father, a naval officer of name and honor, fell
sick and died on a foreign station, leaving my mother
with six little mouths to feed, and six little backs to keep
warm, and six little heads to fill with learning.   To aid

her to do all this, she received a narrow pension allowed
her for her widowhood. It was a sore struggle for the
mother to guard and nourish and cover her large brood
with such narrow wings. Her widowed feathers would
hardly cover us all, and some of us always were suf-
ferers, either for supper, a pair of shoes, or may be a
frock, or jacket, or a necessary school-book.

But Providence takes care of the widow, and so none
of us perished; nay, were ever sick, and what with kind
neighbors, (oh, how many *kind* neighbors there are in the
world!) what, with presents of Christmas-days, Thanks-
giving-days, and the blessed Common-school where we all
went without cost, we managed to weather the beginning
of life bravely.

Charles, my elder brother, through the kindness of
the member of Congress from our district, had his name
presented to the Secretary of the Navy for a midshipman's warrant; but, none offering, soon the same kind
influence placed him in West Point as a cadet, and now
he is a lieutenant, and won, though it is a sister's praise,
a distinguished name on the fields of Mexico. If I dared
name him, sir, you would at once bear testimony to the
truthfulness of my eulogy.

The second child, a daughter, after as good an education as the village school offered, was chosen at the
age of sixteen as its assistant, and after three years she
married a young minister, near Norfolk, Va., who subsequently went abroad as a missionary, and is now a
resident in a far, far land.

The third child was a son, who, inspired by the tales
of his father's exploits on the ocean during the war,
went to sea, before the mast, as he said, "to win a

name." Seven years have elapsed since his departure, and he has not been heard from, and I fear that we shall meet no more in this life. He was a noble, bold, chivalrous boy, and my mother's joy! If he is alive, I know that he is yet worthy of our love and pride.

The fourth child is your humble correspondent, of whom I will speak when I have dismissed the remaining two.

The fifth is a girl; but alas! she is an invalid, having a lame hip, which confines her to the house. She is the loveliest flower of our family parterre! Never were such deep, dark, glorious eyes as hers! They speak! Her face is exquisitely shaped, every feature as soft and spiritual as the gentle angel faces we see in dreams! I can behold her now—the enchanting Ida, seated by my mother's knee on her favorite stool, her heavenly face of pure intelligence blended with love, upturned with a smile. She is now sixteen, but there is so much wisdom in her eyes, so much gravity in her manner, the result of suffering, that she seems twenty. But her figure is child-like, and faultless as that of the chiseled Greek Slave! Noble Ida! If thy eyes should rest on these lines, accept, sweet sister mine, this tribute of love and memory! She is my mother's second self, the partner of her hours, the confidant of her heart's secrets, the angel of her presence.

The sixth is a boy, a buoyant, laughing, rollicking boy, with spirits enough in him for half a dozen girls, of whom, however, he is as shy as if he had no fine, handsome face to commend him to the romping hoydens. He is fourteen years old, and the *baby!* He has no idea of books, and never could bend his fingers to pen-holding. His genius lies in kite-flying, fishing, rabbit-

snaring, bird's-nesting, boating on the river, and in riding the minister's old blind horse to water, full gallop,
a feat, (that is, the galloping,) the minister could never
succeed in getting out of him. This brother is his mother's other joy; or, rather, Ida is her joy, and Preble
(so named by my father after the gallant commodore)
is her admiration.

Now, if you have listened as becomes you to listen
when a "fayre ladye" speaks, you know all about my
family and myself. No—not myself. Be patient, and
you shall have your ignorance enlightened on this score.
Shall I describe myself? or shall I leave you to guess
that my height is five feet four, that my hair is a dark
brown, and worn smoothly so as to hide both ears like a
coif, and knotted behind in very abundant folds; that
my cast of beauty is brunette; that my eyes are said to
be like my sister Ida's, only less, that is to say, a little
more saucy in their brilliancy; that my nose is a very
good nose as noses go; that I have a good mouth and
very fine teeth, which I don't show *too* much when I
smile; that I usually dress in white in summer and ma-
roon in winter, and that my hand is—is—like too many
of the hands of northern maidens, better looking in a
glove than out of one? I do not sing at all. I never
was taught the piano, for you must by this time be aware
that our little cottage had no room for such a costly
affair, though somehow the instrument *does* seem to find
room in a great many houses *too small* for it! I do not
dance, for we had no dancing-school in our village, and
our mother was too sensible to have sent me to one if
there had been. She knew that there were temptations
enough in this naughty world to surround young people,

without adding to them the love of dancing, which tempts many a sweet, good girl into many a folly, afterwards bitterly repented of.   Parlor dancing, in the home circle, where grandpa joins in it, that is the only dancing that is truly innocent and cheerful.   I draw, for my mother taught me; I sometimes sketch, and color my efforts; I speak and write French, being taught this by my brother when he came home at intervals from West Point.   I have mastered German and Italian, and know enough of Spanish to pronounce correctly the names of all our victorious battle-fields,—a no mean acquisition in itself, they are so numerous.   Lastly, I am a governess, and am aiming, with all modest diffidence and deference to your decisions, dreadful sir, to be an authoress.

When I had attained my fifteenth year, I also was advanced to be assistant in the school where I had been educated from a child.   After two years' pleasant toil, I heard that in Massachusetts there were institutions, called Normal Schools, where young females were educated to be teachers.   Having some money, the fruits of my teaching, I applied to be received into this noble school, and after due time I received my diploma, attesting my qualifications to teach.   I soon obtained a school in a considerable town, and had no expectations of doing any thing else than growing gray in my vocation, when, about a year and a half after I had come to the town, as I was locking up my castle one evening after my day's duties were over, my attention was drawn to a handsome private carriage rolling along the road.   In it sat a fine-looking man, with the unmistakeable air and aspect of a Southerner, and by his side was a young girl of fifteen or sixteen, with that rich olive cheek and Italian form of face which distinguishes the maidens of our more sunny South.

My school-house was a very pretty one, with a handsome portico, green blinds, granite steps, a grassy yard, and neat, snow-white fence, while trees shaded as well as adorned the premises. I saw him cast his eyes over the whole with a pleased look, and then his gaze fell upon me. I dropped my eyes, and taking out the keys, put them in my bag, and was turning to go homeward, when I saw the carriage stop. The gentleman, who was a man of fifty, with a fine bearing, and gray and brown locks mingled about his forehead, raised his hat, and courteously beckoned to me to approach.

"Pardon me, Miss," he said, in that half apologetic tone which marked the thorough-bred gentleman, "May I take the liberty to inquire if you are a teacher?"

I bowed affirmatively.

"You will excuse the liberty I take, but I am desirous of obtaining a teacher to go south-west with me, and having applied to the Normal School, I was directed to this town by the Principal, who told me that there was a young lady here whom I could, no doubt, succeed in employing. As he spoke so highly of her, and gave me her address, I have driven here to have an interview with her. You will be likely to know her abode, and will oblige me by directing me to it."

"What is her name, sir?" I inquired.

"Miss Catharine Conyngham," he read off from the back of a letter.

I started with surprise and pleased confusion. He saw my embarrassment, and read plainly the secret in my tell-tale face.

"Perhaps," he added, with a look of gratification, "perhaps I have the pleasure of addressing the very person—Miss Conyngham herself?"

I informed him that I was that person, when, interchanging a glance of satisfaction with the young lady, he handed me the letter, and requested me to read it; but first that I must get up into the carriage and sit down, but this courtesy I declined, and breaking the seal I read as follows:—But I will defer the letter to my next, as I am invited down to look at the slain deer in the back gallery.

Yours,
KATE.

LETTER V.

I HAVE to apologize to you, sir, for not keeping you in "Needles," and I hope you will not say any thing very naughty, because you have not heard from me so long. I have been traveling, and could not devote any time to my pen. You know that it is the custom for planters to leave their homes for the summer months, and *tour* it; and, being governess, I, of course, accompanied our family, in order to keep up my pupils in their books, though little book was learned, be assured, either at the mountains or the springs, for young folks have too much to tempt them at these places to con lessons.

After a pleasant summer jaunt, we are once more in our lovely home, and I trust I shall be able to continue to write you in my leisure. Perhaps, one of these days, I may give you a description of our three months in the Mountains of Cumberland, and at the Springs of Virginia. I will now resume my "Needles" where I left off, which, perhaps, you will remember was when I had just shut up my village school, and broken the seal of a letter handed to me by a strange gentleman in a carriage. The letter was as follows, written by the superintendent of the State Normal School:—

Normal School.

DEAR MISS CONYNGHAM:

The bearer is Colonel Peyton, a planter of intelligence and fortune, who wishes a governess, who will be charged with the education of his daughter. The position seems to be a very desirable one, and I would recommend you to accept it, if he should, after seeing you, offer it to you.

Truly your friend,
B. W.

Upon reading this epistle, I looked up and saw the eyes of both Colonel Peyton and his daughter fixed upon my face, as if trying to divine the effect it had upon me. The gentle eyes of the maiden, who looked earnestly at me, as if she hoped I was not going to say "no," and the gentlemanly, agreeable manners, and the fine expression of the father's face, decided me at once. "If the place is offered to me," said I, mentally, "I will not refuse it. I know I shall be happy with such persons as these." Yet I hesitated and could not speak; for I thought of my little pupils, some of whom had entwined themselves around my heart; and I felt reluctant to leave them.

While I was thinking between hope and sorrow what answer I should make—an answer that would perhaps govern my future destiny—Colonel Peyton was pleased to say kindly:

"I fear, Miss, that you are going to disappoint us. The high terms in which you have been spoken of to me, are confirmed by seeing you. Are you willing to accept the situation alluded to in the letter?"

I hesitated. My eyes filled with tears—tears at the thought of parting with my school—tears of gratitude, that I was thought worthy of so much confidence.

"Oh, do not refuse—*do* say *yes*," cried his lovely

daughter, extending her hand, and clasping mine warmly
in her own.   "You shall be my eldest sister, and I will
make you as happy as I can.   Please, say you will go
with us."

"I cannot refuse," said I, smiling at her enthusiasm.
"If your father wishes, I give my consent," answered
I, without a thought about terms : for I felt that I could
be happy to be one of the inmates of the family, and
call such excellent persons "friends."   My heart seemed
to feel like a daughter's heart towards Colonel Peyton,
and certainly glowed with sisterly love towards Isabel.

"The matter is settled, then," said Colonel Peyton,
with animation.   "We are more fortunate than we anticipated.   Come, Miss Katharine, let me drive you to
your residence, and then leave you to make preparations,
while we remain at the hotel."

When I alighted from the chariot at the door of the
house in which I boarded, there were a great many heads
at the neighboring windows, to see the fine "Boston
carriage," as they called it ; and when they soon learned,
by the cries of three or four little girls, my scholars, that
it had come to take me far away to the South, there was
more commotion than I dreamed such a body as I could
cause.

When I made known to my landlady and to the neighbors, who flocked in to hear the news, my prospects,
some congratulated me, but more said they would not
part with their "school-mistress," that it would break
the children's hearts ; and the children, inspired by their
words, began to cling round me, and take on so dreadfully, that I was near sending over word to the tavern

to Colonel Peyton, withdrawing my consent to go with him.

In half an hour I succeeded in convincing the most zealous of my friends, that it would be greatly to my advantage to go with the Southern family, and, by bed-time, all opposition, save in the form of a lovely little lame scholar of mine, was appeased. This child, to which I was very much attached, would not leave the house to go to its home, but, creeping up stairs, clung to my pillow, and bathed it in tears. Her little prayers of entreaty had nearly conquered me. The result of all was, however, that the succeeding afternoon, I bade fare-well to all my village friends, and left the town by the road passing the school-house. Here, to my surprise, and to the increase of my grief, I found all my scho-lars, some forty in number, drawn up to see me for the last time. They had reached the school-house by a path across the fields. Colonel Peyton stopped the car-riage, and every one climbed up to kiss me—some put-ting wreaths upon my head, and others placing in my hands little tokens to remember them by.

"Don't forget me, Miss Kate!" cried a score of little voices. "We'll never forget you, Miss Kate!" called out others, as we once more drove on. My little, lame pupil was not among them, for I had left her sobbing as if her heart would break, up stairs on my bed. As the carriage turned and hid the town, we heard a shout of "Good-bye, Miss Kate! Good-bye! Come back again, won't you?"

Their voices no longer heard, I gave vent to my feel-ings in a gush of tears. Colonel Peyton did not disturb them.   Isabel nestled her hand in mine, and I felt her tears dropping warm upon it.

The same evening, we reached Boston, and in a few days afterwards were *en route* to the West, by the way of Philadelphia and Pittsburg.

I will not detain you by describing our journey, but close this letter by saying, that after a delightful trip of three weeks, we reached the elegant, interior city of Nashville, from which a ride of two hours and a half brought Colonel Peyton and his daughter home, and me to what will be "a home" for me two years to come.

In my next, I will resume the description of things in the West, which I have interrupted to give you the history of my first coming thither.

I am, sir, yours, respectfully,
KATE.

LETTER VI.

Mr. ——

I HAVE seen in your paper a little notice of my letters by some lady, (I am sure it was a female,) who takes me to task for writing about *myself*. She says it does not matter what the color of an authoress's eyes are, or whether she have small or large hands, or feet; and she takes it upon herself to box my ears for talking about myself. Now, Mr. ——, I think that a great deal can be learned about an authoress, by knowing the hue of the eyes, and the number of the shoe or glove she hides foot or hand in. It don't matter much, perhaps, whether a man who writes an arithmetic, or a woman who writes a geography, have gray locks or red, long noses or short, beards or no beards, for I have seen, (ah, shocking!) women with beards, and they always seem to be proud of them, the way they cherish them! While I write, I recall a "lady" with four moles on her chin, each of which is tufted with a respectable camel's hair pencil. Do not such monsters know there are such inventions as tweezers?

When one writes to interest, and writes one's thoughts, then it is agreeable to the reader to know something about the writer's person. I am sure (now don't call me vain, lady critic severe) that my readers will not like me any thing the less for the description I have given of myself. I see also that one of your readers wishes to know the address of the "Yankee Girl," and that you *decline* giving it. Very good, Mr. ——; and pray, who gave it to you? How coolly you decline to give what you do not possess; for I am sure you could not tell how to reach me by a letter, if you wished to do so. But one of these days, if I see a paragraph in your paper, saying that after my ten *trial* "needles" are written, you will engage me to persevere in authorship, I will then remove the veil.

I have already described to you the happiness I enjoy in my new and stately home, the appearance of things, and the beautiful scenery with which the villa is surrounded. I will now give you some account of the manner in which we pass the day on the plantation, and every day is pretty much the same, save when Sunday comes, or a party of visitors from town, or from some neighboring plantation arrives. About half past four in the morning, I am regularly awakened by a bell, as loud as a college or chapel bell; which is rung in the belfry of the overseer's house, to call the slaves up. Its clear lively peal continues for about three minutes. I open my eyes, see that all is dark, and then sink to sleep again. Or if I lie awake, I soon hear the tramp of the laborers passing along the avenue, and the jingling of horse chains, as the horses and mules are led by to the field. All is soon again still as midnight; for the plantation bell does not disturb the domestic servants in the house, who generally indulge in bed a half hour longer. I believe that I am the only one in the house that the bell disturbs; yet I do not begrudge the few minutes' loss of sleep it causes me, it sounds so pleasantly in the half-dreamy morning.

About six o'clock I am awakened for the day, by the soft footstep of my pretty negress Eda, who steals to my bedside to whisper—"Missy Kate, six o'clock, missy," and next goes to withdraw the curtains, and let in the glorious sumbeams, to gild the atmosphere of the room. She then brings me a laver of cool fresh water from the spring, and snowy napkins; and for the first three or four mornings after my arrival, she brought me a wine mint julep. Yes, sir, a regular mint julep! And when I refused it, spite of its delicious taste and aroma, (for I am a Daughter of Temperance, Mr. ——,) she opened her large eyes with wonder, saying, "Why, missy, dey nebber so nice!" Her assurance, that it was the custom of the house to guests, never moved me, though I must confess they looked very tempting. When she found that I was not to be tempted, she brought me coffee, black, and clear, and fragrant enough for a Turkish Sultana. But I had been raised in the plain, simple, Yankee way, and so had no use for such luxury, and have banished both julep and coffee before I get up in the morning.

My sable maid aids me in my toilet, combs and twists my long hair with the grace and art of a Parisienne, and makes herself most useful. Indeed one does not know of how many uses a servant may be, till one has one, as I have now for the first time in my life. How differently brought up are we Yankee girls from the Southern girls, who never do any thing themselves, being always attended by a shadow of a little negress, or an ancient mammy! For my part, I find it very pleasant:—"Eda, a glass of water;" or, "Eda, bring me such a book from the parlor below;" or, "Eda, hand me my fan;" or, "Eda, a dozen other things." Oh, it is very convenient; and I do believe a Northern girl in these circumstances, will, in a year, render herself more helpless than even a Southerner to the manor born.

At seven, a clear-ringing, silver table bell calls all from their rooms to the breakfast apartment, which is a spacious, cool piazza, shut in by green blinds, and adorned with cages of mocking and canary birds, which sing all the meal time.

Breakfast usually consumes half an hour. Four or five varieties of warm bread load the table, with succotash, and hominy, and ham always. Two men and two negresses, all well dressed and in white aprons, wait on table, and anticipate every wish. The colonel always asks a devout blessing, all being seated, and all respond a loud "Amen." Two noble dogs generally crouch either side of the colonel's arm chair, and a monstrous Maltese cat, having taken a liking to me, seats herself by my chair with a wistful look. After breakfast the colonel lights a cigar at a coal brought him, unbidden, by a negro boy, for he knows his master's habits; and another servant holds a ready saddled horse at the door.

The colonel mounts him, and rides away to overlook his estate, sometimes accompanied by Isabel and me; when we have brave gallops home alone. About nine o'clock we take to our books or our needles, and sit wherever we choose; in our rooms, in the breezy hall, on the piazza, or in the drawing-room. At eleven an attentive servant brings refreshments, when studies and needles are dropped, and we have gossip, music, and sometimes jump the rope, swing, or play at battledore. If we have calls to make, the carriage is ordered at half-past eleven, and after a drive of two hours or three, we return to dine at two o'clock.

The dinner table is placed in the large central hall of the house, and every dish elegantly served. Above the table is a huge silk covered fan, the breadth of the table. Tassels are attached to it, and it is fringed with crimson. From rings in the corners lead red cords, which are pulled to and fro by a little negro, all dinner time. This regular and ceaseless movement of the fan above our heads creates an agreeable breeze, which in this climate is most luxurious. The dinner consists of many courses, with wine and dessert of fruit, sweetmeats, ices, nuts, domestic grapes, and black coffee. The ladies then leave the gentlemen at the table to smoke, and retire to their own rooms to sleep till the cool of the day. The "lords" sometimes at hunting dinners sleep *at the table.*

Towards evening all is animation. Saddle horses are ordered, and away we scamper, now to the tarn, or to climb the lion's head, or to canter along the turnpike. We generally get back by twilight in fine spirits. Tea and coffee are handed to us whenever we choose to have it, no table being ever set for the evening repast. It takes three servants to hand it. One comes with a waiter of napkins first; another follows with coffee and sugar; a third with cakes of all sorts, and sometimes a fourth with purple finger glasses. In the evening we all assemble in the brilliantly lighted parlors, where we have music, play at chess, (the colonel and I take a game at backgammon usually,) read, or talk. By ten we all retire; and soon the house is buried in the repose of midnight. So pass the happy days at Overton Lodge.

Yours,
KATE.

LETTER VII.

Mr. ———

HAVE you ever been fox hunting? If you have, you have seen very respectable, rough and tumble enjoyment; if you have not, there are yet before you certain experiences.

I have already spoken of the fine, broadly spread landscape, visible from the portico of Overton Park Lodge. In the late autumnal months when the crops are well gathered, and there is nothing to trample down in the fields, this wide landscape is converted into a vast fox hunting ground, full eleven miles across. By concert the neighboring planters open their fences with many a gap across the country, and so a clear ride of ten or twelve miles is left free to the adventurous huntsman or huntswoman.

Two evenings ago as I was about to mount my beautiful dapple mule, (don't laugh at my mule, for it is the dearest little fellow with ears like velvet, and feet and fetlocks like an antelope's, a special gift to me for its beauty and gentleness, from Colonel Peyton,) to pace down the avenue to the turnpike, I was surprised to see suddenly appear in sight a party of seven young gentlemen. They were riding at top speed, and in great glee, and all came dashing up toward the villa at that rapid rate the Tennessecan loves to ride.

"Ah, my boys," cried the colonel, who was about to ride out with me, removing his foot from the stirrup, while I hesitated whether to remain on the flight of steps or fly from such a battalion. "Don't go, Miss Kate. They are only some of the young fox hunters come over to make preparations."

And before I could escape—

"Miss Conyngham, gentlemen!"

The young men, who drew up their horses on seeing a lady, lifted their caps and hats, and I was struck with their general appearance; four of them being fine-looking, yet dressed in blue linsey-woolsey, with boots pulled on over their pantaloons; and the other three in thick coats and caps, or broad felt hats slouched behind—a very common head covering in these parts and not unpicturesque. Every young man was armed with a gun, and attended at least by two dogs, and beautiful creatures some of them were—not the young men, Mr. ——, but the hounds.

"Well, colonel, we have come over to settle upon the day," said one of the young gentlemen.

"That is right! I like to see the rising generation prompt to engage in such noble sports. I think that the day after to-morrow we will give Reynard our compliments in person. I will have my men ready, and if you will meet me at the edge of the wood, by the lion's head cliff, at six in the morning, we will do our best for a day's sport."

"We'll be there, colonel," was the response; "and then we shall stand a chance of bringing down a deer or two," added one of them. "I saw one on the ridge by the creek as I rode over."

"No doubt we shall see plenty of sport.   And you must accompany us, Miss Kate," added the colonel turning to me, as I stood with the bridle of my mule in my hand, trying to check his restive movements, for the prancing horses of the young men fired his ambition to prance too.

After suffering myself to be urged a little by two of the young gentlemen, I consented to join the party, if other ladies did so.   The cavalcade then escorted us to the gate of the main road, and the horsemen separated each to his own home; while the colonel and I took a forest road, that, after a league's windings, came out near the villa.   As we rode, the colonel entertained me with a great many anecdotes of hunting, from Bruin to the Hare.   As we approached the mansion on our return, the avenue was temporarily blocked up by not less than fifty slaves of both sexes; for it was now twilight, and they had just completed their day's work, and were wending their way to their village, or *quartier*.

The women carried hoes upon their shoulders, and trudged along, some dull, and with expressionless faces, others laughing and singing.   The men, I remarked, were more cheerful than the women, and had more lively countenances.   One and all were clad in their coarse white cloth, known as negro cloth—the men with straw hats and the women with handkerchiefs upon their heads. I have not yet seen a negro woman wear a bonnet on Sundays, it is only a gayer kerchief.

As we passed, they drew up on each side of the narrow road for us to pass—the men all taking off, or touching their hats, and replying with a smile to their master's salutation of "Good evening, boys!" and the women—

some of them, slightly nodding, but without the smile. One of them had a huge cotton basket upon her head.

"Peep into it," said the colonel, as I rode by. I did so, and beheld four little cunning black babies!—they were nestled together, and quite naked. These babies had been taken by their mothers to the field, and while they were at work, were placed under the care of the girl who had them in charge.

I am already getting reconciled to slavery, since I find that it does not, in reality, exhibit the revolting horrors I was taught in the North to discover in it. There are many things to admire and to interest one in the social and domestic condition of the slaves, and I am almost ready to acknowledge that the African is happier in bondage than free! At least one thing is certain: nearly all the free negroes I have ever seen in the North were miserable creatures, poor, ragged, and often criminal. Here they are well clad, moral, nearly all religious, and the temptations that demoralize the free blacks in our northern cities are unknown to, and cannot approach them.

As we drew near the front of the villa, my mule, not liking the shrill cry of a superb peacock, which conceived the idea of welcoming us with a song, and a resplendent unfolding of his prismatic-eyed tail, started to run with me at top speed. I am a tolerable rider, and as I could not fall far if I were thrown, the mule being so little and low, I did not feel half the alarm the colonel manifested for my safety, who began to ride after me; when finding his horse only gave fresh impetus to the speed of my mule, he drew rein, and called to a negro man to stop my career. But the mule was not to be stopped. Instead of taking the carriage-way, he bolted across the lawn, and made straight for the stable. To stop him was impossible. I found I might as well pull at a granite column as at his jaws. The door of his stable was open, and I saw that he would only stop at his crib. I measured the ground to spring to it, but the dreadful idea that my skirt might entangle with the horns of the saddle, deterred me. In another moment the stable was reached! The door was open. I threw myself forward, clasped neck and mane, and stooping low went safely in with him. The suddenness with which he stopped at his manger, tossed me into the rack, out of which I was taken unhurt, and with many a joke and laugh upon my mule race. But a mule race is not a fox hunt, you say! Bide a wee, sir.

Yours,

KATE.

LETTER VIII.

In my last, I said I would give you an account of a fox-hunt, but ended my letter with a mule-race. But I will now redeem my pledge. Early in the morning, the day but one after the party of young men called at the lodge, we all were up with the ringing of the overseer's bell. By six o'clock we were assembled in the hall, where a lunch and a cup of hot coffee awaited us. By half-past six, ten of us in the saddle, including three ladies, were cantering at a brisk rate down the avenue, in the direction of a gate which led into the wide cotton fields, spread a league away beyond the villa. Not less than seven Africans, mounted, or on foot, brought up the rear of our cavalcade.

Reaching the gate, which one of the impatient young gentlemen opened almost at a speed, managing his horse adroitly the while, we dashed through, and emerged in the old hickory grove, the smooth grass of which glittered with dew-drops. The woods echoed with the tramp of our horses, and the laugh and merry talk of the young men and ourselves, not excluding the white-locked colonel, whose cheerful voice rose above all others. After a spirited gallop of half a mile through the grove, we emerged upon an open field, where once corn had grown, but which, having been harvested, left a desolate waste. In the midst of this field was a ravine, thickly

grown with bushes, which was known to be a favorite
haunt of Reynard. The negroes, who had followed us
with the dogs, were now called up, and ordered to approach the thicket, and stir up such gentlemen of the
red brush as might sojourn therein. The order to advance was obeyed by the negroes and dogs with emulous
alacrity. It was, for the first hundred yards, a laughable
race between quadruped and biped; but the last were
distanced, and the dogs reaching the covert, dashed into
it, a dozen in all, in perfect silence of tongue. But the
negroes kept up an incessant yell as they neared the
bushes, which they began to beat, uttering loud shouts
and challenges to master Reynard to "come out and
show hisself like a gemman, and not to be 'fraid of white
folks."

Reynard, however, did not feel inclined to respond to
their polite and repeated invitations. The dogs, in the
meantime, were busy in the ravine. We could hear
them crashing about over the dry sticks, but not a single
bark from them.

"They know the fox is there, or they would be noisy,"
said the colonel, as he watched the copse.

"Now, Miss Kate, we shall soon have sport. Hark!
hear that! Isn't it music?"

And music it was, such as I had never before listened
to. The whole pack, taking the deep short bark of one
of them as their cue, suddenly opened in full voice from
the ravine. A dozen sonorous canine voices were baying at once. The noise was singularly exciting. It
made my pulse bound, and my heart tremble with ex-
pectation. If you should hear the burst of the full
tones of a pack of hounds, you would never forget the

wild and startling music.   My spirited horse caught the excitement, pricked up his slender ears, and stamped impatiently with his forefoot, yet obediently suffered himself to be restrained by the light pressure of a finger upon his rein.   The barking of the dogs set the whole party on the *qui vive!* Every eye was strained to watch for the appearance of Reynard, when he should emerge from the ravine.   Some of the young gentlemen galloped "like mad" to the south of it, while others swept round to the north of it.   I kept at the colonel's side, who remained in "our first position," as Monsieur Cheffier, the dancing master, says.   "Look! There he goes!" shouted half a score of eager voices, and the fox appeared in full view to all eyes, scampering out of the thicket, and taking a direction straight for us ladies!

"Your whips—lash him as he passes!" shouted the colonel to us.   "We must turn him back, and not let him get into the wood, or the sport is up.   The fox came gallantly on, as if either he did not care for us, or did not see us.   The colonel kept urging "us to whip at him," and turn him.   We three ladies, therefore, placed our horses right across the only way by which he could reach the wood, and prepared to do battle bravely, we being the only persons on that side of the field; the rest of the party having spread themselves over the field, expecting the fox to emerge from cover in a different direction from that which he took.

I must confess I felt some trepidation as I saw the fox, which was a large one, making as straight as an arrow for my horse.   My riding whip was not very long, but I prepared to use it as valiantly as I could.

"He makes for *you*, Miss Kate! Don't let him pass under your horse," shouted the colonel.

In three leaps the fox was within six feet of my steed, and was passing, or rather aiming to pass under him, when I hit him smartly with my ivory-handled whip. The blow had the effect of checking his leap, so far as to give it another direction, and that was *over* the horse. A snarl—a showing of teeth—a dreadful horrid scramble with sharp claws, right up the flank of my horse, and over my saddle—a sweep of his brush in my face—and he was off upon the ground on the other side, with my green veil entangled about his head and forefeet!

"We have him! You've fought bravely, Miss Kate. He's meshed!" shouted several of the gentlemen. "Was any thing ever done handsomer? Never saw a bolder leap than that in a fox!"

The fox was indeed fairly meshed! the veil blinding and fettering him so hard that he did nothing but roll over and over, spit and snarl, like twenty cats tied up in a sack! The colonel leaped from his horse and approached him with his whip. The other gentlemen did the same as fast as they reached the spot. The negroes yelled and laughed with obstreperous joy at the pickle "Massa Fox was in." But Reynard was not yet captured. He now began to tumble and struggle for life so fearfully, that he released one foot from my poor, torn veil, and, thus relieved in part, he managed, by the most extraordinary somersets, to travel at a pace difficult for the gentlemen to keep up with, laughing, too, as they all were, at his perplexity, which was comical enough. The progress of the fox was a one-legged lope, a roll, and a somerset, alternately, varied by a yelp at every new

change in his extraordinary locomotion. He got a dozen
blows with the whips, but still marvelously kept ahead
of his pursuers, till at length he tumbled blindly into a
deep hole, out of which a tree had been taken, when the
dogs plunged in upon him and strangled him. The
brush was brought to me as a trophy, the gentlemen de-
claring that I was his captor. I, however, referred that
honor to my poor veil, which was torn and soiled most
pitiful to behold. The colonel has, since that adventure,
dubbed me as " The lady of the veiled fox."

KATE.

LETTER IX.

MY DEAR SIR:—

I do not recollect whether in my former letter, I have mentioned the rural little Gothic chapel which is on the estate. It was erected at the private expense of the noble-hearted Christian gentleman who is its proprietor. The model is borrowed from an exquisite chapel which the colonel saw on the estate of the Earl of C——, when he was in England. The situation of our chapel is romantic; and, being seen from all parts of the plantation, is an interesting feature in the scenery. It is about fifty-five feet long and built of stone; with turrets and mullioned Gothic windows of stained glass, and a floor of Tennessee marble. Its site is upon the verge of a green plantation, which overhangs the brook, and is, in its turn, overhung by a projecting spur of the lion's cliff. Majestic oaks embrace it, and ivy is trained up its walls. A broad lawn, crossed by graveled paths, surrounds it. These paths lead: one to the villa, one to the next plantation, and one to the African village where the slaves reside; for, be it known to you, that this beautiful chapel, the cost of which was $3000, has been built for the slaves of the estate. The body of the chapel is reserved for them, while in a gallery above the entrance are four pews, two on each side of the organ, in which the colonel's family, and sometimes the families of one or two of the neighboring planters, sit during service. This is performed every Sabbath morning by a gray-headed gentleman, who acts as lay reader, and on week days occupies himself in teaching the classics to two sons of a gentleman who lives two miles off. For his services on Sunday the colonel gives him a salary.

The second Sunday after I came here I was invited to attend service in the chapel with the family. Upon entering it, I found the body of the floor occupied by the black men and women of the plantation, seated in chairs with the utmost decency and quiet, and all neatly and cleanly attired. We took our seats in the gallery, while Isabel placed herself at the organ to play a voluntary. Until the old gentleman who officiated entered, I had time to look at the interior of this bijou of a church. On the right of the chancel was an exquisite group of statuary, executed in Italy expressly for this chapel by the colonel's order, at an expense of $800. It represented the Madonna and her child. The design was full of taste and artistic excellencies. On the opposite side was a table of the purest white marble, surmounted by a dove with its wings extended. It was a memento of the death of a little son of the colonel. There were no pews in the body of the church, only low chairs of oak, a chair to each worshiper, with an aisle between.

The service was very solemn; and my Puritanic objections to praying from a prayer-book, have been wholly removed by this day's experience. The singing was very remarkable. The African women all sing well, having naturally soft voices; with the organ, and full fifty fine voices swelling in harmony with it, the effect was very fine. "Is it possible," I asked myself, "that

these are slaves ? Is it possible that this rich voice
which leads in such manly tones is their master's ? Is it
possible that the fair girl who unites, by an accompaniment upon the organ, her praise with theirs, is one of
the 'haughty daughters of the South ?' "

The responses were all full and timely ; for the slaves
soon learn words by ear ; and many of them go through
the whole service, save the psalter, without a mistake.
The sermon, which was printed, was read well by the
elderly layman ; it was simple, suitable, and practical.
After service, the gray-headed old slaves stood respectfully without the door, and, with uncovered heads, bowed
to the colonel and ladies, the latter of whom stopped to
speak to some of them, and to make kind inquiries of the
old "aunties," as all old female slaves are affectionately
termed, as the term "uncle" is applied to the old men.
I have seen a good deal of the African race since I have
been here, and I am persuaded that they are far more religiously disposed than the lower and middle class of whites.
There are but four negroes on the colonel's plantation,
that are not "members" of the church, and who do not
try to square their lives with the precepts of the Gospel
so far as they understand them. This is the case, I learn,
on all the neighboring plantations, and I am informed
by intelligent persons that it is more or less so throughout the whole South. It would thus seem, that God, in
his providence, has permitted slavery to be the instrument
of christianizing Africa, by *bringing* Africa to Christian
shores ; and colonization by re-action on the shores of
Africa, is completing the mysterious dispensation.

I have an amusing incident to relate of which our
chapel was last Sunday the scene. The annual visita-

tion of the Bishop being expected, the venerable lay-reader got ready some twenty adults to be confirmed, and forty children to be baptized. The Bishop duly arrived, accompanied by two clergymen. Our little chapel, you may be assured, felt quite honored with the presence of such distinguished visitors. There were several neighboring families present, who, with ours, quite filled the gallery.

When the time came to baptize them, the marble font being filled with fair water, the black babies were brought up by their ebony papas. The colonel stood sponsor for the boys, and his sister, an excellent and witty maiden lady, for the girls.

"What is his name?" asked a clergyman who was to baptize, taking in his arms a little inky ball of ebony infancy with a pair of white, shining eyes.

"Alexander de Great, massa!"

I saw a smile pass from face to face of the reverend gentlemen in the chancel. The babe was duly baptized.

"What name?" he demanded of another Congo papa.

"General Jackson, massa!" and by this name the little barbarian was duly made a Christian.

"What name?" "Walter Scott!" "What name?" "Peter Simple!" "What name?" "Napoleon Bonaparte!" Splash went the water upon its face, and another ebony succeeded. His name was "Potiphar." Another's was "Pharaoh." Another was christened "General Twiggs;" another "Polk and Dallas;" another "General Taylor;" indeed, every General in the American army was honored, while "Jupiter," "Mars," "Apollo Belvidere," and "Nicodemus," will give you a specimen of the rest of the names. The female infants received such names as "Queen Victoria," "Lady Morgan," "Lady Jane Grey," "Madame de Stael," "Zenobia," "Venus," "Juno," "Vesta," "Miss Martineau," "Fanny Wright," "Juliana Johnson," and "Coal Black Rose." The water in the font, greasy and blackened by the process of baptizing so many black babies, had to be twice removed and replaced by fresh. The Bishop could scarcely keep his countenance as name after name was given, and the assistant clergyman twice had to leave the church, I verily believe, to prevent laughing in the church. The whole of this scandalous naming originated in the merry brain of the colonel's sister. Of course, the clergyman had to baptize by the name given, and the whole scene was irresistible.

Your friend,

KATE.

LETTER X.

DEAR SIR:

ON Saturday last we all rode into the city, which, as I have told you, is about two and a half hours' fast driving from Overton Park. The road is a smooth turnpike, and runs through a beautiful country of field and woodland, hill and dale. The landscape is constantly varied and constantly interesting. Numerous pretty villas lined the road, which being much used, was thronged with carriages and horsemen.

The number of gentlemen we found on horseback would be matter of surprise to a Northerner, who usually rides only in a gig. A Southerner seldom trusts himself inside of a carriage. If his wife rides out in her finely-appointed barouche, he canters well-mounted by the carriage window. I believe the Tennessee gentleman looks upon it as decidedly effeminate to be seen taking his ease in a cushioned carriage.

On the way we passed the site of an old fort, where the army of Jackson encamped before marching to New Orleans. A few yards from the ramparts, the place where a man was shot for desertion, was pointed out to me. It is a sweet-looking, green spot, and calls up any other associations than those of bloodshed.

The Hermitage where Andrew Jackson, jr., now resides, was not many miles from us. It is a good-looking mansion with a portico, and surrounded by lawns and gardens. At the foot of the garden is visible, through foliage, the snow-white tomb of the hero and statesman.

I was charmed with the beauty of the scenery on both sides of our road. The whole landscape undulated like a mighty green sea. About two miles from Nashville a hill commands a fine view of it. We stopped to gaze upon it as it rose, crowning a sort of lofty island amid a valley, the Cumberland flowing on the east side. The view was exceedingly fine and imposing. For every roof there was a tree, and what with alternate terraces of foliage and porticoes, with the domes and spires rising above all, I was so struck with admiration that I wished for a painter's pencil to transfer the noble picture to canvass.

The highest portion of the city is distinguished by a large mansion cresting it like a coronet. This was the residence of the late President Polk, now occupied by his estimable widow, who, I am told, has shut herself up, a prey to inconsolable grief ever since the death of her distinguished husband. From the distance at which we were viewing the house, I could see that the large columns were craped with black.

Nashville has been celebrated for its gaiety, its wealth, its luxury, its sociability, and the beauty of its females. I was not disappointed in the latter. As we approached the city, we met at least fifty carriages driving out for the usual evening ride, for which these people are so famous. In nearly every one of them I beheld one or more lovely faces. We met also a large cavalcade of school girls mounted on pretty ponies, and every face was handsome. So it was after we entered the city, and

went among the shops. All the girls we met were
pretty; and especially, we noticed an unusual number
of genteel, lovely widows; for men live *faster* than women, and die early.

The equipages of the city are numerous, and some of
them handsome. They drive fast, and usually in open
carriages.

Before leaving the city, which carries elegance and
taste to a high degree, we paid a visit to the Capitol,
which is one-third completed. It is a majestic *new* ruin
in its present aspect, and by moonlight must remind
travelers from Italy of a Roman temple, half dismantled.
Mr. Wm. Strickland is the architect. It has been four
years in building, and will not be completed in five more.
Its cost will be $2,000,000. The material is a white
limestone, with delicately "watered" veins. When completed it will be the finest edifice in the Union, without
exception.

Crowning a cliff that rises like an island rock from
the heart of the city, it will have very much the appearance of the Castle at Edinburgh, and be a distinguished mark for the eye for leagues around. I was
never more disappointed than I was in the air and style
of the city. Everything indicates taste, and the uses
of wealth. There is as much fashion here as in New
York; and the ladies dress far more than anywhere else
I have been. Jewelry is much worn, even in the street,
and especially at church. Riding on horseback is very
fashionable, and the costume *à cheval* is elegant and recherché. The dwellings are richly furnished. One
house I passed, built after the plan of the Borghesé
Palace at Rome, is furnished throughout with furniture

made to order in Paris, and is adorned with European pictures and statuary.

The churches of this city are not handsome or imposing. And who do you suppose I heard read the service, the last Sabbath I was in town? Mr. H——, once an author, who has been for two years past studying for orders in the church. He is also principal of an Academy for young ladies in the city, a position which he holds temporarily, until he shall be ordained. I trust he will be eminently useful as a clergyman.

Speaking of authors, what a change has come over the literary sky! Star after star disappears or falls from it; Mellen is dead; Bryant writes not; Halleck will write no more; Hoffman has changed his poet's pen to an accompter's; Bird is a politician; Simms has become an editor and historian; Poe, poor Mr. Poe, is dead! Hastings Weld has taken orders. Willis has almost ceased to write, except editorially, and very hastily at that; for, give Mr. Willis time to polish and adorn, prune and shape his sentences, and put in the pretty thoughts, and his articles are faultless. No one can excel him therein. But let him write *currente calamo*, as the college men say, and he is not so interesting. Morris is editor, too. I hear his songs sung everywhere in the West. He takes the pianos in fair rivalry with Tom Moore. If he wants to know what posterity will think of him, let him come out West. Willis too, is a favorite this way. In a girl's school the other day, I heard two of his pieces recited by two lovely girls, in a manner that would have made the gentlemanly author feel, had he been present, that he was well repaid for the time and care of their composition. I heard, at the same time, a dark-eyed Grecian looking maiden recite, with pathos and fine taste, Halleck's Marco Bozzaris. The voice of the West is the echo of posterity.

There are no poets among the men West, save Prentice; and few females who write. There is much said of the playful genius of southern women, and the fertile imagination of the men; but these produce but few authors. Amelia of Kentucky is almost the only one known. There is far more poetical *talent* in cold New England, than in the sunny West. Portland is peculiarly favorable to this development, I have heard. It has produced Mrs. Stephens, Mrs. Elizabeth Oakes Smith, the most imaginative of American poetesses; Longfellow who will long be remembered by his noble "Psalm of Life;" Mellen, the forgotten, and others. What country colder than Sweden—what genius greater than that of that sweet writer, Frederika Bremer!

It seems to me that the American press is putting forth nothing new from American authors. Our writers seem all to have turned Magazine writers.*

By the way, French is much studied here, and forms a part of every young lady's education. It strikes me Mr. ——, that if you would add a French department to your other headings in your paper, it would be very well received by the thousand school misses into whose hands your paper falls. I would suggest the regular publication of well written moral French tales, or letters, with an exactly literal translation in the opposite column. It would be quite as acceptable to numerous contributors, as charades, and aid them in their French, while it will

* These letters were written from 1852 to 1855.

improve their minds.   I think it would be an interesting, as well as a new feature in your columns.

This being the last of the test letters I was to write you, to see whether you should judge me fit to be a contributor " on remuneration."   I shall write no further till I learn the decision of your august tribunal.

Yours,
KATE.

LETTER XI.

Mr. ———:

YOUR very kind letter of the 1st inst., conveying to me the unhoped for, but welcome intelligence, that you have decided to enlist me among your *corps* of contributors, was duly received. I know not how, adequately, to express to you, the deep gratitude of my heart, for this decision; for I feel that it was given rather through your kind generosity, than through any merit which my unfledged pen could lay claim to. I shall, therefore, do my best to show you how deeply I appreciate your goodness, and resolve that my "Needles" shall be always sharp withal, that you shall never have cause to regret your decision in my favor.

My simple goose quill already begins to feel its dignity, held in an authoress's fingers! It bristles its snowy mane and curves its polished neck with the pride of an Arabian courser. It realizes its importance. It feels that it is possible that one day it may be knocked off at an auction of "rare curiosities," for not less than ten golden eagles, as authors' stump pens have been before to-day. My inkstand, which is a lion couchant, with the ink in his ears, seems to raise his majestic head with unwonted dignity as he yields it to the thirsty pen. The very paper is eloquent in its spotless robes, and seems to say: "Remember thou art an authoress, and be careful what you trace upon me, for thy words may be immortal!" Oh, the sweet, trembling, timid, happy feeling of author- ship! How the heart bounds at the sight of our *first* thoughts, which we know (yet hardly realize it) have been made visible to the eyes of other in type! We think little of seeing our own ideas *written;* but *printed,* they create sensations indescribable, half delight, half awe, a mingled state of bliss and fear, that none who have not been "in print," can ever experience.

I suppose the young merchant, who, for the *first* time, sees his name heading his showy advertisement in the morning paper, or gazes from the opposite side of the way upon it painted upon his sign in gold letters, upon a blue ground, experiences pleasure, novel and strange. But this emotion is not to be compared with that of the author, who, for the first time, sees the copy of the deep, hitherto unspoken, unconfided thoughts of his soul legible in type to every eye! His *thoughts* thus made public, are more than a mere painted name, they are a *part* of himself, a ray of the outgoings of his spirit! It is like beholding himself with an introverted mirror! Therefore, the poet *loves* his verses, after has subsided his first awe and surprise at beholding them in print, (which a little time before he had found dwelling in the bottom of his soul's deep being,) loves them as a man, with all his faults, loves himself!

Who then will laugh at the dullest rhymer for being enamored with his own verses? We might as well laugh at him for loving himself. He thinks his verses as good as his talk, and what man was ever persuaded that he did not talk well; or else all bad talkers would be for- ever silent! When we can convince a poor talker that he *is* a poor talker, then will appear the Eighth wonder, viz: a poor poet convinced that he is a poor poet. His poetry, like his conversation, is himself, and himself like China on the "Celestial" map, is the centre of the universe.

Now from what I have said, good Mr. ——, you will be fairly persuaded that, write I ever so stupidly, it will be useless in you or anybody else, to attempt to impress upon my mind a healthy sense of stupidity. This is, therefore, throwing down the gauntlet to you and the critics, (if such a little bird as I be worthy of their aim,) not to make the attempt to enlighten my intellectual twilight. I have to thank some friendly pen for a letter addressed to me in your columns; although it appears to come from a juvenile author, it is, nevertheless, worthy of my attentive recognition, as an evidence that some warm heart seeks to express its approving sense of my brief literary attempts. I have also seen a pretty poem, addressed to me, which, albeit, something bold and school-boyish in its audacity, yet it is frank and hearty in its tone, and the writer merits my thanks for his kind wishes. Speaking of poetry, reminds me how little *true* poetry there is written now-a-days. Some one has said that there are fifteen hundred papers printed in the Union; in most of these, weekly, appear one or more pieces of *original* poetry, say twelve hundred perpetrations rhythmical, per week, which multiplied by 52, the number of weeks in a year, would give the amazing number of 60,000 pieces of original poetry, printed in our newspaper columns in a year! Of these not more than sixty annually are worth preserving or republishing, that is, one in a thousand! What a despairing computation!

I am half afraid that, by daring to have made it, I shall be the innocent cause of driving some hundreds of these ambitious poets to running themselves through the heart with their steel pens, or taking ink inwardly.

I have been recently looking over the "Male and Female Poets of America," and I cannot lay my finger on a score of poems of which I could unhesitatingly say, "That is imperishable!" Most of the poems of our book poets, like the editorials of editors, have fulfilled their destiny when once in print. Longfellow has written two pieces, his Psalm of Life, and the noble verses in which the Union is finely metaphored as a builded ship of oak and iron, which will weather all time. Bryant's Thanatopsis, (if he will revise and strengthen by condensing it here and there,) will never cease to be admired so long as men are born to die. Halleck's Marco Bozzaris, it seems to me, holds in suspension the elements of undying life. Simms in the South is a noble poet. One or more songs of the lyric poet, Morris, and two or three of Willis's sacred pieces, are imperishable so long as nature and veneration remain the same as they now are in the human breast. Besides these, I can find none that give promise of surviving the ages to come! We have written a great deal for the nineteenth century, but scarcely any thing for the twenty-fifth! What is literary immortality? Do our poets know what it means, that each expects it? It is the thoughts of one or two individual men surviving the oblivion of 800,000,000 of men, their contemporaries. For of every generation of 800,000,000 of men in all ages past, but *two* or *three* have left their names or works to us! It is but a twenty minutes' task to enumerate all the immortal writers of all nations, from Moses to Chaucer. They are hardly as many for 3000 years as appear in the monthly published list of letters in a city newspaper! They are *one* living man to a hundred millions dead! Who, then, shall dare to prophesy for his productions, or for his name, immortality? Who shall be so vain as to take offence when it is questioned if after the 800,000,000 now on earth have been two thousand years dead, he himself, or aught that he has written, though he be embalmed in Griswold's "Doomsday Book," shall be remembered! Immortality! Perpetuity of memory in the hearts of the myriads of the mighty future! For whose single brow, now on earth, shall the men of the year 6000 wreath the laureled crown? Whose name, of those millions of men who walk the city streets to-day, shall the youths and maidens to be born twelve hundred years hence, have familiarly on their lips, as we have the names of Homer, of Virgil, of Shakespeare, of Milton, of David? Immortality! How few understand thy meaning when they speak of thee! You will see, dear Mr. ——, that I have very little hopes of being immortalized through my pen! I confess the chances are against me, 800,000,000 to 1. You have, therefore, the unique satisfaction of having a contributor who never expects to be quoted by the *literati* of the year 6000, A. M. There is an immortality, however, which all may gain—which springs from the heart, not from the intellect—which looks to the approbation of angels, and not of men—to a world that shall exist when the last year of the last century of this earth shall have closed forever upon all human hopes, compared with which immortality, that of this world is but an echo.

The colonel has just laid on my table Ticknor's Spanish Literature, and Emerson's "Nature." I shall, therefore, feast for the next three days. If I find any thing that strikes me as valuable in either of these books, you shall have the benefit of my reading.

I have heard rifles or shot-guns cracking all the morning in the forest over by the tarn, and therefore judge the game to be abundant. To-morrow I am going deer-hunting! I don't mean to be so cruel as to kill (for I can shoot, Mr. ——, and *hit* too!) the pretty white-breasted does, or the majestic stag, with his proud, antlered head tossing in the air! Yet, I am all curiosity to witness a hunt.

Good-bye, sir,

KATE.

LETTER XII.

Mr. ———— :

My dear sir, did you ever shoot a deer? But I dare say you don't have deer to shoot in Independence Square! Do you think it would be cruel to kill one if you had them there? One week ago I was innocent of the blood of any one of these pretty, brown animals; but, alas! I am sorry to confess that I have shot a deer since I last wrote you, and although it is not dead, I feel as badly as if I had wounded a helpless, human being. Its reproachful, pleading look, as it turned its large, intelligent eyes upon me, I can never forget! I will tell you how it happened.

The colonel had been invited to "Chestnut Ridge," seven miles from the Park, by an old military friend, who is as keen a sportsman as Nimrod ever was, to hunt deer. The invitation was accepted, and Isabel and myself were taken along with the gallant colonel to witness the sport! Sad *sport* to see the innocent animals that so grace the glade of the green forest slaughtered! Rising with the dawn, we took an early breakfast, and mounted our horses just as the sun, like a wheel of gold, rolled up the east. I was no longer mounted on the spirited and pretty little mule, which played me such a runaway prank last November, but rode a handsome black pony, with a long tail and a magnificent mane, and the smallest

ears conceivable.   His pace was as gentle as a cradle,
and he stepped over the grass, as if he trod on velvet
in a drawing-room.   The colonel rode a noble charger,
of a dark-bay color, with a neck arched and proud, like
a war-horse; and such he was, for the colonel had ridden him into many a battle strife on the fields of Mexico.
The superb animal, as he pawed the earth and pranced
along through the woodlands, seemed still "to smell the
battle afar off, and the thunder of the captains and the
shouting."   What grace and strength were united in him!

Next to man, the horse is unquestionably the noblest
created thing.   But of all majestic forms conceivable to
human imagination, I have never seen any thing that
equals that mighty tri-formed figure to be found por-
trayed in Layard's Nineveh.   I mean the sublime form
composed of a body of a lion, of the wings of an eagle,
and of the face of a man.   No one can gaze upon it without admiration and awe.   It represents strength, fleet-
ness, and intelligence embodied, and the result is a
creature that rivals in dignity, majesty, and glory, and
symmetry, man himself!

But I am running away from my party.   Isabel, the
beautiful, Spanish-looking Isabel, rode by her father's
left hand, mounted upon a mottled palfrey that seemed
formed especially for herself.   His small head, his transparent, pink nostrils, his slender fetlocks as neat as a
lady's ankle, his dainty footfall, as his deerlike hoofs
picked out the smoothest way for his mistress, were all
characteristics of the Arabian race, from which it claimed
lineage.   What decided aristocracy there is in the horse!
They differ as widely from each other as men do, and
how widely these are separate in excellency of lineage!

There is nobility of birth as there is vulgarity of birth! There are gentlemen who are gentlemen by nature. I am not a believer in the axiom that all men are born equal, and that education, or the want of it, makes men equal. There is gentility and refinement of feature that education cannot give, and there is vulgarity of feature that education cannot ennoble. When a double-headed, double-jointed plough-horse, or any of its kith, can be educated to win a Derby cup, then I shall believe that a vulgar mind and a vulgar face can, by education, be refined and ennobled. We had a merry ride of it through the grand woods! How we laughed till echo laughed again. One can be as noisy as one pleases in the country. There was a white frost on the ground, and the crisp grass crashed and crackled as we pressed its crystal spears. The birds (for many birds dwell in the forest here all the year round) were singing to the morning with gladness in their tiny breasts; the squirrel bounded from limb to limb, or raced with nimble feet across the sward, and darted up some tall trunk, going higher and higher, and carefully keeping on the side opposite to us; for they are a cunning wee thing, with their bushy tails arched over their round backs, and their twinkling, pretty eyes as watchful as weasels. There was no regular forest path, but we threaded the wood at will, for the trees grew far asunder, and the total absence of underbrush made it like park-land. The surface of the country was undulating and picturesque. At one time we would descend to a gurgling brook rushing hoarsely away from the rocks in its bed, and, fording its translucent waters at another time, find ourselves at the top of a ridge that opened to us a far spread river view.

In our ride of five miles we met but three persons. One of these was an old African with a head as white as *wool*, and a face, venerable and lined with age, and a snowy beard. His appearance was striking, and reminded me of a *black* patriarch, especially as he wore a gray blanket over his shoulder like a mantle. And let me remark, that a blanket completes a negro's winter costume here; sometimes it is made into a coat, but more frequently, for the advantage of having it as a covering at night, worn entire, like a shawl, or a Spanish *poncho*. The African was leading a tall Congo stripling, half-naked to the waist, who had a hanging countenance, as if he were an offender of some sort.

"That is old Juba with his grandson Tom, tied," said the colonel, as they drew near. "Tom has been playing the runaway in the woods these three weeks. So, uncle Juba," added the colonel in the kind, familiar tone in which masters here, who are *gentlemen*, address their old slaves; "so you've caught Tom?"

"Ees, mosse, me cotch de berry bad boy! He nebber raise heself for noting good uf he get de habit ob runnin' 'way dis way! Old Juba feel berry shame ob him. Me gib him frashun, me git him home. He disgrace to de family! Come 'long, you nigger, a'n't you shame youself, run off in de wood like a dog-tief?"

With this appeal, the old man gave the thong a jerk, and, touching his old hat in respectful homage to his master and to ourselves as "young mississes," dragged his ragamuffin grandson of eighteen years on the way back to the plantation.

"That old negro," said the colonel, as we rode on, "has been in my family seventy-eight years. He was

bought by my grandfather before the Revolution from
an African trader that came into Jamestown with a load
of slaves from the coast of Africa. He was then a lad
of fourteen, and is of course now ninety-two; yet he is
never idle, is active and faithful, and is a sort of patriarch over the rest of the slaves, half of whom are his
descendants. He has not yet forgotten his African language, which he still speaks when he is vexed, nor has
he dropped his heathenish superstitions. He wears about
his neck full half a dozen *charms* of one sort or another,
and is a firm believer in the devil, whom he says he has
seen bodily a hundred times. His influence over the
negroes is very extraordinary. They stand in awe of
him. His grandson, you see, is a tall, stout fellow, and
might get away from him; but he would as soon think
of striking the old man as resisting his authority.

We had not ridden more than a mile after parting
with Juba and his captive, when we saw a figure standing
as motionless as a statue in the forest ahead of us. The
attitude was free and commanding, and a nearer approach showed us that it was an Indian. He was leaning on his rifle. He wore a sort of coronet, made of
brass, encircling his crow-black head, and ornamented
with crow and eagle's feathers. He was dressed in a
blue frock, trimmed with tarnished gold lace, and belted
close to his body by a stout leathern cincture. Hanging
upon his brawny chest were several silver medals. On
his left wrist were five hoops or bracelets of brass, close
together, and being riveted on whole, were evidently
meant to be worn till his death. He wore deer-skin leg-
gins, the seams fringed, and his feet were encased in
once handsomely ornamented moccasins, which had seen

service. In his belt were a powder-horn, a long knife
in a sheath of serpent's skin, a pouch for balls, flints, &c,
and another large one for miscellaneous articles. His
rifle was very long, slender, without any groove-stock
for the barrel to rest in, and had a flint lock. I had
time to observe all these particulars, for we stopped and
held some minutes' "talk" with the warrior; for warrior
he was, having fought under General Jackson long years
agone; and two of the medals suspended from his neck
were bestowed upon him, the colonel said, by the "hero."
The Indian was full sixty years of age, but time had
scarcely whitened a hair of his lofty head.   Proud, stern,
dignified as a king, he neither moved nor regarded us as
we rode up to him.

"Good morning, Captain John," said the colonel; "a
fine day for the deer! You seem to be on the chase as
well as we!"

The Indian chief smiled at hearing the courteous and
bland words of the colonel, and answered in a deep bary-
tone, that completely came up to my idea of a "manly
voice."

"Ya, white chief! Good morn'! Deer not much
plenty! Good day hunt, but deer not much plenty!
White man leave no more deer for Indian rifle!" and he
slowly shook his head, cast his eyes sadly to the earth,
and remained silent.

"Why do you and your people not remove west,
chief?" asked the colonel. "You will find vast hunting
grounds there—no white man will intrude upon you--
you can there be happy and powerful!"

"Indian never more be great, white chief!" responded

the old warrior, with a heavy cloud darkening the noble outline of his Washington like features.

As he spoke, he turned and strode away with the air and bearing of Forrest as Metamora, save that the one is imitation, and the other nature.

"Who is that noble looking chief?" I inquired of the colonel, for his sullen pride and solitary condition had inspired me with a curiosity to know his history.

"That is the celebrated Creek chief Nelastora," was his reply, as we resumed our ride, while the chief disappeared in the depths of the woodland. "He was an ally of Jackson's in the Indian wars, and was of great assistance to the cause. The encroachments of civilization upon his hunting grounds, which were once a hundred miles in extent through this region, have compelled most of his tribe to remove to the west of the Mississippi. But he and a few of his friends refuse to go. He has sworn, I am told, upon the graves of his fathers, that he will never desert them, but remain to protect and die upon them! And he will keep his word. Sometimes he is seen a hundred miles south of this, but he is never long absent from the central seat of his tribe, which is a beautiful valley thirty miles to the east and south of us. I have before met him in the forest, but he refused all offers of hospitality, and will cross the threshold of no white man. Crockett and this chief were once like brothers, yet he never sat at the American hunter's board. Three years ago, Nelastora was seen standing by General Jackson's grave at the Hermitage, regarding it in silence; but when he was approached, he haughtily retired."

By the time the colonel had ended this history, we

were winding up an avenue that led to the mansion house of the old soldier, whom we had visited for the purpose of hunting deer with him.

On either hand, the ancient woods were replaced by broad cotton fields, which at this season were unplanted. A quarter of a mile from the house, a white gate, thrown open by half a dozen little shining-eyed negroes, conducted us to the grounds more immediately contiguous with the house, viz: a wide rolling lawn, adorned at intervals with native fruit trees. We approached the verandah of the house at a hard gallop, and were received by our military host with a hearty old-fashioned hospitality, that could only be exceeded by the polished courtesy of his manners. He kissed both Isabel and *me!* But then, Mr. ——, he was full fifty-nine, had gray whiskers, and—and he always made it a point of *kissing* all *pretty* young ladies that came to see him. So, unless you are fifty-nine, and have gray whiskers, you mustn't presume upon this circumstance to think—to think—you may end the sentence yourself, if you please.

Good bye,

KATE.

LETTER XIII.

DEAR MR. ———— :

PLEASE present my smiling thanks to your talented correspondent "Rusticus," of Wilmington, for his graceful verses addressed to me. I feel flattered by his compliments, while I blush that I am not more deserving of them. The thought is singularly pleasing to me, that the crude efforts of my untutored pen find readers who sympathize with and understand me. These kind persons are all my friends henceforward! I see them with the eyes of my spirit, and embrace them with my heart. One day, if not on earth, we shall meet in heaven, and recognize each other, and be friends in sweet communion forever.

When I by chance meet here, in this poor world, a kindred being, whom to know and love is happiness, I think how many such gentle and good ones the world contains, whom I shall never see on earth! When this thought comes over my spirit, I feel sad that we must pass away unknown to each other; but the bright world seen by faith beyond this reassures me, and I take courage and rejoice, believing that in the spaces of eternity all who are shaped in the same mould of love will find each other, and so the beautiful, and good, and lovely of earth, though on earth I meet them not, are not forever lost to me. Is not this a thought to make the lone heart strong? But I must tell you about my deer-hunt. Rusticus seems to question the truth of the account of the fox-hunt, but if he had spent a few days in this region of adventure, he would not hedge in his credulity so closely. Pray, why may not a lady have adventures, and dashing ones, too, as well as the "Lords?" Beshrew me, but the *esprit du camp* is not all under the round hat! I know a young lady not six miles from the Park, who is a celebrated tamer of young steeds, and, mounted upon their backs, whips them bravely into submission. Di Vernon is a tame maiden compared with her. She can shoot a rifle, hit a rose-bud at ten paces with a pistol, and take a partridge on the wing. I will, perhaps, talk about her at another time. I must now make *myself* heroine. Mr. Rusticus Doubtful, I shall rap you over the knuckles, sir poet!

I have told you, Mr. ——, how we were met by the old soldier when we drew rein at his gallery. The house was a long, low, rambling edifice, such as is peculiar to the plantations in the South, with a light gallery supported by slender columns extending along the front. A wide, natural lawn, dotted with huge forest-trees, extended around it, smooth as a green plush-carpet. On it were four or five beautiful horses cropping the sweet grass, two gentle-eyed, tame deer, a heady-looking goat with a beard like a Jew, a little innocent lambkin with a broken leg which was neatly splintered and bandaged by the old soldier's own hands, and a strutting turkey-gobbler with pride enough for the Autocrat of all the Russias, and scarlet enough for a Cardinal's cap. It was a pretty, quiet scene, with the golden bars of sunshine laid along between the openings among the trees, and the birds

singing in the branches, which the morning wind was
waving and stirring with the motion of life. The old
white-whiskered warrior escorted us into his spacious
drawing-room, holding Isabel by one hand and me with
the other, like a gallant gentleman of the old school as
he was. We were no sooner seated, one on each side
of him, than a servant entered with a quaternion of
mint-juleps, in tall silver tumblers, a golden straw of wheat
projecting from each verdant pyramid a-top. Nothing
would do but that Isabel and I should take one. The
old gentleman would not be said *Nay*. He was one of
that class of men who fancy that "no" means "yes,"
when spoken by young ladies; nay, he even went so far
as to asseverate as much. I had to take the julep.
Just imagine me, Mr. ——, seated with a riding-whip in
one hand, and a mint-julep, piled up like "Ossa upon
Pelion," in the other, communicating with my lips by
the hollow tube of straw aforesaid, and imbibing like a
smoker his tobacco, the perfumed nectar of the distilled
and delicate compound. I must confess it was delicious!
Don't tell the good temperance folks that I say so for
the world! but it was truly refreshing. I didn't wish
to sip enough to get into my head; so, after five or six
charming sips, I placed the silver goblet, still full, upon
the salver. Do you not admire my self-denial under the
circumstances?

I spent an hour admiring the pictures and curiosities
in the old soldier's handsomely-arranged rooms. Over
the mantel was a large, full length of the Hero of New
Orleans, at middle age, in the uniform of a colonel. It
was an admirable head, and struck me as the personification of energy of will, a quality for which the "Gene-

ral" was afterward distinguished above all other Americans.

"You admire the Hero?" said the host, as he observed us closely studying the expression of the face of the Iron Man of the New World.

"Greatly," I answered.

"He was a *great* man, Miss Kate!" responded the soldier and companion in arms, with a liquid sparkle visible in his eyes. I love to see tears in brave men's eyes!

"You knew him well, major?" I said, interrogatively.

"We were as brothers, or rather as father and son, for though I am gray, he was twenty years my senior. He was a lion in battle, and an eagle in pursuit. He was born to command. He read men as I read a child's book. They have said he was cruel. It is not true! He loved to exercise mercy. Let me tell you an anecdote to illustrate his character. A soldier had deserted his post to go home to a dying father. He was arrested kneeling at his father's bedside receiving his dying blessing. He begged to be permitted to remain to close his eyes, 'when,' he said, 'he would ready.' He was taken to the camp, then in Florida. He was tried by a court-martial, and condemned to be shot. The General signed his sentence of death on a drumhead. I saw him do it, and I saw a tear drop, like a drop of falling rain upon the hollow drum-head. But those who saw not the tear, but marked only the stern lines of his face, thought him unfeeling!" Here the major frowned, and looked fierce to hide and keep back the liquid drops that had been growing larger every moment, too large for his eyes to hold; but spite of his bent brows, they found their channels and rolled, pearls of price, adown his battle-browned cheeks. What are tears? Can any tell what and why are tears?

"The poor man was at length led forth to execution," resumed the major, who had caught one of his tears slyly on the back of his hand, while the other broke, as he thought unobserved, upon the marble hearthstone; "the detachment which was detailed to execute the sentence, was drawn up about fifty paces from the general's tent. The whole army were drawn up in line to witness the death of the deserter. The general remained in his tent. He was pacing up and down calmly and thoughtfully. There wanted but a minute to the signal for death, when suddenly he ordered the deserter to be brought before him. The man was led blindfolded as he was to his tent. 'Larnham,' said the general to the deadly pale man, 'you have forfeited your life by the laws of war. I therefore signed the warrant for your execution. You have merited life by your filial obedience; I therefore repeal the sentence of the court martial and pardon you; and may every son be as worthy of the name as you have proved yourself to be!' The poor man fell at the general's feet and embraced his knees, and the army without hurrahed as one man; for the filial piety of the deserter had found a responsive chord in every heart, and the pardoning act awakened its echo."

There was a stand of colors in the corner of the room which the major had carried at the head of his battalion; and there were many ornaments around, consisting of war-hatchets, bows, quivers, wampums, crests of eagle's feathers, painted deer skins, fringed and embroidered, all presents from Indian chiefs. The major showed me a war club which was fringed with human hair, and which he said had killed many a warrior in its day. But the sight of it was revolting to my imagination. But he had paintings of favorite horses and hounds, of game and hunting scenes, and the candelabra of his rooms were deer's antlers, with silver tops terminating the extremities to hold the candles. One horned branch held *thirteen* sockets, which he called his Federal Chandelier. He took us to one room which was literally hung around with rifles, old, long, and short, and of all sizes; pistols, fowling pieces, deer's antlers, powder flasks and horns, game bags, dried game, game in glass cases, and all sorts of things which I could not imagine the use of, but which he gravely declared were all essential to the making up of a good hunter.

He would take us to his stables too, to see his blind war-horse. We found the venerable steed occupying a neat brick cottage opening into a green paddock in which he was grazing. As soon as he heard his master's voice he pricked up his aged ears and came trotting along till he was within two yards, when he stopped and felt his way to the gate with his feet. We patted him and spoke kindly to him, and he licked salt out of my hand. His teeth were all gone, and his eyes were as white as those of a fish. How pitiable was the noble wreck! He had been through the Alabama and Florida wars, and bore a scar on his left shoulder from the blow of a tomahawk. His master talked with him as if he were a human being, and as affectionately as if he were a comrade. It was a fine picture; the white-headed soldier leaning upon and talking kindly with the aged war-horse who had seen better days, but had now grown old together with his master.

When we returned to the house we found all ready for the hunt. Our horses were saddled and at the door, each held by an African. We were soon a-saddle, followed by four servants a-foot, two of whom led a leash of dogs a-piece. How the hounds' intelligent eyes spoke of anticipated sport! Our party consisted of our colonel, the old soldier, Isabel, and myself, of the Saxon race; of the four negroes, and a fifth, half breed, who was a sort of forest-keeper to our host. He was a man skilled, the major told us, in every kind of wood-craft, and not to be matched for a deer in all Tennessee. He was mounted on a nag that looked like a half breed, having a head like a bull dog, a mane like a buffalo, and a thick mane on each fetlock. He was shaggy as an Angola rug, black, and ugly in temper. Our elegant, aristocratic jennets shied away from him if he chanced to trot near either of them, with a proud flash of their eyes and a haughty whinny of their nostrils.

We at length reached a noble wood extending to a ridge, from which there was a precipitous path leading to a romantic stream that emptied into the Harpeth which conveys its waters to the broader Cumberland. In this forest the deer usually feed, and, crossing the ridge, descend the winding path to the water side to drink.

After getting through the wood, we took up our position upon the ridge, between the forest and the water. There were four deer paths leading across it, near each of which stood an oak of enormous breadth of branches, with trunks like colossal columns of Thebes. We dismounted on the ridge, and giving our horses to the

Africans, who led them away to a distant eminence, we each of us took a position behind a tree. I would have preferred standing by the colonel's side at his tree, but he and the major insisted that Isabel and I should each have our tree, "so that," said they, "the four paths leading from the forest to the river might be commanded." So for the sake of a military disposition of their forces by the two old soldiers, I had to take post behind one of the huge oaks. Next to me was the major, fifty feet off to the south; and on the north of me was Isabel, with the colonel on the north flank. For form's sake we were both armed. (Isabel and I with small bird guns, London make, and exquisitely ornamented with silver inlaying.) These guns were *ours*,—New Year's presents from the colonel, who regularly gave us lessons in the science of shooting, averring that every American lady ought to know how to take sight and pull a trigger. Now, when I took the post assigned me, I had no more malice aforethought against any deer of the forest, Mr. ——, than I have against that "dear gazelle" the song sings about. I was as innocent of any intention of firing, as a timid young gent who has been dragged into a duello by his "friends" would be likely to have.

The tall half-breed had left us some time before we reached the ridge, and turned off into the depths of the forest with the dogs, about a dozen of them in all. We had hardly well taken our "stands" when, from the bosom of the old wood, came to our ears the low basso baying of the hounds, sounding full a mile off.

"There, they wake them up, girls!" cried the major, with eyes sparkling with something of their old battle fire. "Stand firm and keep your trees when they come.

Take cool aim and pull trigger when you see the color of their eyes. They will be up in about five minutes!"

The baying of the hounds now grew nearer and louder, mingled at intervals with the shrill, human cry of the deer driver. From the colonel I understood that the dogs had doubled round the deer as they were feeding, and were driving them towards the ridge, which they would soon fly across, to dash for the river. Nearer and louder, and wilder was the uproar in the forest! The open mouths of a dozen dogs, cheered on by the half-breed, filled the woods with a continuous roar. Soon were heard close at hand the crashing of branches and rustling of leaves, as the antlers of the deer brushed them in their mad *escapade*. Then came the quick patter of hoofs, and the rush of the air like the "noise of many waters."

"Look! see! they are in sight!" cried Isabel, her dark eyes sparkling like a spirited young knight's, when he first sees his foe advancing against him, lance in rest!

And they *were* in sight! First, a noble stag, leading the van of the flight; then half a dozen graceful does; then two or three smaller stags; then a confused crowd of a score of all sizes. With heads laid flat back on their shoulders, they came up the ridge side with incredible swiftness. As they approached our stands, they divided into four beaten paths, and came on like a rolling sea, bearing a fleet of antlers. Behind them, following hard on their flanks, coursed the dogs, with their heads in the air, and their deep bay deafening the ear.

It was a moment of intense excitement. It was like a battle commencing, with the foe charging! I did not feel fear, but excitement! My pulse bounded! My heart leaped with heroic springs! My spirit caught the wild inspiration of the scene!

"Stand firm!" eagerly whispered the colonel to us, as they got so near that we could see their brown, womanly looking eyes.

"Draw your sight coolly, girls," cried the major.

The next moment they were upon us! The leading stag dashed like a race horse past the oak where Isabel stood, four or five following him at top speed. But I had no time to observe others. My eyes were bent with a stern energy (my brow is hardly yet restored to its natural smoothness) upon a phalanx that was rushing towards me like the wind. An instant, and they passed, leaving a hurricane in the air of their track following them. I shut my eyes involuntarily. (Crack! crack! went rifles on each side of me!) As I opened them again, I saw the last of the party making for my tree like a launched javelin. (At this instant Isabel's gun was heard.) It was a beautiful doe, and as I had, in the bewildering moment of the exciting scene, stepped a little out, and exposed myself unconsciously to her attack, she came leveling her frontal battery unerringly to butt me over. I saw my danger, and was paralyzed at it!

"Fire, or you are killed," shouted the colonel, in a tone of horror.

"Fall down, and let her bound over you!" hallooed the major.

Instinctively I levelled my pretty bird gun and fired. I saw the beautiful animal leap into the air, the red blood pouring down its snow-white breast, and plunge forward headlong at my feet. I sunk, almost insensible, upon the warm body, scarcely hearing the cries.

"Bravo!"

"Capital shot!"

A shriek from Isabel, who believed me wounded by the doe's hoofs, and who flung herself by my side, recalled me from the momentary stupor which the mingled emotions of my danger and my escape, and my horror at the sight of the bleeding breast of the deer, had produced.

Judge my happiness, Mr. ——, when it was found that the doe was not mortally wounded. The major, at my entreaty, said it should be taken to his house and nursed for me till it recovered. This was done, and I have the pleasure of assuring you that it is rapidly convalescing, and it seems to be grateful to me for riding over every day to see how it fares.

The result of the day's "sport" was two stags, three does, and one rabbit, which Isabel caught alive on our way home, after running it down on horseback. She also wounded a deer, which escaped from her.

Now, then, you have a veritable account of my deer hunt. When you make your promised tour of the Union, "á la President," and come to this garden of the West, Tennessee, we will get up a hunt especially for your edification, fox, deer, or rabbit, as may chime in with your fancy.

Yours, respectfully,
KATE.

LETTER XIV.

My wounded deer has quite recovered. You cannot imagine my joy at this result. If it had died, I should have carried the poor, affectionate, mild-eyed creature's death upon my conscience to my last hour. It already knows my voice, and suffered me to lead it by my saddle-horn yesterday, from the major's to the Park; though, to confess the truth, it came twice near bounding away from me when it discovered a herd of deer, which, scared at our approach, went scampering down the glades. But a gentle word and a pat upon the neck re-assured and quieted it. The worst part of bringing it over was to keep two hounds, that always ride out with Isabel, from tearing it in pieces. They could not comprehend the mystery why man should one day hunt deer down and slay them, and the next, pet and protect one. Brutes are not very able logicians, and are beyond the comprehension of mixed motives. No doubt a great deal of the conduct of their intelligent masters puzzles them vastly. Brutes follow instinct that never deviates from a straight line, while intelligence is unconfined. Buck and Wolf could not be reasoned with, so I used my whip smartly; and, thus seconded, at length got my protegée safely housed at home. What splendid orbs the mild creature has for eyes! Their expression is soft and pleading, with a slight glitter of timidity. I have seen a beautiful

woman who had just such eyes as my deer has. To
keep my treasure from the dogs, I have shut it up in the
paddock for poultry, which has a high fence around it;
I have had to whip the hounds half a score of times to
teach them not to stick their black noses through the
palings and yelp at it, half terrifying it to death.

By the way, talking of hounds, I was awakened this
morning at sunrise by a great uproar in the kennel, where
at least twenty hounds are kept. Every dog was in full
howl, and such a noise! It was not the clear, heart-
stirring bay they utter when they are in chase, but a
melancholy, cross, snappish wailing and howling, as if
some hitherto unheard of tribulation had befallen them
generally and individually. The whole house was roused.
The colonel first reached the scene of the canine turmoil, and, upon inquiring, ascertained from a black woman, that they were "mad because *she* baked their corn-
bread for dem."

It appeared that old, purblind mam' Daphny, who
does nothing but cook for the hounds, was sick in bed
"with the rheumatics," and delegated her duties to
another for the day. The hounds, whose alimentary
tastes, as well as olfactory nerves, are keenly sensitive,
had detected the new and less skillful hand "at the bel-
lows," and so bellowed forth, in the fashion I have
described, their grief and rage at this innovation upon
established usages. They left the corn-bread untouched,
and would not eat until old aunt Daphny—good-hearted
Congoese—crawled out of bed, and made up a "batch"
which was no sooner placed before the epicurean quad-
rupeds, than they devoured it greedily. It takes as much

good bread to keep these hounds as it does a dozen negroes.   They, the dogs, are dainty wretches.

I was witness, yesterday afternoon, to a scene that
afforded me infinite amusement.   The negroes had presents all round at Christmas and Newyear's; but, on
Washington's birth-day, old George, a favorite and venerable slave, whose father once belonged to Washington,
argued that. *he* ought to have a special present!   The
colonel therefore sent into Nashville and bought him a
new violin.   A more acceptable gift could hardly have
been made to him, as he has a fine ear for music, and is
the Orpheus and "Ole Bull" of the plantation.   It has
been his custom of evenings, after the day's work is over,
to seat himself upon a bench beneath a large elm that
grows in the centre of the African village or Quartier.
Here, at the sound of his fiddle, would gather the whole
ebon population to dance.   At such times he gives *regular* lessons to the young negroes in dancing to the
banjo, and teaches their juvenile voices the classic airs
of Mondango and Guinea; hereditary tunes, that have
been brought from Africa, and which are now spread over
the land to such words as "Juliana Johnson, don't you
cry," " Old Daṇ Tucker," " Long Time Ago," &c.

We had just risen from the tea-table, last evening,
when old George made his appearance at the steps of
the gallery, and, baring his bald head, he bowed with a
politeness that Lord Chesterfield would have envied, and
made us this speech:

" Young Missises and Massa colonel; old George
take de liberty to 'vite you to come to de dance out
door by de ol' elm.   Massa hab giv' me new fiddle,

and I takes pleasure to giv' de white folks a consart, and show de young ladieses how my scholars dance."

We accepted George's polite invitation, and as the moon was full we went over to the village. We were guided to the tree by the bright light shed from half a dozen pine torches, held in the hands of as many African animated statues, whom George had conspicuously stationed to throw light upon the scene.

As I approached the spot, I was struck with its novelty, for I have not yet been long enough here to become familiar with all plantation customs. I have told you that the negro village of the estate is picturesquely disposed on the borders of a pretty *mere*, a few hundred yards from the house. We crossed the water, by a wicker bridge, and had most of the dwellings of the slaves in full view, occupying two streets and three sides of a square. The lights of pine-wood flung a red and wild glare upon their fronts, and upon the lake, and upon a group of more than a hundred Africans of both sexes, who were assembled about the tree. It revealed, also, here and there an old man or woman, helpless through age, seated in their hut-doors, in order to enjoy as much of what was going on as they could.

We already found the dignified George seated upon his bench, fiddle in hand. On his right stood a short, fat negro, holding a banjo, and on his left was another slave, with eyes like the bottoms of China cups, holding two hollow sticks in his hand. Behind George was a toothless negress, having before her a section of a hollow tree, shaped like a drum, with a dried deer-skin drawn tightly over it; in her shining fist she grasped a sort of mallet. Chairs, assiduously provided, were placed

for us, and the buzzing of pleasure, occasioned among
the numerous company of Ham's posterity, having subsided, at a majestic wave of George's fiddle-bow, the
concert began! The first tune was a solo, and new to
me, and so beautiful and simple that I made old George
play it for me to-day in the house, and I copied the
music as he did so. He says his father taught it to him.
Certainly the negroes have striking native airs, charac-
terized by delightful surprises and touching simplicity.
Their chief peculiarity is cheerfulness.

George having first played a soft strain, the banjo
struck in a second ; then came the hollow sticks, like castanets, but five times as large, hollow, and more musical ;
and, lastly, the old negress thumped in a base on her
hollow drum. The perfect time, the sweet harmony, the
novelty of the strange sounds, the singular combination
enchanted me. I must confess that I never heard true
music before ; but then I should acknowledge I have not
heard any operatic music in an opera-house. But do
not smile if I say that I believe George and his three
aiders and abettors would be listened to with pleasurable surprise, if they should play as I heard them play,
by a Walnut street audience. *Real* African concert-
singers are not, however, in fashion. White men blacked
are only *comme il faut*. Is it not odd that a city audience will listen to *imitation* negroes, and yet despise a
concerto composed of the Simon pures? After George
had played several pieces, one of which was "Lucy
Long," as I had never heard it before, and had received
our praises, he said, always speaking with the dignity
of an oracle :

"Now, if massa and de young ladieses please, we

hab de small-fry show demselve! Come, tand out here,
you litty niggers! Show de white folk how you dance
de corn dance!"

Thereupon a score of little darkies, from five years
of age to a dozen years, girls and boys together, sprang
from the crowd, and placed themselves in the space in
front of us. Half of them were demi-clad, those that
had shirts not being troubled with any superfluous apparel, and those that had trousers being shirtless; in a
word, not a black skin was covered with but one species
of garment, and this was generally a very short and very
dirty, coarse *camisa*.

"Now make de dirt fly!" shouted George, as he struck
up a brisk air alone—banjo, hollow sticks, and drum being silent.

The younglings obeyed the command to the letter.
They danced like mad! The short-skirt flaps flew up
and down, the black legs were as thickly mixed up as
those of a centipede waltzing; woolly heads, white eyes,
glittering teeth, yells and whoops, yah-yahs, and wou-
wous, all united, created a scene that my shocked pen
refuses to describe. The little negroes did full credit to
old George's skill, and he evidently felt it. He sawed
away desperately till the sweat rained from his furrowed
brow. He writhed, and rose, and bent over, and stood
up, and did every thing but lie down, playing all the
while without cessation, and in a sort of rapturous ecstasy. Banjo caught the inspiration, and hollow sticks
started after, while drum pounded away like young thunder, yelling a chant all the while, that, had her grandmother sung it to Mungo Park, would have driven him
from the shelter of her hut to the less horrible howls

of the desert. The little Africans danced harder and harder. Their parents caught the spirit of the moment, and this one, dashing his old cap down, sprang into the arena, and that one, uttering a whoop, followed, till full fifty were engaged at once. I never enjoyed any thing so much! I could fancy myself witnessing some heathen incantation dance in the groves of Africa! The moonlight shining through the trees, the red glare of the torches upon them, their wild movements, their strange and not unmusical cries, as they kept time with their voices to their quick tramping feet, their dark forms, their contortions, and perfect *abandon*, constituted a *tout ensemble* that must be witnessed to be appreciated.

Suddenly, in the height of their diversion, the plantation bell began to strike eight o'clock. When the first stroke was heard from the turret of the overseer's house, there was a burst of mingled surprise and regret. They shouted to each other to "do their best;" and between the first and eighth stroke, take my word for it, Mr.——, more dancing was done, and harder, and faster, and noisier, than was ever done before in so small a limitation of time. It seemed they were all determined to heap as much pleasure into this fleeting space as it could contain. With the last stroke, every man, woman, and youngling, uttered a yell, gave a final leap into the air, and with the dying vibration of the bell's sound, all was quiet. George even was arrested with his bow in the air, in an attitude of expiring delight, as if

"Dying of a tune in Orpheanic pain,"

"Good night, boys," said the colonel, in the cordial frank way he has when he speaks to his people; "you

have enjoyed yourselves, and so have we.   George, your
pupils, young and old, do you credit."

"Tankee, Massa Colonel; I know'd you'd be berry much
gratify.   I hope de young ladieses is ekally charmed."

"We *are* charmed, George," I answered; at which he
made me a superb bow, when we took our departure.
The slaves also retired each to his own cabin, the torches
were extinguished, and before we reached the house,
stillness reigned in the green moonlit square of the African quarter.

"Now let us have some of *your* music, Bel," said her
father, as we entered the dining-room, which was richly
lighted with a solar sphere of ground glass.   As my
eyes fell upon the superb furniture, the gorgeous carpet,
the luxurious drapery of the windows, and the golden
harp and rosewood piano, and the peerless beauty of the
young girl seated at the costly instrument, I could not
help contrasting the refined character of the whole *ensemble* with that we had just borne a part in.   It appeared like a transition from one world to another!
Isabel's voice is surpassingly rich in compass and sweetness.   She sings much like Biscaccianti, and warbles in
her throat in the same dulcet, dove-like manner.   She
can soar too, to the same lark-like notes, taking the soul
far up on the wing of her song, to the very skies, till it
melts into heaven.   Don't think me extravagant, but
music ever needs adequate language to describe its effects.
Types, transpose them into any shape of words, fail to
express the impression music makes upon the soul.

While I was looking at the African dance, and listened
to their voices, which went to the tune of the dance in a
continuous chant, I was led to the reflection that the

dance, even in our assemblies, is a barbaric relic, and
that civilization in retaining, has only rejected the vocal
feature which characterizes it among all barbarous people. We dance *mutely;* Indians and Africans *singingly.*
Who shall judge between us?

Since I wrote the above, I have seen the gentleman
who rode the bull six miles on a steeple chase, half
across the country! He called to see the colonel on some
business, and was presented to us. He is a young man,
resolute, and rather dissipated looking; and I discerned
the butt of a small pistol sticking out of his pocket, which
did not prepossess me favorably, for it strikes me that
a brave man will not go armed day-by-day. Carrying
weapons is a sign either of a quarrelsome temper, or a
cowardly heart! After our visitor left, the colonel told us
that three years ago he laid a wager that he would ride a
famous fierce bull twice around a pasture. The bet was
taken, and the young man managed to get astride the
bull with only a stout whip in his hand. The bull, as
might be expected, at being thus taken "a-back,"
plunged, roared, pawed, and set off at full speed. At
the first dash he broke through the fence, and laid his
mad course straight across the country. The young
man, putting his whip in his teeth, and grasping a horn
in each hand, held on for his life. Unable to guide the
enraged brute, unable to check him, and fearing to throw
himself off, he committed himself to the creature's will,
which led him two leagues to the Cumberland, into which,
sans peur, the bull plunged headlong, and so gave his
involuntary rider liberty. It is needless to say he won
"the stakes."

Can you tell me, Mr.——, if General Morris has

lately published any new pieces? Next to Tom Moore's, his songs are admired in the West. If the gallant general should come out here, he would have a pretty fair notion of what *post mortem* fame is; for the appreciation which an author receives in a strange land, as I have said, is equal to the voice of posterity.

Respectfully,
KATE.

LETTER XV.

My dear Mr. ———

I CAN convey to you no adequate idea of the picturesque character of the scenery of this estate. It is made up of groves, uplands, cliffs, grotto-like springs, level, green meadows, and undulating fields. In whatsoever direction we ride or walk, there are interesting features to please the eye. Our drives from the villa are all charming. Eleven miles in one direction, eastward, we come to the venerated tomb of Jackson, at the Hermitage; in another we find ourselves, after three hours' ride, in the beautiful and wealthy city of Nashville. A longer ride, south, brings us to the handsome village of Columbia, where President Polk was born and lived, and where is one of the most eminent collegiate institutions for females in the United States; and beyond, an hour's ride farther, lies Ashwood, the princely domain of the four brothers Polk, whose estates extend for miles, in continuous and English like cultivation. Of this lovely region I shall write you by and by. A shaded road, leading four miles north of us, terminates on the pebbly shore of the romantic Cumberland, where, as we sit upon our horses, we can watch the steamers pass, and the keel boats and huge barges floating down with the current. Here, too, we sometimes catch fish, and have a rare picnic time of it.

Be sure of it, Mr. ——, you never will have enjoyed
life till you come to our Park. If I dared tell the colonel
what I was doing, he would heartily invite you through
me; but I would not let him know for the world that I
am "takin' notes an' printin' 'em," so pray don't send
your paper to him. He doesn't read much, save politics,
or I should tremble lest, when he rides to the city, he
should fall in with my "Needles." But, then, I have
not said any thing in them very naughty, have I, Mr.
——? I am sure all is love and kindness that I write;
at least, I see them in my inkstand when I dip my pen
therein.

My deer follows me like a greyhound. It has a heart
that holds gratitude as a full cup holds rich wine. When
I look into its intelligent eyes I seem to be looking down
into a pair of deep, shadowy wells, at the bottom of which
I see visible the star of its spirit. It seems to have
almost a human soul! It loves, and is grateful, and is
dependent like a woman! Nothing pleases it so much
as to have me talk to it. It listens, moves its graceful
ears, and smiles out of its eyes, its calm joy! "What,"
asks Emerson, "what is a brute?" Who can answer?
What a mystery they are!

By the way, I nearly lost my life defending my pet
yesterday. I had walked down to a spring that gushes
out of a cavernous rock in a lovely green glen, a short
distance from the house. My deer followed me. As I
sat by the spring and read "Willis's People I have Seen,"
—a very readable book, by-the-bye, my deer ambled off
to a little emerald knob, and began to browse. It was
a quiet scene, and the idea of danger never entered either
of our foolish heads. All at once I heard a wolf-like

bay from a deep throat; then a swift rushing of a bloodhound so closely past me, that I felt the warm breath
of the animal upon my face.   The next moment he was
within a bound of my deer!   With a cry of warning,
I thoughtlessly hastened to the rescue of the deer, which
no sooner saw its danger than it sprang into the air,
completely over the dog, as he crouched *couchant* to
pounce upon him, and flew to me.   The bloodhound
doubled and came back after him.   The deer stopped
and stood trembling at my side.   I threw myself forward, and endeavored to intimidate the red eyed monster
by shaking Willis at him!   But, I know not from what
influence, he turned aside from me and leaped upon the
animal's shoulder.   The helpless deer sunk upon its
knees, uttering a piteous cry.   At this my courage was
roused, and grasping like a stiletto the steel inlaid paper-
cutter I had been using, I was in the act of driving it
into the fiery eye of the savage brute, when a loud voice
caused the dog to release his hold, and me to suspend the
blow.   With a growl like a bear robbed of his prey, the
bloodhound slunk away, evidently fearing to encounter
the owner of the voice, who proved to be the overseer.

"You had an escape, miss," said the man, politely
raising his broad black hat.   "I did not know any one
was in this field, or I should have kept him close by me.
It was the deer he was after.   I hope you were not
hurt?"

"Only frightened for my poor deer," I answered.
"Her shoulder bleeds, sir."

"It is only a tooth mark through the skin.   Let me
see that dirk, if you please.   If you had stuck him with

that in the eye you would have killed him outright. It is a little, but sure weapon."

"It is a paper-cutter, sir," I said, mortified to think he should suppose I carried a dirk.

"It is as good a cutter as a knife. I am glad you did not strike the dog. He is worth a round hundred and fifty dollars, and he is the only one we have. They will track a footstep for miles," he added; "and the negroes fear them so, that one on a plantation is enough to keep them from running away. I keep this ugly fellow more as a preventive than really to hunt them. Come, Tiger," he said, calling the dog; and in a few moments I was left alone with my wounded deer. It was not, fortunately, badly hurt, and in an hour was as lively as ever.

On my way home, I called at a neat hut, built under a shady catalpa tree. A clean, broad stone was the door-step; white half-curtains were visible at the small windows, and an air of neatness pervaded the whole. Before it was a small yard, in which grew two "Pride of China" trees, for shade, and a cabbage and gourd plat were on either side of the doorway. In the door sat old Aunt Phillisy, a negress withered to parchment by extreme age.

She says she is over a hundred years old, of which I have no doubt. She is African born, and still retains many words of her native dialect, with a strange gibberish of broken English. She was smoking a pipe, made of corn-cob, and rocking her body to and fro in the sunshine, in pure animal enjoyment. Her husband, old Daddy Cusha, who was nearly as old as his wife, was seated on a low stool in the room, but where the sun fell upon him. He was the most venerable object I ever beheld, in his way. He was stone blind, his head bald, and shining like burnished copper, and his beard white as fleeces of wool. His hands were folded upon his knees, and he seemed to be in silent communion with the depths of his own spirit. These two persons had not labored for years, and their master was providing for them in their old age. On every plantation you will find one or more old couples thus passing their declining years, in calm repose, after the toils of life, awaiting their transfer to another state of being. The care taken of the aged servants in this country is honorable both to master and slave.

I had often seen Mammy Phillisy and old Daddy Cusha —as Isabel, who was attached to them, almost every day brings them, with her own hand, "something nice" from the table. The first day I took dinner at the Park, I noticed this noble girl setting aside several dainties, and directing the servant in attendance, in a whisper, to place them on a side table; and I was led from it to believe some person, some very dear friend in the house, was an invalid. But I soon found that they were for Aunt Phillisy, Aunt Daphny, and Father Jack, and other venerable Africans of the estate, whose age and helplessness were thus tenderly regarded by the children of the master they had once faithfully served.

"Good morning, Aunt Phillisy," I said.

"Eh, goo' mornee, Mishy Katawinee," answered the old slave, with a brightening expression, "howee do, Mishy ?"

"Very well, Aunt Phillisy," replied I, "I hope you and old Cusha are doing well."

"Yeesha, Mishy, we welly wellee. Takee seatee,

Mishy," she said, rising and handing me a wicker chair. So I sat down and had a long chat with them. Old Cusha could recollect when he was taken prisoner in Africa. He said his people and another tribe fought together, that his tribe was beaten, and he, and his mother, and brothers, and sisters were all taken by "de oder brackee men for gold backshee; den dey put me board de leety ship," continued Cusha, "and, by'm by, we come to land, and dey sellee me in Wirginny. Oh, it long time 'go, Missee!"

Aunt Phillisy's memory traveled no farther back than "the big blue sea." Her life in a slaver seemed to have made such an indelible impression upon her that it had become the *era* of her memory. Before it, she remembered nothing. Her face, breast, and arms were tattooed with scars of gashes, as were those also of her husband. While I was talking with them, one of their great-grand-children came into the cabin. It was as black, as thick of lip, as white of eye, as long of heel, as thick of skull, as its genuine Afric forebears; which proved to me that the African loses none of his primal characteristics by change of climate and circumstances, nor by the progress of generations. The reflection was then forced upon my mind that these familiar looking negroes, which we see every day about us, are indelibly *foreigners!* Yet what Southerner looks upon his slave as a barbarian, from a strange, barbarous land, domesticated in his own house, his attendant at table, the nurse of his children? Yet no alien in America is so much a foreigner as the negro!

What a race they are! How naturally they fall into the dependence of bondage! How familiarly they dwell in Southern households! How intimately they are associated with the inmates! How necessary to the happiness and comfort of the beautiful daughter or aristocratic lady of the planter, is the constant presence of an Africaness, black, thick-lipped, and speaking broken English, —a black daughter of Kedar—whose grandmother may have danced the Fetish by the fires of human bones, and whose father sacrificed to idols more hideous than themselves! How little, I say, does the Southerner realize who and what the negro is! Yet these descendants of barbarians and wild Afric tribes are docile, gentle, affectionate, grateful, submissive, and faithful! In a word, they possess every quality that should constitute a good servant. No race of the earth makes such excellent domestics. It is not in training! They seem to be born to it! Look at the American Indian, and contrast him with the African.

In the early history of the United States, many of these were forced into bondage, but soon pined and died! In the West Indies the Spaniards would have made the native Indians slaves, and did compel them to toil, but in what island of the West Indies are now to be found any of their descendants in bondage? Perished all! The proud spirit of the Indian will not brook vassalage. His will bends not, but breaks! A few months' subjection to imprisonment broke the great heart of Osceola! Oh, when I think on the base act of treachery (and by an American officer, too) by which that gallant and chivalrous chief was inveigled into the hands of the Americans, my pulse throbs quicker, and I feel my cheek warm! It is the darkest act that stains American history! And our government connived at it!

Our government, which, next to God's, should be supreme in greatness and glory, justice and mercy, over the earth, our government availed itself of the treachery, and so made it its own! Shame on the American arms! Infamy on the name of an officer, who, under a flag of truce, could thus violate every principle of honor!

There is just now a good deal of talk about the dissolution of the Union.* We ladies even engage in the discussion, and, if not with ability, at least with warmth and patriotism. With but one exception, I am glad to find all the Tennessee ladies I have met are firm unionists. This lady said she hoped to see the "North cast off," Nashville the capital of a new republic or kingdom, when Charleston would rival New York, and New Orleans would be the Constantinople of the world! How my heart pitied her! Dissolve the Union! It is to expatriate ourselves. It is to blot the name of America from the scroll of nations. I have no patience with such talkers. They know not what they say. What a speech Mr. Clay has given the nation! Last and mightiest effort of all. As he advances in years, his intellect seems to catch glory from the splendor of the world to which he is near approaching! His speech will be remembered through all time.

Why should such a man as Mr. Clay or Mr. Webster wish to be President? This position can add no new lustre to their names. As Presidents they would be lost in the long list of Presidents that is to be unrolled along the tide of time; but simply as American Senators, (titles, than which none are more dignified on earth,) they will descend to posterity as the Cicero and

* Written in 1852.

Demosthenes of the early ages of the republic. I would say to them, "Senators, if you wish to be great for all time, lie down in your sepulchres with the senatorial mantle folded upon your breasts."

You must pardon my bit of politics, Mr. ——, but the Tennessee ladies are all politicians, I believe the most zealous to be found anywhere, and I have caught their spirit. It strikes me that every true American woman should understand the affairs of government, political motives, great men, and exciting questions of public interest. So did the Roman matrons, and, doubtless, the Roman maidens.

But, my paper tells me I must close.

Respectfully yours,

KATE.

LETTER XVI.

DEAR MR. ———:

I HAVE just finished reading Emerson's great book,
"Nature." What a well of thought it is! What a
wonderful man he is to write such wonderful things!
He is a metaphysical anatomist. He lays open the universe to the soul's eye. He is one of those few writers
that put in words for us, our own unspoken thoughts,
those great thoughts that come upon us in the waking
hours of night, and in the still, holy hour of twilight.
How many thoughts that I never dreamt of uttering,
not dreaming they could be written in words, have I
been startled and pleased to find in this book! He
seems to comprehend the mystery of life, and teach us
what and for what we are. The questions which a child
asks, and which puzzle a philosopher to answer, this
philosopher answers with the simplicity of a child. He
delights us, because we feel that he has felt, and thought,
and wondered, as we have felt, and thought, and wondered! His book must make its way to the hearts of
all who think; of all who look at the stars, and ponder
with awe and solemn curiosity thereupon; of all who
look downward into their own spirits, and meditate upon
the mystery they are!

Mr. Emerson calls the visible universe the *scoria* of
spirit! He says, that all spirit has a tendency to visi-

bility—hence result the visible world, the heavens, and the earth. A visible creature is the *ultimatum* of spirit. The physical powers of Deity are visible in the grandeur of creation—the moral were made visible in the person of Jesus Christ, who was the "Godhead visible." These are wonderful sayings to think upon. They help vastly towards unfolding the mighty thoughts that rush upon the soul at times. Mr. Emerson's must delight all right minds. The whole scope of his Christian philosophy, however, I can not accept. He stops short of revelation, and all true philosophy should point to the Christian doctrine of the cross.

Ticknor's charming and elaborate work on Spanish literature, I have just completed. How shall I express my thanks to this laborious and elegant scholar, for the delight and instruction I have been recipient of from its pages! How little have the best Spanish students known of Castilian literature! The educated world, both sides of the sea, are under infinite obligations to Mr. Ticknor for this book. The only fault I can find with it, is the obscurity in which he has left the question touching the authorship of that fascinating work, Gonsalvo de Cordova. I have two books with this title, but am at a loss to know which it is he describes, whether the one commencing "Castas musas," or another. But one fault is a spot on the sun. I have no doubt Mr. Ticknor's work will create a taste for Spanish literature. There is none that surpasses it. The best of it is still in MS., and some of it remains locked up in the Arabic character. It is odd that the bulk of Spanish literature should consist of comedies, when we reflect that the Spaniards are the gravest people in Europe. The

French, who are the lightest people, excel most in tragedy! These facts need accounting for.

Last evening Isabel read to us one of Mrs. Lee Hentz's finely conceived and gracefully penned stories. We were all charmed with it, and the colonel, naughty man! who thinks ladies are good for nothing but to stitch and sew, play the guitar and piano, marveled "that a woman could write so well." He even goes so far in his prejudice as to refuse to read a book written by a female! Isabel read Madame de Stael's "Corinne" in French, to him, lately, and he was as charmed with it as the authoress could have desired. He would even forego his afternoon nap and cigar after dinner, to come to the drawing-room to listen. We have a conspiracy against him, and mean he shall yet confess that books written by women are the only books worth reading.

We are somewhat puzzled to know who wrote "Shirley," a man or woman! *I* am satisfied it is a woman. It is a well told story, but does not deserve half the praise that has been lavished upon it. Mrs. Ann S. Stephens has more talent, and can write better than the author of "Shirley." If this book had been trimmed of full one hundred and fifty pages of prosy verbiage, the balance would have entitled it to a place by the side of the "Vicar of Wakefield;" but as it is, it will not live two years,—it will never become a library book. Poor Goldsmith! What a pity he is not alive to enjoy the sunshine of his posthumous popularity! Last week I saw a copy of Shakspeare, superbly illustrated. It cost $150. I sighed that "Witty Will" was not living to read his own works in such splendid drapery. How such things mock all human glory! Great men live and struggle, and toil, not for themselves, but for the future. They die ignorant that they leave an imperishable name on the earth.   How few men have cotemporaneous fame! Washington Irving, Bryant, and Tom Moore, have it! and they say poor Moore has become imbecile. I mentioned this to a young lady whom I heard singing one of his songs.

"Is he?" she replied, in a half inquiring, half indifferent tone, and went on with her song.

"Such," thought I, "is immortality! Such is human glory! A great man dies—a great poet becomes insane—and the world says, 'Is he?' and rolls on as before!"

I have been for a couple of days past on a visit to a neighboring estate.   Upon it is a large, green mound, which the proprietor excavated for our entertainment. The result was the dishumation of several beautiful vases of lemon-colored clay, baked like porcelain; arrow heads, beads, bones, amulets, and *idols*. One of the last weighed seventy pounds, was the size of a boy six years old, carved out of limestone.   It was seated *à la Turk*, and had a hideously ugly face.   It, nevertheless, proves that the Indians had notions of sculpture.   It is precisely like the pictures of such deities in Stephens' book on Central America.   It is to be sent to the celebrated cabinet of Professor Troost, in Nashville, a collection not surpassed in the Union.   The doctor is a venerable Dr. Franklin looking man, is an enthusiastic geologist, and is polite to the ladies, especially the young and beautiful, for though he has seen eighty-one years, he can distinguish *specimens* in that way.

A young friend of ours, who lives not far distant, and

is a frequent visitor at the Park, after paying a visit to this cabinet, was seized with the cacoethes of geologizing. He passed two weeks in the woods and hills, and wandering along rivulets, till he loaded himself and two slaves down with specimens. With them he made his way to the presence of the worthy doctor, whom he intended both to gratify and surprise with his rich donations to science.

The venerable professor received him and his treasures with his characteristic courtesy, and when he understood that the specimens were destined to enrich the cabinet, his fine old Franklin face brightened with delight. I will describe the scene in our friend's own words :

" The first rock he took out he glanced at, and tossed it aside, with some indistinct sounds I could not understand. I thought it was German. The next rock, which I took to be a fine agate, he tossed away with the same muttering. So he went on till he had thrown away a dozen, each one with looks of increased disappointment and unconcealed contempt.

"'What is that you say about them, doctor?' I asked.

"'Vater vorn—all vater vorn.'

"'Water worn? What is that?' I asked.

"'Worn smoot'; not'in' but bebbles. Dey goot for not'in', if dey all de same!'

"'They are all the same,' I replied, chop-fallen.

"'Den dey all good for not'in'.'

"I told the boys to shovel them back into the bags, and as I saw a shy twinkle in the professor's eye, I dissolved!"

Perhaps no state is so rich as Tennessee in geology.

A bare inspection of this cabinet will show this. The doctor has some rare diamonds and jewels, which he takes great pleasure in showing to the ladies; and his collection of polished stones will shame even the most brilliant show-case of your much extolled Bailey & Co. Among the curiosities is a bowie-knife wrought out of a thunderbolt, (magnetic iron,) which fell in this state.

The iron of this description is beautifully crystalized, unlike any thing belonging to terrestrial geology. The "water worn" specimen collector, above mentioned, was, not a great while since, the subject of an amusing incident. He has been for some time an admirer of a cousin of Isabel's, a belle and a fortune: and it was settled they were to marry. But one evening when he called, he found her unaccountably distant and cold. She would only answer him in monosyllables, and with scarcely an opening in her lips. If he drew near her, she would draw back; if he demanded an explanation, she replied only by silence. At length he arose and left, and she silently bowed him "good night." Unable to account for such conduct, and wondering how he could have offended her, he early next morning came riding at spur-speed to the Park, to unfold his distress to his fair friend, Isabel, and beg her intercession to heal the breach.

He had hardly got through his story and received Isabel's promise, before her cousin was announced. She entered, arrayed in an elegant green riding costume, with a snow white plume pending to her shoulder. She looked earnest and anxious. But, seeing her lover, she was about to smile and address him in a frank and usual manner, when his cold bow and haughty air chilled her. She turned away, and, embracing her cousin, walked through the folding doors into the farther room with her. Here she told her how she had offended her betrothed, and had ridden over to get her to explain matters.

"You must know, Isabel, that the doctor prescribed for my sick-headache, yesterday, six onions, cut fine, eaten raw, with vinegar, pepper, and salt. Well, I followed the prescription; and I assure you they were very nice; and they cured my head. So I went into the parlor to practice a new waltz, when, without my knowing he was in the house, Harry entered the parlor. I instantly remembered the horrid onions and felt like a culprit! I would have fled, but it was too late. What should I do? I had to remain and entertain him. But mercy! I dared not open my mouth, lest my breath should betray the fatal secret! So I monosyllabled him —kept as far off from him as possible; and at last he went off, his handsome eyes flashing like two stars. Now you must go and tell him how it was, and make it up."

You may be sure, Mr. ——, that with two willing hearts the reconciliation was not long in being effected; and the lovers rode away together perfectly happy. Poor Harry! water-worn pebbles, and onions with vinegar and pepper, are now his abhorrence!

I have half a mind to try my pen at a tale for you, Mr. ——. Mrs. Lee Hentz's beautiful stories have inspired me with a desire to attempt something in the same way. I feel diffident of my ability to adventure into the higher field of literature—but I can try.   If it will not pass "the ordeal of your critic's eye," you have only to call it "water worn;" and throw it away with other *pebbles*.

Respectfully,

KATE.

LETTER XVII.

My dear Mr.————:

When you hear I have been to the great "Nashville Convention," I fear me you will have no more to do with me. It was curiosity that tempted me, and, being a "Yankee Girl," I felt the greatest desire to be present at a meeting which was drawing the attention of the whole Union, if not of the whole world. The colonel is a true Southern man in interests as well as feeling, and, at breakfast table on the morning of the 3d inst., he said, in his badinage manner:

"Kate, what say you to going to the Convention?"

"The Nashville Convention, sir?" I exclaimed, with a start of innate horror.

"Yes; it begins its session to-day. It is but three hours' drive into town, and I am going in to see what they are going to do. Isabel is desirous of being present, as ladies are especially invited to grace the assemblage."

"I thought they were to meet with closed doors, colonel," I said, in my innocence, having the ghost of the Hartford Convention before my eyes.

"No; they will do all open and fearlessly, Kate. If you can overcome your scruples enough to be of the party, we should be delighted to have you go."

After a few moments' reflection, I concluded to con-

sent, though I must confess with some compunctions of
conscience, Mr.——, for I religiously believed the Convention to be traitorous in its spirit, in its views, and in
its tendencies.

The carriage was at the door as soon as breakfast was
over, and, after three hours' drive, we entered Nashville,
a city, as I have before remarked, presenting the most
charming aspect to the approacher of any inland town in
the Union.   The tall, Egyptian towers of the Presbyte-
rain church, the Gothic battlements of the Episcopalian,
and the pointed turrets of the Baptist, the fortress-like
outline of the half-finished Capitol, and the dome of the
Court house, with the numerous cupolas, galleries,
groves, and bridges, together form a *coup d'œil* that
enchants the eye.   On our road, we had overtaken an
open traveling barouche, containing two South Carolinians, on their way to the Convention.   One of them
being known and recognized by the colonel, we had quite
an animated conversation, as we rode side by side.

Arrived in town, we stopped at an elegant mansion,
the abode of a relation of the colonel, where we were
made as much at home as we could have been at the
Park.   We found the city thronged with strangers from
all the Southern states, and the houses of the best families were hospitably opened to entertain them.   Upon
expressing my surprise to an eminent whig jurist opposed
to the Convention, that he should have thrown open the
largest and best rooms of his house to the members of it,
he remarked that " he could never forget the laws of
hospitality, and that it was his opinion that strangers
visiting the city should be received with kindness and

civility." I honored the venerable gentleman for this specimen of old Roman feeling.

The Convention at first convened in the Odd Fellows' Hall, a large and beautiful edifice, but not being found convenient for the accommodation of spectators, especially the *ladies*, the McKendree Church, which is the most spacious in the city, was offered to it and accepted. As we entered the vestibule, which was thronged with gentlemen, I noticed a placard, reading in large letters as follows : " The pews on each side of the church on the floor, reserved for ladies ; and no gentleman without a lady to be admitted on the floor unless he is a member. This rule will be strictly enforced."

Upon entering, we found the house filled, the members occupying the body of the church, the ladies, like borders of flowers, (that is a gallant delegate's figure of speech,) enclosing them on each side, and the galleries packed with lookers-on and lookers-down, some of them with their hats on their heads, for there are some men that don't know when they ought to keep their hats off. Through the politeness of General ——, a gentleman as distinguished for his patriotism as for his politeness, we were escorted to an advantageous seat near the platform, although we did not turn any gentleman out of his seat in order to get places for ourselves.

I know of nothing more uncivil or worthy of being rebuked, than that rudeness so common among ladies, which leads them to make a gentleman sacrifice to them a seat, which, perhaps, he has with much difficulty obtained for himself. It is the duty of every man coming into a crowded room with ladies, to *find places for them without discommoding other men*. I saw two "ladies" come in and

stand before a pew, and look steadily at an elderly gentleman in it, as if they were resolved to look him out of
his seat, though his wife and daughters were with him in
the pew; but the height of impertinence is for a man
with females under escort, to ask another gentleman to
rise and give his seat to the ladies; yet, during the session
of the Convention, I saw this thing done repeatedly.
Madame de Stael says, in her admirable " Corinne :"
"l'idée que les grands seigneurs de Rome ont de l'hon-
neur et du devoir, c'est dé ne pas quitter d'un pas ni
d'un instant leur dame." I fully subscribe to this law
of manners in its application to the present purpose.

When we entered, Mr. Hammond, of South Carolina,
was addressing the chair, which was filled by a dignified,
Andrew Jackson-looking man, who, I learned from the
colonel, who knows almost everybody, was Judge Sharkey,
of Mississippi. Mr. Hammond's head struck me as very
fine. He is of a pale, intellectual aspect, with a high
forehead, white and polished; indeed, his whole face
was almost as colorless as alabaster, and seemed chiseled
out of marble. What he said was moderate and conservative, and what particularly surprised me throughout
the nine days sitting of the Convention, was the calm,
dignified, and impassioned attitude taken and held by
the South Carolina delegation. They spoke little, giving the lead to others rather than taking it themselves,
yet it was perhaps the most talented, Mississippi alone
excepted, delegation in the Convention. Barnwell Rhet,
of South Carolina, spoke during the day, and made a
favorable impression. He is a strong-minded man, with
a head something like late Attorney-General Legaré's,
and a manner highly courteous in debate; and this

finished courtesy seems to me characteristic of these Carolinian gentlemen. Mr. Barnwell (since chosen United States Senator in place of Mr. Elmore) also made a short reply to one of the delegates. He is a strong man, and holds rank with the leading intellects of the South. His intellectual weight will be felt in the Senate. Mr. Cheves, of the same delegation, is a hale, white-headed old gentleman, with a fine port-wine tint to his florid cheek. He has a high reputation, I believe, but during the session he said but little. The most eloquent man of this delegation is Mr. Pickens. He made a speech on the sixth day that surpassed any thing in the way of forensic eloquence I ever imagined. He has a face like one of the old Roman emperors, which I have seen on a coin, Nerva, I think, and his oratory is worthy of the Forum. By turns, calm and tempestuous, gentle and strong, witty and withering, logical and imaginative; at one moment, the audience would be startled with the thunders of the rock-beating surges; and at another, soothed by the soft zephyrs of a summer sea. His rhetoric was profusely ornamented with figures and metaphors, like an exquisite mosaic. Altogether, he is one of the most finished orators it has been my good fortune to listen to; and the colonel says, his speech on this occasion was worthy to be compared to the most noble efforts of Wirt and Patrick Henry. South Carolina, in truth, sent her jewels here, and their talents have won them golden opinions. Be assured, Mr. ——, that the sentiments of this state have been misrepresented. Throughout the Convention, her sons were *models* of conservatism and healthy patriotism. Seated near them was the Mayor of Charleston, called "the handsome

Mayor," Mr. H——, a worthy descendant of Colonel
Hutchinson, of Cromwell's time, and of the Mrs. Hutchinson, whose memoirs are so well known. He was
pointed out to me by a lady with: "Don't you think he
is the handsomest man in the house?" He is not a delegate, but only a "looker-on in Venice." He has been
to the Mammoth Cave, near here, within a few days
past, and his description of it to me I must give you, it
is so truthful: "The sensation," said he, "on beholding
it when standing beneath the main dome is precisely like
that experienced in gazing upon Niagara; *it is Niagara
in repose.*"

The Virginia delegation took a very active part in all
the debates. It was, if possible, more ultra than any
of the rest. The Hon. Beverly Tucker, a half brother
of John Randolph, spoke often, but what he said did not
please me. He is, moreover, past his vigor, and entering his dotage. His speech was exceedingly bitter, and
out of temper. It was the only one that was recrimi-
nating against the North; for a spirit of forbearance in
this direction has peculiarly marked the whole body.
The North is alluded to as "our northern brethren," or
"our sister states," &c., and there is almost, as I have said,
a total absence of vituperation. Mr. Tucker, however,
something in the spirit and something in the *manner* of
Randolph, of Roanoke, let out his bitterness, and was
sometimes forgetful that ladies were present. He is a
venerable and gentlemanly-looking man, and bears a high
reputation, I believe, but it is rather for what he has
been. The most able and patriotic member of the Virginia delegation was Mr. Gordon, who spoke always well,
and to the purpose. He has something of the massive-

ness of Webster in his manner of speaking, and was always listened to with deep interest. The several delegations from the several states, (nine states in all,) were seated each by itself. The two places of honor, the front pews on each side of the broad aisle, directly in front of the President's chair, were given to South Carolina and Mississippi; on the right of the latter was Virginia, occupying two pews; on the left of Carolina was Florida. In the rear of South Carolina was Alabama, and in the rear of Mississippi were placed the Georgians. The Tennessee delegates, among whom was General Pillow, in a military white vest, and Major W. H. Polk, the late President's brother, occupied the side pew on the left of the pulpit. In front of the pulpit is a carpeted platform, within the chancel-railing, on which a dozen little green tables were placed for editors and reporters.

In the centre, before the desk, sat Judge Sharkey and the vice-president, Gov. McDonald of Georgia, supported by their secretaries. What, with the vast assemblage before them, and the reflections upon the important subject which had convened such a House, the whole scene was imposing and solemn in the extreme. Perhaps since the meeting of the Signers of the Declaration of our priceless Independence, no Convention has been assembled in the Union, so fraught with profound and sober interest as this. It was no assemblage of young politicians, ambitious for notoriety. Everywhere, as I looked over the house, my eyes fell on gray heads venerable by wisdom. The majority of the members were men whose names are known to the world with distinction,—men who are the pride, and glory, and honor of the South. Governors, Judges, ex-members of Congress,

eminent jurists, and distinguished orators, composed the
assembly.   Dignified in its character, calm, and delibe-
rate in its debates,—as if impressed with the solem-
nity of their combined attitude before the country and
the world,—they struck me as forming, for the time
being, the *true* Congress of the country; for the consti-
tutional assemblies at Washington seemed to be suspended in action while this one was in session, as if waiting for the result of its deliberations.   And there is little doubt but there was as much talent in this Congress
as in that.   All its proceedings were marked by the
severest parliamentary etiquette; and I heard gentlemen,
who dined at the house where we were guests, say that
the whole tone and temper of the proceedings and
discussions were not unworthy of the United States
Senate.   You see I am getting to be quite a Southerner
in feeling.   But I must describe as I saw, and write as
I feel.   Opposed as I was to the Convention, I cannot
withhold justice where it is due.   At first the citizens
of Nashville were opposed to it; but day-by-day, as its
sessions advanced, it grew into favor.   The galleries
(the people sovereign) thundered applause, and the ladies
smiled approbation.

The members beguiled the tedium of the reading of
the resolutions in going from pew to pew, chatting with
the beautiful women, and the sessions were thus varied
by some interesting flirtations on the part of the handsome widowers, and married men, too, to say nothing of
bachelors, who seem to live single in order to flirt.
Brilliant parties had been given nearly every evening to
the delegates, and dinner parties were the order of the
day.   The whole city, all the time of the session, was in

delightful excitement; and fair widows and beautiful girls reigned in all their splendor and power. Many a heart was lost,—and some of the most firm disunionists brought over to the opinion that *one kind of union* is at least very desirable. Probably Nashville has never seen so gay a fortnight as that during the sitting of this brilliant Convention.

The most talented and active member of the Mississippi delegation was a Mr. McRea, a young man, but who has made himself a man of mark, by the display of his talents for debate on this occasion. The most exciting speech made, was by the Hon. Mr. Colquitt of Georgia. He is athletic, short, compact, and iron-looking, with a large intellectual head, thick with wiry, gray hair, growing erect all over it; a jutting, black brow, and a firm mouth, the whole man and the whole face being stamped with a rough, fiery energy. He rose to reply to some moderate member, against the Compromise, I believe,— and growing excited, he jumped from his pew into the broad aisle, to have more space. Here he spoke with perfect *abandonment!* His voice rung like a bugle! He would rapidly advance, sometimes five or six steps, as if about to leap the chancel railing at a bound, and then stopping full, terribly *stamp*, *stamp* his right foot, and discharge his artillery-like thoughts, which seemed bursting for more vehemence than he could give them; (and never man had more;) at another time he would re-treat step by step, speaking slowly in whispering irony, half down the aisle, when suddenly leaping into the air, his voice would explode like a shell, and electrify us all. Now he would turn round and appeal to this delegate— now face an opposite one; now he would advance like a skirmisher, and utter hoarse, denunciatory whispers to the President in the chair, as if for his especial ear. In a word, he made a most extraordinary speech, in which the manner of all the best orators of the land was mixed up with that of some of the worst. It was in oratory, what a medley would be in song! It was wild, fierce, terrible, dreadful, *mad*—yet most wonderful to listen to. It was eloquence tied to the back of a wild horse, Mazeppa-like!

General Pillow also spoke several times, and spoke well. I had the greatest curiosity to see him, having heard so much of him. He lives in elegant and opulent retirement, not far south of Nashville, and is very popular in this state, and may be the next governor. All those foolish stories told about him by the papers, have been proved to have no foundation, and ought to be dismissed from the public mind. He is in the prime of life, decidedly a handsome man, with a marked military air. There is a smile in his eyes, and which generally plays about his finely shaped firm mouth, that renders the expression of his countenance singularly pleasing. He looks like a gallant and chivalrous gentleman, and his speeches were all patriotic and to the point. This distinguished man has been called vain, because some suppose he wrote a self-commending account of the battle in which he had fought so well.

There is classic authority for such a sentiment, which I believe is not an unworthy part of human nature. Pliny says, in his nineteenth letter, book ninth, to Rufo: "In my opinion, every man who has acted a great, a distinguished part, deserves not only to be excused, but approved, if he endeavors to secure immortality to the

fame he has merited, and to perpetuate an everlasting
remembrance of himself." Frontinus forbade a monument to be erected to him, saying, "The remembrance
of me will remain if my actions deserve it!" Some men
call this modest in Frontinus, but in my opinion it is the
perfection of vanity; for he is so impressed with the cer-
tainty that his actions will be remembered, that he pro-
claims it to the world. I think every man who performs
noble actions, should take pains that they are set right
for the eyes of posterity; and if such a course be vain,
then is Cæsar the vainest of men, as he was among the
bravest and wisest.

Why is it, Mr.——, (listening to the debates has led
me to the reflection,) that men *talk* to one or *two* persons, but *declaim* to a hundred? You see the absurdity
of making a loud and oratorical harangue to a single
auditor, yet let another and another be added, till there
is an assembly, and the conversation is elevated to oratorical declamation. Pliny, who is a great favorite with
me, speaking of the same subject, says:

"The reason I imagine to be, that there is, I know
not what dignity in the collective sentiments of a mul-
titude, and though separately their judgment is, perhaps, of little weight, yet, when united, it becomes respectable."

Major Wm. H. Polk spoke two or three times early
in the session. He has a remarkable voice, deep as a
volcano. He is a handsome man, but is bearded like
an Ottoman chief. His manner of delivery is striking,
from his emphatic enunciation. With every word, he
makes an energetic nod forward, and the vowels are all
enunciated with the precision of an elocutionist, in

particular the terminations *ion*, which he pronounces round and full in *two* distinct syllables, like a Spaniard speaking his own sonorous tongue. He always spoke to the purpose, and with great boldness.

To show you how little popular applause can be appealed to as a criterion of opinions, I heard the galleries one hour applaud a suggestion of "non-intercourse," and the next hour a defence of the Union. After passing their series of resolutions and "Address to the Southern States," on the ninth day the Convention adjourned to meet *again* at Nashville, where they have been so agreeably entertained, the sixth Monday after the adjournment of Congress, if the action of that body prove hostile to Southern interests. Moderate men regard this as an imprudent challenge, and perilous to be taken up.

After a few local resolutions, voting thanks to the citizens of Nashville for their hospitality and to "the ladies for their smiles," the president made a neat farewell speech, and the house adjourned. The gallant Charleston delegation won high favor by making a present to the church of a superb carpet to compensate for the wear of that which covered the floor during the session. These South Carolina gentlemen have a thoughtful *savoir faire* way of doing just what ought to be done.

Now, Mr.——, I have given you a sketch of my impressions of this famed Convention. I hope you will not deem it treasonable to publish it. What the result and influence of the action of this body will be, is not for a female pen to venture to say, but I believe firmly that it will have a tendency to consolidate the Union. The whole temper and tone of the proceedings cannot fail to command the respect of the North; and I hope and

heartily pray that the end of this unhappy difference will
be to settle upon a firmer basis, the noble political institutions which command the admiration and homage of the
nations of the earth.

Respectfully,
KATE.

LETTER XVIII.

MY DEAR MR. ———:

I HAVE a secret for your especial ear-trumpet, but, perhaps you are not old and deaf, and so don't use a trumpet; but the only two editors I ever saw, were both deaf, and kept clapping their ear-trumpets to their tympana, like two sportsmen bringing Colt's rifles to their eyes. The secret is this: Last evening, Juba, who brings our mail from town, placed a letter in my hand, addressed, "Miss Catharine Conyngham, care of Col.———, &c." I thought the hand-writing was my brother's, the midshipman, and tore the seal with fingers trembling, and heart bounding. But it proved to be from an editor —yes, Mr. ———, a real editor, and publisher of a weekly literary paper. And what do you think was the purport of it? I dare say, if I left it to you to say, you would be wicked enough to reply, "A declaration of love." It was no such thing! It was a very polite request that I would contribute some "Needles" to his paper, and if I could not furnish him with a series of "Needles," to oblige him with a series of "Tales." Tales? I, who have not the least grain of imagination, write tales! My reply I shall defer, till I hear from you and have your permission; for, I do not feel that I can, in justice, contribute to any other columns without your *full* consent—for you are my literary god-father, Mr.

——. Suppose I write a tale for *you*. I will try. Perhaps it may turn out a simple affair, in that case you won't publish it, and so no harm will be done. It is one thing to write sketches, and quite another thing to write a thrilling tale. In a week or two, I will see what I can do, and send you the first fruit of my venture into the world of fiction. "Perhaps it may turn out a song, perhaps turn out a sermon."

You will be interested to know that I have not heard a blow struck on this estate, and the colonel says he has not punished one of his slaves in seven years. It is true all men are not like the good colonel, yet for the most part the planters are kind and considerate towards their slaves. They often give them Saturday afternoons, and all day Sunday, when they appear in holiday attire, gayest of the gay. They are all great lovers of going to meeting, and delight in hearing *preaching*, and their fixed and earnest attention in church, might be an example to their superiors. Marriages are performed by the planters themselves, with great show of ceremony, by gravely reading the service from the prayer-book. We had a wedding last week; Jenny, the sempstress, a pretty mulatress, being married to Charles, the ebony coachman of Dr. Bellman, who lives three miles from us.

At seven o'clock, the whole party made its appearance in the great hall, at one end of which stood the colonel, Isabel, myself, and several friends from the neighboring plantations. Dressed in white—a white satin petticoat, with book-muslin robe worn over, and with a wreath of flowers, which Isabel had gathered from rare plants in the conservatory upon her head, with a high comb, and long lace veil, ear-rings, bracelets, and satin shoes with spangles, the bride first entered, attended by her two bride's-maids—one of these, my handsome negress, Eda. The bride's-maids were both dressed very richly, Isabel having given one of them one of her beautiful dresses, and loaned her diamond pin and ruby bracelets. I also decked out my Eda in a figured white muslin, two bracelets, a necklace and brooch, and she really looked superb, with her large, fine eyes and graceful figure. From the neighboring estates were several females, handsomely dressed, and wearing their mistresses' willingly loaned jewels, so that, at this wedding of slaves, shone more jewels (thanks to the kind indulgence of masters and mistresses) than are often seen in more elegant assemblies.

The hall was soon filled, and as far as I could see into the piazza beyond, was a sea of woolly heads, of "cullered" gentlemen and ladies. Dr. Bellman, a hale gentleman of the most frank and cordial manners, white hair, ruddy cheeks, portly form, and always laughing, and telling some funny story—he himself "gave away the bride." The colonel read the service for the ceremony in a clear and solemn voice; and all passed off with the utmost decorum and gravity. The bride was not kissed by the colonel! The marriage ended, the whole party, full three hundred Africans in all, went to the lower gallery that half surrounds the house, and is full one hundred feet long, by eighteen wide, and here they formed into cotillions. The gallery, enclosed by venetian blinds, was lighted up for the occasion, and three fiddlers, and a banjo, and castinets, were perched upon a platform at one end, where they played with a zeal and unweariness that I had never seen equaled. At eleven o'clock, they were invited by the colonel to supper, which was laid in the gallery of the kitchen, itself a long structure, enclosed by a broad piazza. We all stood by and enjoyed the happiness of the Congoese festivity. One young "cullered gentleman," brother to the bride, and something of a Beau Brummel in his way, remarked to me, with a low bow, and with his hand on his heart—

"Nebber see, young missis, nebber see so much beauty afore, at no weddin'. De ladies looks splendid, specially de purty Miss Edy! She de belle ob de party!"

Throughout the supper the utmost order prevailed—nay, *politeness* reigned! Give me "cullered gemmen" at a "cullered" party for your true and genuine politeness! The white gemmen are not one half so courteously polite to us white ladies, as *they* are to their "fair sec!" Bows and smiles, and Brummellian bends of the body, displayings of teeth, and white perfumed pocket handkerchiefs, and glances of adoring white eyes, were the chief features of the scene.

In the course of the evening, a strange, odd, amusing sea captain dropped in. He had been all over the world, and lived longer on a ship than on land. He was now on a visit to his sister, who was married to a planter who lives near us, and where we visit intimately, and whom he had not seen in twenty years past. Among other curiosities which he brought her, and which included two live monkeys, to say nothing of ugly-faced gods of all the heathen nations on earth, was a Bengal tiger! The animal had been given him when a cub, for some service he had performed for some Rajah, and he had kept it as a pet till it had got nearly its full growth, and too large to stay in his ship. Indeed, he said that it had, on the voyage home to New Orleans, nearly killed one of his seamen. So he brought him up to Tennessee in a cage, and his monkeys in another, and some half score of splendid foreign birds in a third. No wonder, as he laughingly says they did, that they took him for a menagerie exhibitor. His sister was delighted with the birds! amused with the pranky monkeys! and horrified at the Bengal gentleman in velvet!

This famous captain, having, as he said, "boarded us in the midst of the sport," after looking on awhile, came to the resolution to show us a regular built "Guinea Coast fandango dance," which he said he had often witnessed on the coast of Africa. Never was any thing so ridiculous as the scene which now took place. The captain, having selected eight of the genteel "cullered pussons," four men and four women, the former in white waistcoats, the latter in white muslins and net gloves, proceeded to explain the dance to them with amusing minuteness.

He seemed to be much surprised that they showed so little aptitude to learn, expressing it as his opinion that the dance ought to come to them *naturally*. But he soon found that the fashionable African gentlemen and ladies, whom he was trying to initiate into the heathen mysteries of their ancestors, had no more *penchant* towards such outlandish doings, than other *civilized* people. Indeed, the cullered circle upon which he would have forced this "old country" cotillion, felt their feelings hurt by the insinuation which his efforts conveyed. The civilized negro is very desirous to bury his pagan juba-jumping ancestors in oblivion. He wishes to forget his heathen origin; and the more removed he is from them, the more aristocratic he is. A newly-imported African is decidedly vulgar! The merry captain at last gave up his pupils in despair, and entertained us for an hour after we reached the drawing-room, with graphic and well given stories of what he had seen in far lands, "beyond the rising place of the sun."

At twelve the party broke up, and the invited guests from other plantations mounted their plough horses or mules, loaned for the purpose, and sought their own dwellings, galloping away in the moonlight, and laughing and talking like children on a holiday, till they were out of hearing.

I forgot to say that the supper had been gotten up by Isabel and myself, and that it was both handsome and costly. A dozen frosted cakes, jellies, preserved fruits, pies, custards, floating island, blanc mange, and other nice things too numerous to mention, were upon the table. In the centre, and at each end, was a pyramid of cake, wreathed with flowers. Indeed, had the colonel given a party to Isabel, her supper could not have been much more elegant or expensive.

The captain, who accepted the colonel's hospitality for the night, caused a great deal of sport this morning by trying to ride! He absolutely knew nothing about a horse; hardly can tell the stirrup from the bridle! With a horse-block to aid him, he got into the saddle, but the horse had not trotted six steps before he was out of it on the ground, having lost his balance. After three attempts, each of which ended in his being tossed out of his seat, by the motion of the horse, he insisted on being tied by the feet, or "lashed under the keel," as he called it. Peter, the black hostler, always accustomed to obey, gratified him by performing this favor for him, and thus firmly secured, he gave the animal the bit and a blow with his fist simultaneously on the haunch. The consequence was that Arab, who is a spirited fellow, set off with him at full gallop, and as the park-gate was fortunately not open to the forest, he swept with him at full speed round and round the circular carriage-way of the lawn. Isabel and I were already in our saddles, for we were going out on a morning gallop, and we began to feel some anxiety for the worthy captain, who passed us bare-headed, his teeth set, and his hands grasping Arab's mane, while the reins flew wildly in the air. If the rope, by which his feet were tied, had parted, he would have been dashed to the earth. As it was, he began to slip, and hang sidewise upon the horse's neck, and I really believe if the colonel's commanding voice had not caused Arab to stop, the captain would the next minute have been underneath the horse, with his feet bottom upwards over the saddle!

"I would rather ride out an equinoctial gale, lashed to the fore-top gallant cross-trees!" cried the captain, as he was relieved from his perilous situation, "than mount a live animal again! Nature never intended the critters to be backed!"

I like the captain, because I have discovered that he saw and spoke with my recovered brother in the Mediterranean, where he visited his ship; and I felt with him in his defeat, and declined to ride.

How necessary it is that we should behold men in their *proper* position and pursuits, in order to know and give them due honor! *Out* of them they are often ridiculous, helpless, and ignorant. Here is a man who could battle with a storm on the ocean, and ride upon the wings of the hurricane, its master! who would unerringly guide a mighty ship across the pathless waste of waters, and who, by his skill, had belted the round earth; whose courageous eye had met fearful perils without quailing, and whose manly voice had given courage and rekindled hope in the sinking bosom of the timid—here was this man, *on land*, in unfamiliar scenes, surpassed and laughed at by the least, ragged, black urchin that can bestride a wild colt.

Yours respectfully,

KATE.

LETTER XIX.

DEAR MR. ———— :

You will remember that I promised to write a tale,
or rather to make the attempt. I have written one, and
will send it to you for your decision. I hope you will
be very severe with it, and reject it at once, if it is
wanting in the points that go to make up a "thrilling
story." Do not let any consideration for my vanity
(what woman is without vanity, especially one who writes
for printers?) prevent you from judging and condemning
impartially; for candor on *your* side may save me on
my side from many a foolish perpetration in the literary
way hereafter. If editors would show more courage and
candor, there would be fewer scribblers, and more ster-
ling writers. So, if they complain that periodical literature is at a low ebb, they ought to blame their own
indolent criticisms, and not fasten the guilt upon poor
literateurs, who only live upon the nod of the editorial
tribunal. It depends wholly on you editors, sir, whether our manuscript sees print or lights candles. You
will now understand, Mr. ————, that I am honest in
wishing you to be so; for if you, in the goodness of
your heart, and because "I am a lady," publish my
story, and it is a poor one, I shall write nothing else
but just such poor tales all my life! There is my forefinger up with the caution. Do you know that Isabel

has a very neat talent for writing? I have some of her MSS. which would delight you, and if you will never tell, I will send you some of it, but you must not publish it for the world, if you like it never so much, for it is a " dead secret."

I have a beautiful story to tell you of Isabel. A few days since she went to C——, twenty miles distant, in the stage. Among the passengers was a white-headed, poorly-clad man, with his arm in a sling, and lame from a bullet in his knee. He was pale, and seemed to suffer, yet was cheerful, and related to her deeply thrilling stories of his war scenes in Mexico, where he received the wounds which now disabled him. He had been for some months in a hospital, at New Orleans, and was now just returning to his family, after two years' absence, and moneyless. At the inn, at Columbia, he alighted with difficulty, and appeared so ill that Isabel told the land-lord that if he would send for a physician, and have him well attended to, she would be responsible. Isabel was then driven to the elegant residence to which she was going on a visit. After tea, she took a bundle of com-forts, and in her friend's carriage drove to the inn, sought out the old soldier, who was very sick in bed, bathed his temples, and even assisted the doctor in ban-daging his arm. She remained nursing him two hours, and then left money to hire an attendant. After an illness of a week, every day of which saw Isabel at his bedside, the old white-headed soldier recovered so as to pursue his journey, his expenses paid from the purse of this benevolent and generous girl, who is as good as she is brave and beautiful. How few girls of seventeen would have thought a second time of the old soldier after leaving him at the inn! When Isabel was asked by a fashionable friend, "how she could do so?" she answered like a true Tennessee girl, "Soldiers fight the battles of our country, and the least we can do is to cherish them in their helplessness, and bind up their wounds. Every true American woman, who loves her country and the defenders of its glory and honor, would have done as I did."

Her father heard this spirited yet modest reply, and taking her in his arms, he kissed her on both cheeks, and smiling with pride called her a "true soldier's daughter."

A letter came this morning from the old man, to Isabel, and every line is glowing with praise of her, and warm with grateful words—though some of them are spelled wrong. But the heart has little heed of orthography. I know a lady who always slips in her spelling, when she writes a letter under any deep emotion. I do not go so far as a certain matter of fact, but warm hearted doctor, whose early education had not been done full justice to, whose maxim was "correct spelling and a cool head go together; but a warm heart don't stop to pick letters." If the old soldier had not written so heartily, therefore, it is very likely, we see, that his orthography might have been less erratic.

You recollect that I alluded to a Bengal tiger, in my last. I have quite an incident to relate of which he was the hero, and I *one* of the heroines, alas! a poor heroine you will say when you hear the story.

Three days ago, the colonel, Isabel, and I, were invited to spend the day and dine at the plantation of Mr. Henry Elliott, the gentleman who is husband to our riding sea-

captain's sister.   After half an hour's delightful drive in
the carriage, along a picturesque road, with a brawling
brook on one side, running at even pace with the horses,
and woods and rocks overhanging on the other, we
reached the tasteful, English-looking mansion which was
to terminate our drive.

After dinner, while Isabel was standing by a marble
table, looking over a superb copy of Boydell's Shakspeare, by her side, Harry Elliott, a handsome young
collegian, at home on vacation, admiring *her* rather than
the pictures to which she was drawing his attention, and
while I was seated in a lounge, reading Simms' last novel
to Mrs. Elliott; and the colonel, and "the captain," and
our host were smoking their cigars on the front portico,
suddenly, with a bound as noiseless as that of a cat, the
Bengal tiger entered through an open window, and
pounced into the drawing room.   Mrs. Elliott sprung to
her feet, and pointed in speechless horror at the terrible
and beautiful creature, as it stood for a moment where
it touched the soft carpet, and gazed slowly and fearlessly around as if selecting its victim from one of us.
Isabel and her young friend had not yet seen him, their
backs being towards the window.   As for poor me, I sat
like a statue, motionless and without power of motion.
The blood froze in my veins !   I caught the glittering
eyes of the tiger, and, for an instant, was fascinated ;
and I do not know, if he had not turned away his look
with dignified contempt, that I should not have risen up
and advanced irresistibly, like a charmed bird towards
the serpent.   He moved a step, crouching.   I looked at
Mrs. Elliott.   I saw courage coming into her eyes, and
she said to me, whispering, "If I catch his eye, I can

detain and cower him." But ere she could catch it, the tiger advanced three fearful bounds, and then Isabel, for the first time, beheld him! Harry Elliott no sooner saw him, than he laid one hand on the wrist of Isabel, who seemed to gaze more with wonder than with fear upon the mottled Bengalese, and pointed with the other to the piano.

"To the piano, Isabel! Play, quickly! Music, or he will do mischief—music, quickly!"

The tiger now slowly sunk down *couchant* upon the carpet, and I could see him unsheath his curved white claws, and his eyes burned as if fires were kindled in their orbs. He seemed about to spring upon Henry, who fixed his gaze resolutely upon him with a courage I could not but admire, terrified as I was at such a drawing-room companion. My fears were not lessened by the recollection, which just then came upon me, that I had been told that day as one of the feats of the "captain's pet" that he would snap off a cat's head at a bite, and make nothing of it. I always knew my head was small, and I felt that it was now smaller than ever. The horrid creature *gaped* all at once, as if to increase my apprehensions, and I was now certain he would make as sure of my head as a guillotine would do it.

Isabel glided backward, pale as snow, and as cold,—glided backward, step by step, so as not to seem to retreat, and reached the piano. Running her icy, cold fingers over the keys in a fearfully brilliant prelude, she commenced a superb cavalry march,—a new Hungarian piece—with a world of war music in it. The tiger, as soon as she began to play, rose from his crouching attitude, and moved with a sedate step to the piano, and took his stand by Isabel, and so near that her snowy arm, as she reached to the distant keys, would nearly touch his glossy shoulder. *We were as still as death!* We began to have faith in the music, seeing that he noticed it in so marked a manner, for he stood as if listening, charmed.

White as a Medician statue, yet Isabel played on. I expected each instant to see her fall from the music stool, or pause in pure terror, when I felt confident the fangs of the terrible creature would be buried in her bosom. Yet we dared not give the alarm! The voices of the three gentlemen could be heard on the gallery, yet we feared to call for aid lest we should draw the tiger to spring upon us. So silent, and nearly dead with awful fear, we waited the issue, trusting to Providence, or the music, for a diversion in our favor.

Henry Elliott, in the meanwhile, leaving Isabel playing, stole out of the room, unseen by the tiger, and reaching the portico, made known to the gentlemen, in scarcely articulate words, the state of affairs in the drawing room. Mr. Elliott would have run for his rifle, and the colonel was calling for pistols, when the captain, motioning for them both to preserve silence, hastened to the scene of danger. When I saw him enter I felt inexpressibly relieved, for I believed in him that he could help us. He moved noiselessly across the room, and coming round at the end of the piano, he faced the animal, and bending his glance upon him, he caught the glittering eye of the tiger full with his own! The effect of his fixed and commanding gaze upon him was wonderful. The monster gradually dropped his body upon his haunches, and sank quietly into an attitude of submission at Isabel's feet. The captain then placed himself at a bound between her and the animal, and grasping him by his jaw, he spoke to him in a tone so absolute and bold, that he rose and suffered himself to be led out of the room like a hound, and locked up in his cage in the poultry yard. He had no sooner disappeared than Isabel, who had not ceased to play, dropped to the floor, but half-arrested in her fall by her father's embracing arm. Mrs. Elliott fainted outright. As for myself, I did nothing but cry for half an hour, I was so happy we had all escaped so well. Even the courageous Harry's voice trembled two hours afterwards when he was congratulating me on my escape.

And was it not an escape, Mr. ——? To be called upon by a gentleman tiger, and only saved from being eaten up by him by treating his lordship with music. It appeared, on inquiry, that the captain had let his "pet" out for air, and tied him to a chestnut tree that stands in the centre of the yard, from which freeing himself, he had taken the liberty of bounding into the parlor, through the window which opens directly upon the lawn.

You may be sure, we, and Mrs. Elliott in particular, gave the captain a good rating for bringing such a *pet* into a peaceable neighborhood, frightening young ladies out of their senses. Mrs. Elliott roundly informed her brother that the monster must be shot, or she should not sleep a wink all night for thinking he might get into the bed-room.

The captain, who had been terribly alarmed at our perilous situations, promised he should be shot, but said he could not have the heart to be the death of his old friend. It was decided that the negro driver of the estate should kill him, but the black objected from some superstitious feeling, when Harry Elliott proposed that he should be turned loose in the forest and hunted down! This proposition, so promising of a new kind of sport in the way of Western hunting, was warmly accepted, and would, no doubt, have been carried out, if some one had not started the objection that he might not be easily shot in the chase, and if left to roam the park, might do some fatal mischief. Whereupon, Mr. Elliott went out and shot the handsome, wild brute through the head, with a rifle, at five paces. The captain would not see the deed done, and remaining in the house, jammed his fingers in his ears, to shut out the report of the gun that sealed the fate of his friend. The poor tiger died instantly, and we all went out to look at him as he lay on the green grass, now quite harmless, yet looking strong and terrible in death. He was a beautiful fellow, with the glossiest, silkiest hide, barred and spotted brown and black. The captain says it shall be made into housings for Isabel's saddle and mine. Moreover, he has given me two monkeys and a superb bird of paradise, his sister, Mrs. Elliott, having been made so nervous by the late tiger adventure, pointedly refusing to have any more of the outlandish citizens of earth or air on her premises. Two monkeys, Mr. ——! And merry, ugly, little men they are, wrinkled as a negro a hundred years old, and mischievous as two imps satanic. They are both with chains round their bodies, fastened one at one pillar and another at another pillar of the gallery, so that they can run up and down at pleasure, and all the little "miniature humans" do, is to take their *pleasure*.

They have done nothing all day but eat nuts and cakes,

mow and chat together, and make faces at the negroes.
The old slaves seem to look upon them with an evil eye
and a spice of fear. Our old African says they are
"Goobah—no good—hab old one in 'em!" The young
fry among the blacks—the little niggers—go mad with
delight at witnessing their pranks, wonder at their having
tails, and seem to regard them as in some sort cousin-
germans of their own race, mysteriously tailed, an addition which they evidently look upon with envy. My
magnificent bird of paradise has a disagreeable voice,
like a creaking cart wheel, and yet his plumage is splendid
beyond description! With all his prismatic glory, the
little brown mocking-bird that sings under my window
half the night long, by moonlight, is worth a score of
them. The eye soon wearies with the monotony of
beauty, but the ear never with the harmony of sound.

Yours respectfully,
KATE.

LETTER XX.

DEAR MR. ———:

DID you ever go a fishing? If you have not, I advise you to buy a rod and line, and start brookward on such an adventure; if you have been, you will know how to appreciate my happiness yesterday, when I tell you that I spent it in fishing! Early in the morning my Afric maid, Eda, stole softly by my bedside, and waking me gently, as if half afraid she should wake me, reminded me that "we were all to go fishing to-day." I was soon dressed in my stout pongee habit, which I wear when I go into the forests, and which just fits my figure. Eda brought me a broad-brimmed leghorn, which I put on, with the brim flapping over my eyes, and shading me like an umbrella,—a sort of man's hat, which the colonel's care for our "fair complexions" had provided for both Bel and me. I also wore a pair of masculine boots; real Wellingtons, Mr. ———, but made of the softest calf-skin, and setting to the foot like a glove. The high heels added full an inch and a half to my stature, whereat I was not a little vain. Upon descending to the hall, I found Isabel all ready, in man's hat and boots, and a jockey looking tunic of green cloth, elegantly embroidered over the bust, to which it was charmingly confined by a broad, glazed, black belt, "clipping the slender waist," and secured by a silver buckle. Her small feet looked perfectly bewitching in her huzzar-like boots, and she wore her sombrero with such a dashing, don't-I-look-like-a-very-pretty-boy air, a little tipped over her left ear, that, with her fine Spanish eyes and expressive face, she looked bewitching enough to fall in love with.

How is it, good Mr. ——, that pretty girls always become additionally attractive in masculine costume? A woman never looks so young as in her riding costume, and for the reason that it is partly copied from the dress of the other sex. And have you never been struck with the youthful look a boy's hat, worn upon the side of the head of a woman of thirty years old imparts to her, giving to her face the juvenility of a handsome lad of sixteen? Solve me this mystery, sir Editor, for editors are, of course, supposed to be able to solve everything!

The colonel was in his brown linen hunting coat, with six pockets therein and thereabouts. Having complimented us upon our good looks and becoming costume, he escorted us to the room, where a nice hot breakfast was awaiting us. After a hearty meal, partaken of in high, good spirits, we prepared to mount our ponies. Two servants were already in attendance upon the gallery; one of them with long rods, for each of us, full twenty feet in length, with hair lines neatly affixed, and boxes of bait—writhing ground worms! The other was laden with a basket of provisions, nicely covered with a snow-white napkin, in spite of which, peeped out the red-waxed neck of a claret bottle, and also there was just visible the wire-tied cork of a champagne bottle! But don't tell the temperance people, Mr. ——! You know, or if you don't know, you know now, that nobody can go fishing

without such mystic appurtenances in the dinner-basket—
at least in these parts. All being a-saddle, and in high
pulse, we started on our expedition to war against the
innocent fishes. We proceeded in the following order.
First, astride a half-broken colt, as shaggy as a bear,
rode a young negro urchin in a torn straw hat, and with
naked feet. He was pioneer to open the several gates
that lay in our road across the plantation. Next rode
the colonel, smoking a cigar, and gaily talking with Isabel and myself upon the probability of our being joined
by the "tiger captain" and young Harry Elliott at the
Seven Oaks, and questioning whether the former could
be prevailed upon to mount a horse! Behind us came
the gray-headed servant who carried the basket and bait,
mounted upon a horse as venerable as himself, and
whose ribbed sides he ceaselessly thumped with his two
heels, keeping time thereat with every step made by his
Rozinante. He was followed by black John, so called
to distinguish him from another John on the estate, who
is not quite so dead a black as the "*black* John." He
rode a sober, long-eared mule, and carried the slender
fishing rods on his shoulder, which as he trotted, bent
with the motion like whale-bone. The mule had an odd
fashion of throwing out his left hind leg at every third
step, which created a rolling motion to his rider, that
was infinitely ludicrous.

What a merry ride we all had! The colonel sang,
and his manly voice made the old woods ring again.
Isabel laughed to listen to the laughing echo, and I
shouted! The Africans were delighted in our delight,
and laughed after their fashion, and the little ragamuffin
Peter, our gate opener, who always takes liberties, and

is notably saucy, whooped and turned somersets on his pony's back from excess of animal spirits.

Three miles from the house we crossed the turnpike road which leads to Nashville. A stage coach was going by at the time, and the passengers looked at us with hard curiosity, and seemed to be amused at the appearance of our motley cavalcade, the rear of which I ought to have said was brought up by three dogs, one of whom was a majestic full-blooded Newfoundland. Not far behind the stage, came a handsome traveling carriage, from the window of which a gentleman hailed the colonel. As we rode up he was presented to us as a General P——, one of the most distinguished officers whose valor in Mexico elevated the military glory of our Republic. After some conversation we separated, he to drive on to his princely estate, a few leagues southward, we to enter the forests and wind our way to the stream. Half a mile from the pike we came to the Seven Oaks, a noble group of forest trees standing by themselves in an open area, where several woodland roads meet. We had hardly reached it when the colonel shouted—

"Here they come! *Voilà* the captain."

Looking in the direction he indicated, we beheld Henry Elliott riding by the side of an old doctor's sulky, in which was harnessed, a tall, long-bodied steed, which as it drew nearer, proved to be stone-blind. At first we could not distinguish whom the ark-like vehicle contained, but a loud shout to us like Neptune hailing a war-ship in a high wind, left us in no doubt as to the personality of the occupant. Harry, mounted on a superb hunter, and dressed with picturesque effect, but without foppishness, which he is too handsome and sensible to be guilty of, on

discovering us left his companion and galloped forward
to join us.   How superbly he rode! yet with the ease
and natural attitude of a Comanche chief.   He was
laughing as he came on, and well might he laugh.

The sulky was shrieking in anguish at every revolution of its rattling wheels; the horse reared behind and
pitched before with a double-jointed, spasmodic locomotion,
that shook the captain from his seat within at every jerk.
The vehicle, the horse, the sulky, and the wheels had
each a several and independent motion of progression,
which four being combined, produced a compound movement of the whole, unlike any thing on the earth, or under the earth, or in the sea.   We all shouted!   The
captain reached us and then tried to stop his headway;
but the ancient horse had an iron jaw calloused by long
use, that no bit would twist or hurt, and it was plainly
apparent that, once under weigh, and propelled by the
complex motions of the entire machinery, he could not
stop if he would.

"'Vast heaving ahead! Luff!—Luff you beast!"
shouted the captain, with stentorian energy, as he was
passing us, pulling at the reins.   "This land craft is the
crankiest clipper I ever g-g-got a-a-bo-ar-d-d of!" cried
he, the last words being jolted out of him by one of
the four motions.   "'Vast there and heave to! What
an infer-fer-na-nal *sea* is running!—Co-co-co-co-col-on-
n-el, heave us a rope! Bear a hand here, some of you
darkies, or I shall soon be hull down and out o' sight to
leeward!"

The colonel rode ahead of the blind and still des-
perately-plunging-forward animal, and had no sooner

touched his head lightly with his whip than he stood stock still.

"Thank'ee, colonel, thank'ee," said the old seaman, as he scrambled over the wheel to the ground; "that craft is the hardest thing I ever steered! Catch me aboard of one of your land craft again, if I can help it! You see this mad-cap nephew of mine wanted to tempt me to ride a horse; but I have had enough of that. Don't laugh, girls,—but it is true. So, cruising about the stables, I run athwart this old lugger, stowed high and dry, and covered with dust and cobwebs. Elliott said it had belonged to a doctor who once lived at the plantation, and it was now condemned as unseaworthy. But so long as it didn't leak, and the spars were sound, I didn't care. So I had her hauled out into the stream, her old rigging overhauled, and this blind horse o' my own choosing, out of a score o' faster and better ones to tow it along. And here you see me, with my innards shook out, because I forgot to put ballast aboard to keep her trim; and then, for yawing wide before the wind, I never saw the equal of that blind beast; and as for shortening sail or coming-to off port, he doesn't know what that means."

We all enjoyed the captain's professional account of his *voyage*, and, as the stream was yet a mile off, we set forward, the captain once more aboard his land craft, but with the precaution of having one of the negro men lead the blind horse along, with his hand on his head-stall. Relieved "by this towing," as he termed it, from the direct command of the vessel, the captain lighted a cigar, lolled along and smoked as well as he could for

the rough sea produced by the resumption of the quadru-
plex motion of the whole apparatus.

We at length reached the creek, though Isabel and
Harry were somehow loiterers, and always were, *somehow*,
on *such* occasions, and did not come up till we had
alighted. What a delightful spot it was where we stopped
to prepare for our sport! Mighty trees overshadowing
us, a limpid stream eighty feet wide at our feet, its clear
waters sparkling over snowy sands, and gurgling and
rushing around and between gray mossy rocks lying in
its bed.

Higher up was a waterfall, with a constant murmur,
and to the left of us the bank receded, leaving a dark,
deep pool, in the depths of which, the darting fish, in
their silvery armor, gleamed like meteors in a lower
sky. Just where we alighted was a verdant carpet of
soft thick grass, with three or four fine old rocks scattered over it like granite lounges, which use we made
of three of them; the fourth having a shape somewhat
tabular, being converted by us into a table for our pic-
nic dinner. Altogether, the place was romantic, secluded,
and still, and would have delighted dear good Izaak Walton, whose shade we invoked as we prepared our lines
for the sport! Sport! ah, poor Pisces! what was to
be sport to us, was death to you! But so goes life,
Mr. ——; one half of God's creatures, both brute and
intelligent, pursue their pleasure at the expense of the
other half.

. The tiger-captain attached himself assiduously to me
for the day, no doubt seeing that Isabel was well provided
for in young Elliott's devoted attentions, and taking pity
upon a lonely demoiselle. He taught me how to cut

bullets half through, and affix them to the line for sinkers;
he gave me a lesson in making and fitting a quilled cork;
initiated me into the mysteries of "bending on a hook,"
which good Mrs. Partington could do, as it is done by
knitting stitches upon the shaft, as one would upon a
needle; and he gave me a horrid lesson in the art of
scientifically putting a worm upon the hook. The squirmy
creatures, how they did curl about my fingers! yet I was
afraid to incur the captain's contempt by even shrieking
or throwing them from me. But isn't it a cruel murder,
sir, to cut in three sections a living worm, and then
thread longitudinally your barbed hook with one of the
soft, cold, twisting pieces? But a lady who goes a fishing with a sea-captain who has tigers for pets, must have
no nerves. I found the captain an admirable instructor.
He showed me where to find the deep pools, and how to
cast my line thirty feet outwardly at a sweep, without
bungling or lodging it in the branches overhead. He
instructed me how to watch the little green and red
painted cork, and how to spring the line when it bobbed
under—in a word, he proved a valuable comrade for a
tyro in fishing like me, and an unexceptionable beau,
except when I once let a large trout drag my hook, line,
pole, and all out of my grasp, and dart away with it
down the stream like a rocket, when he "made a great
swear," as I heard an Indian say of another great personage. With this nautical exception, the tiger-captain
was a delightful companion on a fishing picnic.

After three or four hours of various successes, during
which some eighty-five fish were caught by the whole
party, negroes included, one of the servants announced,
"Pic-nic ready, Massas and Misseses!"

As the captain and I, after winding up our lines, hastened to the spot, I passed the little negro Pete squatted on a rock, fishing, holding a huge stick for a pole, with twine for line, and, for bait-box, the *captain said* that he made use of his enormous mouth, which he kept full of live worms ready for use! Oh, shocking, Peter!

It took some time to find Isabel and Harry, who, at length, made their appearance from up the stream, but with only three fish between them. I suspect they passed their time so pleasantly in each other's society, that they thought little of the little fishes. The captain rallied them on their ill luck, and made them both blush. We had a capital feast under the trees, with the grass for our seats, and a rock for our table. I placed a chance copy of the Picayune before me for a table-cloth, and thus, reading and eating, I enjoyed "a feast of reason," as well as a more substantial one. We had ham, sandwiches, pickles, cold-chicken, cold broiled pigeons, salad, pic-nic crackers, Scotch ale, champagne, and claret. The two negro men waited on us with the precision and etiquette of the dining-room. Our horses, and ponies, and mules, picturesquely tethered around us, cropped the grass, or stood, meditating, doubtless, upon our conduct, our laughter, our toasts, our uproarious behaviour, so in contrast with *their* sedate gravity, which never departs from its propriety. Especially the captain's blind horse looked melancholy and lonely, tied to the wheel of the sulky, with a basket of corn hanging at the end of his venerable nose. At every Borean burst of quarter-deck laughter from the captain, he would crop his overgrown ears, and roll his white, fishy-looking eyes about as if in bodily apprehension.

We toasted, in lady-like sips of the iced wine, the President, Henry Clay, Daniel Webster, and Jenny Lind, and, in silence, drank to the memory of the warrior-sage of the Hermitage, who sleeps not many hours' ride from where we were.   It would be difficult to impress persons out of Tennessee with the veneration with which the green memory of the Hero of New Orleans is held by all Tennesseans.   Through the rolling ages, his secluded tomb will be the fane of pilgrimage for the sons of this state.   We intend shortly to pay a second visit to the Hermitage, of which I will give you an account afterwards.

After our pic-nic dinner was over, the table-rock was vacated to the servants, and the gentlemen laid at length on the grassy bank, smoked, and entertained us with stories.

KATE.

LETTER XXI.

I HAVE had a mind to make this a literary "Needle"
and talk book; for I have lately been reading so many
delightful authors, that, like the busy bee, the wings of
my soul are laden with their sweets, and I must, *per
force*, make honey.   The last work I have laid down, is
"Emerson's Representative Men."   How suggestive is
this book!   How it teems with thought, and food for
thought!   How deep he goes down into the being of
man, and how he walks among the stars!   What a faculty
he has for putting mind into type!   He touches nothing
that he does not find a kernel in it, where most other
writers and thinkers see only a husk.   He beholds with
the eye of the poet, and the contemplation of the sage,
the "splendor of meaning" that plays over the visible
world, and by its light, he looks down, down into the
human heart, and then tells us with terrible strength of
word, all he discovers there!   We tremble before the
man who thus boldly drops his plumb-line into the abyss
of our being, and reports to us its depth.

Mr. Emerson has a great mind.   Grave errors of
theory he has, but new and hitherto untold truths so
burn in his pages, that his discrepancies are lost in their
light.   His sentences are a "carved thought," every one
of them.   He uses words for the frame work of his precious thoughts with the economy of a jeweler, his gold

in setting precious stones.   Every page is an intellectual *pabulum* on which the intellect of a man may be
nourished.   He sets you thinking, and thinking, and
thinking! He has the rare talent of expressing to the
eye the deep and unbroken musings of the spirit of man
about God, about Nature, about the mystery of the past,
the awe of the future, the riddle of life, the infinitude of
the Universe—musings that all indulge, but never impart
the secret of what they think.   Mr. Emerson puts such
twilight and star-light thoughts into shape, and startles
us at recognizing them, as much as if we had seen our
own ghosts rising from the misty emptiness of space!
We all love to discover that our own speculations upon
the mysteries that surround us, have been the speculations of another mind; and if that other mind will lead
us farther than we have gone, we follow with a charmed
awe, confident in his pilotage, though he lead us into the
unfathomable!

Some of Mr. Emerson's propositions and opinions
savour of Swedenborg, of Grecian philosophy, of Jewish
skepticism, of German transcendentalism, neither of
which by itself complete, yet in combination they produce a synthetic whole, that is the just representative of
the modern mind of philosophy.   If Mr. Emerson could
only combine a fifth element in his circle, the humble
faith of the New Testament, his philosophy would be in-
destructible.   How so great a mind can approach so
near the Cross and not see it, and be dazzled by its
glory, is to me a cause of the profoundest marvel.   Aside
from this radical defect in his philosophy, his book is
laden with the richest intellectual ore which the wise
searcher will gather, and know how to free from the

alloy. Did Mr. Emerson live in the days of Plato, he would have founded an Academy of Philosophy, to which the youth of that classic land would have flocked to learn wisdom! Why do not our learned and wise men now become teachers like the old philosophers? Such a man as Emerson might crowd his rural retirement with intellectual young men, and establish a school of thought, that would produce a positive effect upon the age.

But rather let our able divines become such teachers in Christian Philosophy, such men as—but I will not give the names that come to my pen, lest it should seem invidious; if these able doctors of divinity would open their homes, they would be filled with disciples. If eminent retired physicians would receive young men as discipuli, how many would avail themselves of the privilege! If retired lawyers and statesmen would thus become teachers of legal and political philosophy, how many talented youths of our land would become rivals for these inestimable advantages! Suppose it were understood that Henry Clay (God bless him) or Daniel Webster (all honor be to his mighty mind) would, the one at Ashland, the other at Marshfield, receive a limited number of disciples, to instruct them in "the things of their wisdom," what price would be counted by ambitious young Americans, if they could attain to the honor of sitting at their feet? Schools of politics are needed in our country, where statesmen should be graduated!

Dear me! Mr. ——, how boldly I am making my pen write! Only a young woman, perhaps I ought not to touch upon such weighty matters; but please permit me to suggest that there *ought* to be a Diplomatic College at Washington, where our Foreign Ministers, Chargés,

&c., should be educated, and take out diplomas, certifying their qualifications to hold those important positions, by the incumbents of which our country is judged by all nations. The requisites should be a thorough knowledge of international law, of the elementary principles of our Federal Constitution, and those of the thirty States, of the history, products, resources, and commerce of the country, the history of political parties, and the internal operation of our domestic institutions. Lastly, as a *sine qua non*, they should write and speak French fluently, the ignorance of which in nearly all our foreign ministers renders them incompetent, and often ridiculous.

There, Mr. ——, I've done on this hobby.

Another book I have been reading is Dickens' " Copperfield." I do not read novels often, nor do I read them ever for the story or plot, but for the thoughts which the writer may string upon it. Dickens' stories seldom have any but the most indifferent *plots*. He never invents surprises, but writes you a story as transparent as gossamer. Nobody looks for plots in this charming writer, but for his witty sparklings, his quiet humor, his inimitable sketches of character, his pictures of every-day people, whom we afterwards do not so much seem to have *read* about as to have known. This deficiency of plot, which characterizes Dickens' stories, and their wealth of original ideas, is what renders young people somewhat indifferent to reading them, and more mature heads fond of them. Like Emerson, he is an analyzer, but Emerson builds theories on what he discovers, while Dickens works his discoveries into practical life. Like Emerson, in his knowledge of the springs of our being, Dickens is a philosopher, but rather of the heart than of the intellect. Emerson will unlock the abyss and unveil to us the foundations of the universe, and even the spirit-world beyond. Dickens will take us to these beings, and make us know and love them. Emerson would explain the temple; Dickens would present to you the worshipers, maid and and mother, child and patriarch, the poor widow with her mite, and the haughty Pharisee. Emerson's pen records discoveries in the world of thoughts; Dickens' pen records experiences in the world of hearts.

I have heard of the death of Fanny Osgood with much and deep sorrow. She was a bright spirit, with a noble nature and taste cultivated in the highest degree. I once met her, and the remembrance of that interview, short as it was, will ever be fresh; my only regret was the feeling that I had not known her intimately. If she had lived, for she has fled the earth young, she would have done great deeds with her pen. But God be thanked, there is a world of reunion, where death will no more intrude his severing scythe, where the poet's immortal mind shall have scope measurable with its immortality.

KATE.

LETTER XXII.

AFTER the literary letter which I sent you last month, you will no doubt feel particularly grateful to my learning, if it will dispense with such lofty writing in future, and give you something more in the descriptive and gossip way. It isn't every day I get my head crammed with "book," but when I do, it must be emptied; for, as you have before been informed by me, my head is a very little one, and won't hold a whole library. Having relieved its fulness in my last, I now begin perfectly *in vacuo* (this Latin my brother taught me) to write you, solemnly averring to you that I havn't read a book through for a month. This epistle will, therefore, be about what I have seen, and of that of which I have been "a part."

Last week it was resolved, after several days of doubting and of deliberation, that we would all go and spend a couple of weeks at Beaver Dam Springs, in this state, not that we were any of us invalids, but as all our neighbors had gone packing either to the North or some of the watering-places, we had to imitate them, in self-defence, to get rid of the loneliness of the neighborhood. One morning, for instance, we would take a gallop over to Kenton Hall, only to be told that "Massa, and Missus, and all de young people had gone to de Nort'." Or, in the evening we would canter to Bell Park, to find every soul away, and the noble halls in charge of an African housekeeper. In a word, the country was deserted, and as one might as well be out of the world as out of the fashion thereof, the order was at length given for *our* departure also.

It seemed to me a great pity to quit the elegant mansion, and beautiful grounds, and sweet retirement of Overton Park, for unknown inconveniences at some uncomfortable and crowded watering-place, but as Isabel insisted that there would be a great many fine beaux there, and dancing, and all that, I was reconciled to the change; for, though I don't care much about beaux till they have got a little gray, and therefore a little wisdom withal, and seldom dance except with the colonel, or the tiger captain, at a parlor *reunion*, yet I knew *she* would be very happy there, and so I turned my sighs into smiles for her sake, and went cheerfully to work packing. Mr. ——, did you ever pack a trunk? If you have not, and resolutely intend never to pack one, you are an enviable gentleman. The great art, especially in fixing away for the springs, is to cram the contents of four large trunks and a wardrobe into one small trunk; at least, this was the system Isabel and I went to work upon, for the colonel said, very positively, that we must have all baggage put into two trunks, for the traveling carriages wouldn't carry any more. More than once in our stowing processes I wished for the aid of the cotton-press, and believed, at last, we should have to send the trunk to the gin, to be placed underneath the cotton-bale screw, in order to consolidate the contents. But, as this would utterly have demolished cologne and rose-water bottles, ruined silks and lawns, and generally and miscellaneously annihilated every thing, we called in two stout African dames from the laundry, and, making them stand together upon the top, we caused two negro boys to draw the straps, one at each strap, and another to watch the opportunity, when the women on top sprung up in order to make the cover go down, to turn the key in the lock. But the efforts of the latter were entirely unsuccessful, and with the trunk only strapped and buckled by the extreme ends, we pronounced that it would do, no rogue would know the difference. The next question was, what should we do with our hats? The colonel had forbidden bandboxes, and yet we must carry our bonnets in some way. It was in vain the colonel assured us we should have no need of bonnets at the springs. We did not know what might happen, and determined to take them. The bandbox finally was safely smuggled under the feet of Phillip, the driver, the hammer-cloth scarcely covering it. This important matter being arranged, we took an early breakfast, and set forth on our journey, which was to occupy us two days.

You should have seen our cavalcade, Mr. ——. Let me describe it to you. First and foremost rode Charles, the colonel's intelligent and well-dressed serving-man, well mounted on a serviceable traveling horse, and leading by the bridle his master's noble battle-steed, which he still keeps as his favorite riding-horse. The horse is a large, finely-formed animal, and with his gorgeous Spanish saddle half covered with silver, and his plated bridle, half of which was massive silver-chain, he moved on his way, tossing his head, and stepping off as if he "smelled the battle afar off." Next came our family coach, a large, Philadelphia-built carriage, as roomy as one could wish, with drab linings, luxuriantly soft, broad, comfortable seats, that one could almost use as sofas. There were a dozen pockets in the sides, the two larger ones crammed for the occasion with books, magazines, and newspapers, to read on the way, when we should tire of each other, for the most social folks, with the most praiseworthy loquacity, can't always talk while traveling. One of the others was charged with cakes, and another thoughtfully teemed with peaches and apples, the foresight of the careful housekeeper, who had traveled with her mistress in her younger days, and knew how to make "white folk comfortable." A fifth, which was long and narrow, was neatly packed with cigars, to be conveniently in reach of the colonel, the only smoker in our party; this care for making "white folks comfortable" being referable to the attention of Charles, who was *au fait* in all things appertaining to his master's habits. A sixth pocket, in the front, contains a box of lucifer matches, to light the cigars with; and from a seventh projected the brass top of a small spy-glass, with which to view distant prospects as we rode through the country. In each corner swung a brilliant feather fan, ready for our use, and in a rack over Isabel's head was a silver cup with which to drink from the springs or running brooks. There was an additional contrivance to the carriage I have never seen in any other; this was an arrangement by which the lower half of the front could be let down under the hammer-cloth, and so make room for an extension of the feet of an invalid to recline at length; a luxury that the indolence of voluptuousness, rather than the comforts of indisposition, originated. Behind our carriage rode a little mulatto of fourteen, who is taken along as a pupil to initiate him into the mysteries of his future duties, as body-servant to the colonel when Charles grows gray: he is an intelligent lad, and has a thirst for books that it is my delight to gratify, and it is amusing to witness the expansion of his large, handsome eyes at every new idea his little books give him. He thinks there is no one like Missy Kate, and says to me frequently: "When you get marry, Missy Kate, me wait on you' husband—me love b'long to you, Missy."

Beyond being in the possession—the property of *somebody*—the born slave has no idea. Like the beautiful daughters of Circassia, who look forward to a harem as the crowning honor of their sex, and the completion of their happiness, the Afric youths in slavery, of both sexes, contemplate only, as a second or rather their first nature, the condition of servitude: so strong are habits and the influence of education. The little fellow is in raptures with his journey and at every thing he sees, putting his smiling orange-tawny face round the corner of the coach to speak to me in the window, to point out to me something strange to his optics, but familiar enough to ours.

In the rear of the carriage, at a sufficient distance to avoid our dust, and not to lend us theirs, rode on ambling nags two female slaves, one of them Isabel's maid, who attends her every where, and Edith, who has been installed from the first, as my factotum. It was useless for me to say that I did not wish to take her along, that I could do without her. Go she must, first because I should need her; secondly she wanted to go and have the pleasure of the trip; and thirdly, Jane, Isabel's maid, *uould* be lonesome without her companion to gossip with;

and servants are better contented when they are together. So I had my maid. They were both dressed in well-fitting pongee riding-dresses, were mounted on side-saddles; and at the horns thereof hung the neatly tied bundles that contained their respective wardrobes. They paced along side by side after us, as merry as two young black crows in a corn field, and made the air ring with their mirthful and not unmusical laughter; for musical ever are the voices of the dark daughters of Afric; and I am not surprised to hear that there is a prima donna of this race in Paris, filling it with wonder at the richness of her notes.

I can name half a score of negresses, on the estate of the Park, whose voices are charming, and, with cultivation, would surprise and enchant the cultivated listener.

In the rear of these two "ladies," who only cease their talk with each other, to switch up their nags, comes the coachman's boy, a fat-faced, oily, saucy-lipped son of Ham, black and brilliant as a newly japanned boot. He is the coachman's page, and boy of all work about the stable and horses; and rubber-down and harnesser-up; the polisher of the stable plate and the waterer of the horses; for your true "gentleman's coachman," is a gentleman in his way, and there are the "meaner things" of his profession, which he leaves to the "low ambition" of such coarser colored clay as Dick. In a word, the theory of division of labor is completely carried out into practical working system on a southern estate with its hundred slaves. The carriage-driver must not only have his deputy ostler, but the laundress must be waited on by a little negress, to kindle her fires, heat her irons, and do every thing that the dignity of the "lady" in question deems it "derogatorum" for her to put her hands to. The chief washer-woman has from two to four ebony maids, who do the grosser work while she does the "fancy washing." The cook must have a strapping negress, with eyes like anthracite, to peel and pick; a strapping lad, with feet like two copies of Mitchell's School Atlas for breadth, to chop the wood, bring water, and be at hand whenever he is wanted; and two or three small fry to catch the poultry, turn the spit, and steal all they can. The gardener has his aids; the "marm-nurse" hers to *tote* the children; the housekeeper hers; and all this army of juveniles are thus in full training to take the places, by-and-by, of those to whom they are appended.

Thus every negro child is brought up (educated shall I say?) to *one* thing, and comes to understand that particular branch *perfectly* by the time it gets to be a man or a woman, hence the admirable, the *perfect* servants, one always finds on a well-regulated plantation. Out of their particular province they know nothing—absolutely nothing; and no judicious master ever thinks of exacting of them, duties out of their regular work. Dick, the ostler's boy, doesn't know horse-radish from a pumpkin-vine; and Bob, the gardener's boy, could solve a problem in Euclid as easily as he could place the harness on the carriage horses. The cook never enters the house, and the nurse is never seen in the kitchen; the wash-woman is never put to ironing, nor the woman who has charge of the ironing-room ever put to washing. Each one rules supreme in her wash-house, her ironing-room, her kitchen, her nursery, her housekeeper's room; and thus, none interfering with the duties of the other, a complete system of domesticdom is established to the amazing comfort and luxury of all who enjoy its advantages.

This, however, is a digression; but, as I am not writing by the rule, whatever ramblings my pen takes should be regarded as a regular part of my letter, as a deviation contemplated in the beginning. I will now return to Dick, or *Dickon* as he was called "for short," as Charles saith.

Dick was mounted on the same low, black, shaggy, Mexican pony I have before described, his feet dangling as if they were two weights to balance him, and encased with a pair of brogans, the bottoms of which were still of that fresh polished leather-brown, which showed they had not yet touched mother earth, but were span new. Indeed, I had seen Dickon mount his Mexican bare-footed, and then cause one of his black companions to put his shoes on for him, in order that they might shine with newness, and as long as possible delight the eyes, and kindle envy in the bosoms of all "darkies" whom he might encounter on the road. In this vanity, Dickon was not peculiar, for the whole race are more pleased with a pair of new boots or shoes than any other portion of apparel. I have seen both men and women, in going to meeting with new Christmas-gift shoes, walk half the distance on the Virginia fence, in order that they might reach the "meetin' hus" with the *bottoms* of their brogans "spick and span." White "gemmen," I believe, think most of a new hat, if one might judge from the habit of betting a hat, and the gentle pleasure they seem to enjoy in smoothing its glossy coat down with their palm or a kid glove, and the jealousy with which they protect it, when it is new, from all soiling. The new coat may sit down in a dusty chair without much compunctious visitings to the trembling conscience of the wearer; but did any lady ever see a gentleman deposit his hat upon a table barely susceptible of dust? Between us, Mr. ——, fear of such contact with its immaculate ebon causes gentlemen to keep their hats in hand in parlor visitations, protesting, with a hypocritical smile, if you try to deprive them of it, that it is really *the* fashion! Bless me! If the fashion should change, what would be the substitute? There can be none; for I have seen fine beaux use their castors as if they were pet kittens, stroking down and stroking down the soft fur with affectionate endearment, as if it were a baby, tapping and smoothing its glossy crown, as if it were a fan, with which to cool their be-whiskered faces, or a pocket handkerchief, to hide a temporarily missing tooth, or wine-tainted (more's the pity) exhalations of breath, or an escritoire to pencil a letter upon, and as a mail-bag, to put one in!—as a weapon of war to drive a wasp or a bat out of the room, as an individual fire-screen, and for illustrating any ideas in conversation: as, for instance, I have seen a hat called (only for the sake of illustration, Mr. ——,) a steam boiler, a new novel, a church, the Mexican general Santa Anna; while the coal-scuttle stood for General Taylor, Mount Vesuvius, the tomb of Mahomet, a patent coffee-mill, a newly invented horse-shoe, and a negro's head. It has enabled many a diffident gentleman to retain his self-possession, and give a use for his hands for a whole evening, who, otherwise, would have suffered excruciatingly from the embarrassment of being alone with himself. You might as well ask some

nervous gentlemen if you should take their boots, as to
ask them if you should "take their hats."

It occurs to me, Mr.——, that only one thing is wanted
to perfect the drawing-room hat. This idea has been
suggested to my mind more than once, when I have seen
gentlemen, during a pause in the conversation, gaze ab-
stractedly down into the recesses of their castors, as if
they were trying to discover stars at noon-day in a well.
The idea is this: That in the next issue of fashionable
hats by your tonish *artistes*, Oakford of Chestnut street,
or Genin of Broadway, there should be elegantly inserted
within the crown, where the maker's name usually is
found, a small mirror, encircled by the manufacturer's
name.* Ladies have them in their fans, and the hat is
the gentleman's fan. Such an arrangement would meet
with favor, I have no doubt. The gentlemen at a loss
for ideas could catch inspiration from the depth of their
castors; for what will inspire a person with such a flow
of agreeable ideas as the contemplation of himself?

The introduction of this hat would be productive of
the highest social benefits, and impart a charm and
vivacity to drawing-room conversations that cannot now
be properly estimated. Dear me! Let us go back to
Dickon, whom I have fairly taken for my text; for
what I understand by a text, is some point which gives
the preacher a starting vantage, like the starting pole to
the foot-racer, who, once leaving it at his back, never
expects to behold it more.

But we won't lose sight of Dickon, nor of his brogans.
When we came near any dwelling, to the front of which
any of his sooty brethren might be drawn to gaze on us,

* This has since (1853) been done.

he would throw out his legs horizontally, in order to display the full glory and splendor of his pegged shoes, the soles of which were three-quarters of an inch in thickness, and the leather of which they were made, as thick as the hide of a rhinoceros; yet they filled his dark soul with delight, and he rejoiced in them as if they had been as beautiful as the slippers of Cinderella.

He led by the bridle Isabel's riding horse, the handsome creature I have before described, fully caparisoned, and *my* beautiful mule, accoutred with Mexican magnificence. These accompany us in order that, when we are tired of the carriage, we can ride, and also for our convenience while at the Springs. My mule is a perfect beauty! He is none of the Sancho Panza donkey race, but as symmetrical as a deer, with an ankle like a hind of the forest, or like a fine lady's; with hide as glossy as that of a mouse, ears not too large, and well cut; a pretty head, a soft and affectionate eye, with a little mischief in it, (observable only when Isabel would try to pass him,) and as swift as an antelope, and thirteen and a half hands high. It comes at my voice, and does not like for any one but me to be in the saddle. The value of this mule, Mr. ——, is three hundred dollars. You have no idea of the beauty and cost of these useful creatures in this country, and how universally they are used. Out of nine private carriages at the Church last Sabbath, four of them were drawn by beautiful spans of mules. Even our own traveling carriage, which I have described to you, is drawn by a pair of large mules, sixteen hands, and which the colonel has been offered one thousand dollars for. It is only the rich that can afford the luxury of the use of these elegant animals. So don't smile at my saddled mule, which I have named "Jenny Lind."

Having now introdued you to our traveling party, Mr. ——, I will in my next give you some account of what events took place on our journey.

Yours,
KATE.

P. S. Many thanks to the kind editorial people who have been pleased to treat my faults as a writer so leniently, and to encourage me with such words of approbation. I will do my best to merit their esteem.

LETTER XXIII.

MR. ———:

My Dear Sir,—It is all up now! Everybody knows
it! The secret is out, and I am distressed beyond measure. I wouldn't for the world it should have been
known I write these letters; and I have done my best
that it shouldn't be suspected; and if it had not been for
certain over-wise busy bodies, the colonel and Isabel
would have been none the wiser; for they never see your
paper—I have taken nice care of that. I will tell you
how it was, Mr.———. You must know that on the evening of the day we left the Park for the Springs, we
reached the village of Columbia, where there is a celebrated Institute for Young Ladies, romantically situated
near the town. Isabel had a friend or two there, and
proposed to call and pay them a visit. The colonel said
he would accompany us; and off we set on foot through
the principal street. On the way we passed a one story
white cottage house, with a little shaded green yard in
front. This, the colonel told us, was the residence of
Mr. Polk, when he was called to occupy the White
House. It is wholly unpretending, and might rent for
one hundred and fifty dollars per annum. In coming to
Columbia, six miles out, we had passed a small country
dwelling, of the humblest aspect, which we were told was
his birth-place.

After looking a moment at the plain dwelling on the street, and reflecting from what various positions of society our Presidents spring, the abode of Madam, the venerable mother of the late President Polk, was shown to me—a two story brick house, without ornament or grounds, and approached only by an uncomfortable looking side-walk. She is greatly beloved, and is said to be both an intelligent and witty old lady. Near her resides Mrs. Dr. Hays, a sister of the late President, and said strikingly to resemble him in talents and appearance.

At length we came in sight of the Gothic turrets and Norman towers of the battlemented structure towards which we were directing our steps. It is truly a noble edifice, commandingly situated, and complete in all its appointments to the eye. Its color is a grayish blue. It is approached through imposing gate-ways, by winding avenues that bring the visitor soon upon a green plateau. The entrance is spacious, and hung with pictures. We were ushered by a well-dressed female slave into a parlor on the left, handsomely furnished, but not a single book to be seen in it. This showed that the proprietors regarded books as *tools* in that place, and kept them for the *shop*—that is the study-room. The colonel sent up our names to the Rector; for the Institution, which numbers three hundred pupils, is Episcopalian, and is under the charge of a clergyman of the Church.

A gentleman shortly made his appearance, dressed with the nicest care and attention to his personal appearance. He was rather a handsome man, inclined to genteel corpulency, wore gold rimmed glasses, nankeen trousers, white vest, and full whiskers accurately trimmed

to a hair.   He was the *beau ideal* of preceptor-in-chief
of a large and fashionable boarding-school of young
misses.   He was the most polite man I ever saw.   Lord
Chesterfield would have embraced him with demonstrations of enthusiasm.   Yet, with all this formality of
courteousness, which the head of a ladies' school must
of necessity get into the habit of exercising towards all,
his face bore the impress of a scholarly mind.   I always
note with great particularity the peculiarities of those
who educate youth, for so much depends upon example,
and is learned by involuntary imitation.   The young
ladies, whom Isabel had sent for, soon made their appearance, both dressed plainly in white, and I observed
that they both eyed me askance and curiously in a peculiar way, and then both whispered to Isabel, and then
looked mysteriously again at me harder than before.

At length, we rose to accompany the courteous Rector
over the vast establishment which calls him lord.   I was
amazed at its extent, at the number of its rooms, at the
profusion of its pictures and maps, hanging from all the
walls, at the crowd of girls, so many of them, and so
full of the promise of future loveliness, and the perfect order and system which prevailed throughout.   But if these
gratified me, I did not a little marvel at finding myself
waylaid and watched by knots of juvenile belles, with
rosy lips buzzing, and their handsome eyes flashing and
staring at me as if I was a "show" of some kind, while
Isabel and the colonel were scarcely noticed.   "What
can have happened to me?" I asked myself, and imagined I had in some way disfigured my face, and so made
a fright and sight of myself; but happening to pass a
mirror, and finding my "beauty" unimpaired, and my

appearance as it should be, I was excessively annoyed
and curious to know why I was stared at and whispered
about so.   It was not done rudely, however, but civilly,
and with a sort of pleased reverence.

I did not discover the secret of it all until we had returned to the inn, when a gentleman, who is a poet, but
I believe has never published any thing, called and sent
in his card for me, his name written gracefully in a scroll
held in the bill of a dove, all done with shining black
lead.

When he was admitted, he approached me with a dozen
bows, and said he was happy to have the honor of welcoming me to Columbia.   He had just heard from some
young ladies of the Academy that I had honored it with
a visit, and he begged to assure me that I was appreciated, in the most distinguished manner, by all intellectual persons who had had the pleasure of reading my Letters from Overton Park, published in the Model Courier.

" I trust I have also the honor," here the young gentleman turned and bowed low to the amazed colonel, " of
seeing the celebrated colonel whom your pen has immortalized, and this"—and here he made two very low bows
to the puzzled Isabella—" is, without doubt, the bold
and beautiful Miss Peyton, whom I have learned to admire, though I have never before had the happiness of
paying my respects to her."

Mr. ——! can you appreciate, have you nerves and
sensibility enough to appreciate my position at that awful moment?   I felt that the crisis had arrived!   I did
not open my lips, but pale and motionless I sat and
looked him into annihilation, and then I moved my eyes
towards the colonel and Isabel, in a sort of helpless

despair, to see the effect of this *contretemps* upon their unsuspecting minds.

"What is this, Kate, eh? What is it the gentleman would say?" he asked, in an amusingly bewildered way.

"I can explain, dear father! Don't look so like the white lady in wax, dear Kate!" added Isabel, smiling. "I heard something of it at the school, and the girls all wondered I had never heard of it before, especially as I was spoken of in the Letters."

"What letters, Bel?" asked her father. "You mystify me! I heard something once, I now recollect, but it passed from my mind."

"Why, sir, the truth is, there is a spy in the camp, dear father," answered Bel, with an arch smile, and glancing aside at me, "and this gentleman has been so good as to let the poor kitten loose in sight of everybody. Kate has been writing letters to a paper in Philadelphia, which have been printed, at least, so I was told at the Academy, a score of them, and every one of them dated at Overton Park, and descriptive of every thing that she saw or experienced there that she thought would be interesting; and in these letters she has been so naughty as to speak of both of us, at least so I was told, for I have not seen one of the letters, but I am dying to do so."

"Nor I," said the colonel. "So! so! Then we have a literatteuriste in our family, 'takin' notes an' printin' 'em' too, i' faith! You sly rogue, Kate," he added, turning to me, "you have got the advantage of me. So you have been making us all sit for our portraits, poor innocents!"

"But she has not written one word, she would be afraid to have us read, that I know," said Isabel.

"That I'll vouch for, Kate! so don't look so blank!"

"That she hasn't, sir," officiously exclaimed the wretched poet, as if he were eager to atone for his *faux pas.* "Dear me! I didn't know but—but—every body knew—or—! But sir! but, Miss! you may rest assured that not a word is written, that,

'Dying, she would wish to blot.'

She has alluded to you in every instance in the most princely, and affectionate, and respectful—"

"My very good sir," interrupted the colonel, "the lady needs no apologist. We know well she has not. Now, Kate, if I had these Letters, I would, as a punishment to you, make you read every one of them aloud to us when we get back to the Park."

"It *would* be a punishment," I said, smiling and taking heart again, at the kind and affectionate manner in which the discovery had been received by my two dear friends. "But if it will be received in full atonement—"

"Full—complete," answered the colonel.

"I have most all the Letters, sir; seventeen in number, sir, up to the last week," eagerly remarked the poet; "they are at your service, sir!"

"And so, sir," said I, half angrily, "you would complete the mischief you have involuntarily done by a voluntary proposition to contribute to my punishment."

' "Ten thousand pardons, Miss Kate—I beg pardon, Miss Conyngham—I will withhold the Letters, then."

"Nay, since you have them," said I, "and are willing to part with them for a time, (they shall be returned to your address again,) I will accept the offer; for, Colonel,

I wish you to see all that I have written, and the sooner my mind will be relieved."

"I am full of curiosity to read them," said Isabel eagerly.

Thereupon the blabbing poet departed to bring them, when the colonel and Isabel, feeling for my chagrin, succeeded in reconciling me to myself; and when the miserable youth came back with the bale of Couriers under his arm, I was in a mood to receive them with a merry laugh, though still a tear or two of vexation trembled in my eyes, that the discovery had been made, and I heartily wished I had never written a line. But, who ever dreamed of my Letters being read here, *out West*, or being thought of a week after they were written? You know, sir, how insensibly they were drawn out from paper to paper, and increased to their present number, almost without my knowledge.

"If I had reflected," as I now said to the colonel and Isabel, "that what is published in an Eastern paper is read as well in the West as if it had been printed there, for newspapers circulate everywhere, I should not have written, or written less freely in my use of names and places. I did not then understand that communications sent out from Tennessee, to a widely circulating paper in Philadelphia, will as certainly come back to Tennessee, and be read by all the next door neighbors of the writer, as certainly as if they had been printed in his own town. I did not understand, as I now do, that newspapers are without geographical limits and boundaries, but that their *voices*, like those of the stars, 'go into all lands, and their words to the end of the world!' that to them belong neither climates nor latitudes; that the same journal which is read around the elegant fireside of glowing anthracite in Walnut street, is also read, word for word and column for column, before the light of the log fire in the woodman's hut on the Mississippi."

I have decided to continue to write my Letters, Mr. ———, for the colonel and Isabel have read all which I have written, (this being the third day since the discovery,) and find nothing that I should not have set down, save names, and, as they say, giving them both better characters than they deserve. I shall therefore resume my "journey" and give you an account of a delightful day passed at Ashwood, en route to the watering place, seven miles west of Columbia.

The unlucky poet felt so badly at the scrape he had unwittingly got me into, that in the morning, when we left the inn, he came to the carriage, and bidding me good bye, begged me to pardon him, a request which I very cheerfully complied with. The last I saw of him, as the carriage turned the corner, was standing fixed to the spot where I had charitably shaken hands with him, his hat raised, and his body bowing, with his left hand frantically placed on his heart.

Mr. ———, if you receive a piece of poetry from these parts, addressed to *me*, "On meeting me" in Columbia, I implore you not to insert it, for I saw the mad phrensy of such an act in his eyes as I parted with him, and he will be sure to perpetrate the deed there fore-shadowed.

Respectfully, yours,
KATE.

LETTER XXIV.

THIS letter, my Dear Sir, is addressed to you from the loveliest region of this state, and from the "Garden of Eden" of this loveliest region. Maury county, (pronounced here Murry,) you must know, is the gem of Tennessee. It contains the most beautiful hills, the clearest brooks, the prettiest vales, the stateliest trees, the handsomest *native* parks, the richest farms, the wealthiest planters, the most intelligent population, the best seminaries of learning, and the loveliest ladies of all Tennessee; at least the good people of Maury say so, and who should know so well as they, pray? They also boast of having given a President to the United States, and its greatest astronomer to it—Lieutenant Maury, of the Observatory at Washington. So far as my experience goes, I am ready to endorse all the good folks say; for Ashwood, which is the *setting* in the ring of Maury, and where I now am, is enough in itself to give grace to a much more inferior country. I will describe Ashwood to you.

Fancy yourself, Mr. ——, (where you may be in person whenever you take it into your ambulatory brain to ramble this way,) seated in our roomy and luxurious carriage, by *my* side, if you are not too stout, and don't fill up too large a space, for, of all things, I love to ride comfortably; or by Isabel's side,—but then she is so

handsome, I dare say you would rather sit opposite to
her, where you could watch the intelligent play of her
beautiful features; or, perhaps, better still, imagine yourself on horseback, riding by our window, with no object
to obstruct your view of the country; this will be best,
after all—especially as you are supposed to be traveling
to see and print the country; for I conceive that everything is viewed by an editor—typically—not as it really
is, but how it will look in type—how many squares or
paragraphs it will make! Fancy yourself thus *á cheval*,
and riding by our coach windows as we sally forth from
the village of Columbia, with its one broad, rocky, side-
walkless street. On your right you will not fail to notice
the former cottage abode of the late President Polk, and
on the left, the plain residence of Madame, his aged
mother, to both of which I have before drawn your attention.

A few minutes farther will bring you opposite the
castellated edifice known far and near as the Columbia
Institute, where I had "the honors" paid me the day
before, and where is preserved a conservatory of loveliness, each virgin flower awaiting her turn of annual
transplanting into the great wilderness of the world.
Ah, girls! if you knew the storms and clouds, the sad-
nesses and sorrows, the cares and anguishes, the biting
frosts ánd chilling winds that wither the heart and blight
the spirit in the open world, you would hug your present shelter, and long linger,—dreading and shrinking
to go forth,—within its protecting and safe embrace!

This reflection is supposed to be made by yourself,
Mr. ——, in the philosophical mood which becomes an
editor *en voyage* to see the earth he lives upon. After

losing sight of the Institute, you will come to the top of the hill, and glance back to take a parting look of the village of Columbia, which is nestled picturesquely amid trees, with a tower or two peering above them, on the banks of the romantic Duck! Yes, Mr. ——, the classic, and erudite, and scholastic Columbia is situated on the "Duck river." "What is in a name?" you ask—

"Duck, or Doddle, or Dunkins, or Dumplins; all very good names in their way, if they mean good. A rose by any other name would no doubt smell like a rose." Suppose a rose were called "Quashee," would you name your lovely daughter Quashee? Ah, Mr. ——, can you fancy your smiling babe looking as sweet with the name of Quashee indelibly fixed upon her, as she now does? One of these days, we have no doubt that the refined polish of the Columbians will lead them to see the affinity between Duck and Quashee, and at least adorn their rock-cliffed river with a more euphonious name.

After losing sight of the village, you will find yourself pacing smoothly along a level and broad pike, not roughened by even a pebble to disturb the even roll of the carriage wheels. The fields on one side are green and undulating—on the other is a fine wood. In a few minutes a dark brown villa meets your eye, some distance from the road, on the left hand, with a neat gate-way opening into a well-kept carriage-way, that sweeps handsomely round a lawn up to its portico. The grounds are ornamented, well kept, and neatly enclosed, and the whole place has an air of scholarly seclusion, combined with the most enviable domestic comfort. This is the abode of the Right Rev. Bishop Otey, of the Tennessee Diocese of the American Episcopal Church. This residence is the seat of true clerical hospitality. Bishop Otey is indeed the reverend father in God of all his clergy, who look up to him with a filial love, combined with a fraternal confidence, that speaks volumes for the traits of character of a Bishop, who can command such voluntary affection. Bishop Otey stands among the very first Prelates of the Church, which his piety and learning so eminently adorn. If you will turn your eyes in that direction, you will discover him in a brown linen coat, and home-made trowsers, and an old straw hat, working amid his shrubbery. That bright-eyed young girl, with a shade hat in her hand, and a cloud of sunny hair, is his youngest daughter, the pride of her father's heart, who has recently laid beneath the green earth two still more beautiful ones. It is only the hope of the Christian that can strengthen and bind up the heart broken by such heavy strokes as these. Calm and holy confidence in a life beyond the stars, where the severed here shall entwine in each other's embrace, holy lip to holy lip, loving heart to loving heart,—can only lend endurance to separations in this. Without this sure and steadfast hope, what a bottomless pit of crushed affections would the grave be ?

The road now divides a green and verdant landscape, more woodland than field, but made up of both, with here and there a tenement of some small proprietor. You are pleased with the beauty of the trees, the height and majesty of the silver-trunked sycamore, overshadowing some rock-bound crystal spring, or by the graceful bendings of a group of willows bordering a rivulet; or by the breadth of the broad-armed oak on the sunny hillside; or by the feathering and stately elegance of the

Indian salex; or the columnar altitude of the poplar, marking the site of some hidden cottage.

I see you gaze with admiration into the sun-dappled forests, whose broad patches of light and shade look like scenes in Claude Lorraines's pictures, and remind you of them. You wonder at the green sward beneath the trees being *so* green and soft, as if it had been the work of trained English gardeners; when the extent of these lawn like forests convinces you that they are as nature's gardening left them. I see you stretch your neck to see where the deer are. They seldom come near the road, and in the vicinity of towns are rarely seen now. There are few or no deer in this county of Maury, but those that are tamed and kept for gentle adornment to the vicinage of some villa.

Did you ever trot over a smoother road, sir? For the last three miles, not a stone the size of your watch seal has been encountered by the polished wheel-tire. Does not the stately span of mules move with a truly equinine bravery and speed? I see by your eye, as you are watching their pace, that you mean to have a pair for Broad street, or whatever other avenue you Philadelphia gentlemen make a fashionable driving thoroughfare. The colonel offers you a cigar out of the window. Don't refuse it, Mr. ——. They were brought from Havana by the tiger-captain, and are pronounced *nonpareil*. I love to see a gentleman smoke who knows *how* to smoke; but, bless me! when they *do not* know how, what filthy work they make of it! The awkward way they embrace the cigar with the unskilled lips, as if it were an unusually large stick of bitter barley candy—the jaundice-colored exudations of juice, which must be expectorated twice in every minute—the—but enough: if these may not be written about by pens polite, how can the spectacle be endured as it is by hundreds of polite eyes and polite nerves daily?

Oh! ye monstrosities of smokers—ye caricaturists of a cigarilian luxury—ye unsuccessful imitators of the inimitable!—chew tobacco at once, but don't—don't join together in one operation what was ever intended to be kept asunder. I see you smoke your cigar like a true smoker, Mr. ——. You use it as familiarly as the jockey his whip, or the fine lady her fan. You handle it as delicately as if it were made of gossamer, yet puff it as vigorously as if it were of the consistency of gutta percha. You do not so much *smoke* as inspire and exhale *azurely* —as if it were as natural to you as to breathe ordinarily. You never remove it from your mouth, save to laugh, for you converse with it as if it incommoded you no more than your lips or teeth, and then you touch it delicately and regard it affectionately. An admirably finished and endurable smoker! Such smoking is not unlawful, and can never be indicted as nuisable. Colonel, please hand Mr. —— another cigar.

KATE.

LETTER XXV.

Mr. ———:

My Dear Sir,—There is probably no purgatory on earth (for purgatories abound in this world) so effectually conducive to penitence and repentance as a watering place. If good cannot come out of evil, nor light out of darkness, nor laughter out of sorrow, neither can any thing interesting proceed from a watering place. Nevertheless, I have to fly to my pen for solace. I have read till reading is insufferably tiresome—I have walked till I could walk no longer—I have talked till I am tired hearing my own voice and the voices of others—I have jumped the rope till I have blistered the soles of my feet, and made my hands burn—I have drunk the waters until I shall never bear to hear water mentioned again— I have danced under the trees, and looked on in the old dancing-room, till dancing is worn out—I have yawned till I have nearly put my jaws out—and I have sat till I could hardly keep my eyes open, looking at the trees, the hot walks, the listlessly-wandering-about people, that look as if they could take laudanum, hang themselves, or cut their throats, "just as lief do it as not," if it were not so impolite and wicked to shock people's nerves by perpetrating such dreadful things! I have slept till my eyes won't hold any more sleep, and are swelled and red like two pink pin-cushions. I have rolled ninepins

till I have nearly broken my arm with the heavy balls;
and it is too hot to sew, to knit, to net, to do any thing
but write! This I can do when all other things fail.
I can write off a headache, write away care, and bury
miserable thoughts in the dark depths of my inkstand.
Therefore, Mr. ——, I fly to my *escritoire* for relief
from the tedium which everywhere surrounds me.

It is just half-past twelve in the morning. Let me
describe to you what I see from the open window, before
which I write. Directly in front is a broad lawn, intersected in every possible direction by foot-paths, some of
which lead to the dining room, others to the bowling
alley, others to cottages and cabins, others from these to
the springs. This lawn is now hotly waving in the undulations of the heated atmosphere. The sides and roofs
of the cabins are also trembling with the quick waves
of rarified air, vibrating along their sun-heated superficies.
A solitary negress, in a blue frock,—for most of them
dress in blue check,—is slowly gliding along the path
from the spring, with a jar of water balanced upon her
head, for her mistress. She is singing in a low, musical,
unintelligible tone. She is the only moving object visible.
At the foot of the lawn runs, in a shadowy coolness, a
brawling brook, now flowing like a melting mirror over
a smooth, flat rock—now gurgling in a dozen mimic falls
of white foam—now rushing hoarsely between narrow
channels—and now whirling and hissing in eddying
circles about the roots of a tree that have temporarily
dammed its progress.

Beyond this romantic brook, the sight of which is
enough to cool a fever, ascends irregularly a green bank,
dotted with beech and birch trees, to the summit of a

ridge, along which winds the road by which we came to the Springs. The whole scene before us is rustic, quiet, and wild, and would have been pronounced a perfect wood-scene by good old Izaak Walton; for not even trout are wanting. There sits an elderly lawyer, with his back against an oak, a long rod in his hand, the hook at the extremity of which has been baitless for the last hour, while the angler sleeps with his mouth wide open; and I fancy I hear his sonorous snore mingling not unharmoniously with the guttural noise of the brook. Not many paces from him is stretched, in ponderous length, a huge brown horse, his head a little cast to one side, as if he were eagerly listening; but it is all a deception; a little closer scrutiny will show you that his large eyes are both shut, and that he is also as sound asleep as the old lawyer, only he doesn't hold his mouth open. Brutes always sleep, I have observed, with dignity. An eastern sage has said that men and beasts are on a *level* when they sleep! There is, doubtless, something deep lying under this observation, if we could think it out; but it would take other heads to do that! The bowling alley is in full sight. Its thunder is silent—its thunderbolts repose. The negro boy who sets up is now lying down upon the broad of his back, in the sun, and seems to be enjoying sleep as only an African can. On the benches are stretched gentlemen in various picturesque attitudes, some sleeping, others smoking, and idly conversing. The air is so still, the buzzing of the flies is heard in the sunny air, like the distant murmur of a busy spinning-wheel. The mosquitoes are the only things that seem to be taking time by the fore-lock. There, under an opposite gallery, reclines a fat gentleman in an

arm-chair, and doing his best to get to sleep, in order to
forget that he is at these horrid Springs. Now he slaps
at a mosquito with his right hand, then he hits at another
with his left, his eyes both shut all the while; now he
brings his fleshy palm down upon his forehead, with a
slap loud enough to wake the ancient lawyer with the
fishing-rod; and now he grumbles out a half-choked
oath, and throws his great red silk-handkerchief over his
face. But I see they bite through this, for he kicks out
his short legs in a kind of frenzy of desperation. I can
see the Etna-like tip of his nose pointing upwards underneath the handkerchief, a fair mark for a sharp pro-
boscis. A shrewd mosquito has found the place vulne-
rable, and the victim, seizing the end of his nose, wrings
it as if he were wringing off the head of a chicken; at
the same time being bitten on the knee, the fat gentleman roars and kicks fiercely out, and the chair, which
was never manufactured for such trials of strength as
this, refuses longer to sustain him in his freaks, and dis-
solves into its primitive parts, every round and leg unglu-
ing and separating from its bed, and letting him down
bodily amid the wreck like a huge globe fallen from its
sphere. What a change! Presto, how the Springs are
alive! The crash, heard all around, starts fifty sleepers,
one hundred and fifty idlers, two hundred dozers, black
and white, and all run to the scene of disaster, to see
what has happened; for, at the Springs, *an incident* is
worth five hundred dollars, Mr. ——, if it is worth a
dime. The fat gentleman finds himself the cynosure of
all eyes, and the butt of all possible inquiries of—

"What is it? How did it happen? Who's hurt or killed?
Bless me, my dear sir, are any of your bones broken?"

The latter inquiry could never have been satisfactorily responded to by the fat gentleman, as, without doubt, he had lost sight of his bones many years before, underneath the masses of superincumbent flesh which lay larded eight fingers deep thereupon.

There is no describing the effect this little incident has produced upon the whole circle of animated life. The bowlers, once aroused, are playing at mimic thunder again—the ancient barrister has shut his huge mouth, opened his eyes, put on his spectacles, and resumed his occupation of fishing for subaqueous clients. The old brown horse has thrust out his two fore-legs on the grass, and pulled himself heavily up from his haunches to his hoofs, and begun to crop the sward. The cabins, lately so quiet, resound with the laughter of young girls, and the octave voices of ladies calling to their maids to prepare them for dinner, for the hour of this important event is at hand. In half an hour the dancing-room will be filled with beaux and belles, papas and mammas, buzzing, and walking, and gazing, and waiting for the dinner-bell. We shall have a dinner, such as it may be, but luxurious enough for people who will leave pleasant homes to go to watering-places!

TEN O'CLOCK, P. M.

The day is past; and as it is our last day at the Springs, therefore rejoice with me, Mr. ——. I am impatient to be back once more to my dear, familiar room, with its thousand and one comforts. I want to see my pet deer, my doves, my squirrel, my flowers, my books, my own looking-glass, for I don't look like myself in these at the Springs, which look as if they had been made while a stiff breeze was rippling across their molten surface.

I write to the measure of the dance in the hall, and the merry jingle of violins and castanets. The young folks are enjoying themselves while they are young. The happiest persons I saw in the ball-room, however, were the blacks. You who live in a free State, have no idea of the privileges this class are permitted in a slave State by the white people. They stand in the doors and otherwise vacant places of the ball-room, and laugh, and are as much at home as "massa and missis." They go and come around or across it as they please; a favored aunty will even ask you, "Please, missis, stand dis way little bit, so I can see!" and "missis" complies as readily as if a lady had asked her.

One reason of this is that the system is so intimately interwoven with domestic arrangements, and associations, and habits, that, to all Southerners, slaves are necessary appurtenances in all places. If they see not their own slaves, they see those of others, and pay no attention to their goings and comings. The slave will even attend her mistress with her umbrella or cloak to her pew, and, leaving them, go *out* again down the broad aisle, no one noticing her. I have seen slaves sent from one part of a church to another, during service, without attracting observation; nay, even into the pulpit, to restore the clergyman his pocket-handkerchief, which he had let fall. But in the North, who would *suffer* "negroes" to appear in such places? A Southerner never objects nor thinks of objecting to the presence of a servant anywhere. I might travel with Edith in a stage from Memphis to Savannah, and not a Southern gentleman in it

would speak of it, or think of it; while from a New England coach, she would be ejected. Tell me, Mr. ——,
why is this so? How is it, as it is certainly the *fact*,
that the Northern people have a positive *dislike* for the
negro? But I will not discuss this question.

These Springs have only within a few years attracted
attention. They are embosomed in the depths of a wilderness far from village, or civilized habitation. The road
by which we reached them after quitting Mount Pleasant,
a pretty and dirty village this side of Ashwood, lay for
twenty-eight miles through a forest, which was scarcely
invaded by the woodman's axe. For fifteen miles we
did not see a habitation. The solitude was grand. The
surface of the country was undulating, and we could see
long vistas into the depths of glens, where I imagined
lay the deer in covert, and where once crouched the wild
beast in his lair. It seemed at every winding in our
road that we should come upon some Indian hunter.
But the red man was not there. Wasted "like the
April snows in the warm noon," he had disappeared before the sun of civilization. Now and then a squirrel
would cross our path, or a gray-plumed woodpecker startle the echoes with his busy knocking at the doors of
the insects' homes, in the bark of the trees, for them to
come out and be eaten. Once a huge black snake lay
directly in our path, and would not stir till Charles
lashed him with the whip, when he moved off as deliberately as if he did not care for us,—a spice of the old
Eden pride of power left in him. Of all things, why
should a serpent have been made use of by Sathanas to
tempt Eve? It were more likely to frighten her. Perhaps, however, that to Eve, before the Fall, all things

(all of God's creatures) were beautiful,—for it is sin only that deforms and brings deformity!

That Eve is not surprised that the serpent has a voice, is, because she and Adam spoke, and it was natural for her to suppose, until experience taught her to the contrary, that all brutes were likewise gifted with speech. We see her evince no amazement at the vocal powers of the serpent.

Dear me! if I had been Eve—but nobody knows what a body would have done, had a body been Eve!—the probability is, that I should have eaten two apples instead of one.

The arrival of our cavalcade at the Springs produced a sensation, as new arrivals always do,—but nobody seemed to notice its size and variety. Indeed, since we have been here, quite a dozen of arrivals quite as formidable in largeness of retinue have occurred. Nay, one young lady had a wagon bringing up the rear containing her harp and guitar. Some of the parties brought an extra wagon for baggage.

Last Saturday, quite a horse troop of lads and lasses, from the adjacent country, broke in upon us like a foray of Highlanders upon the lowlands. Some of the young men, every soul of whom was full six feet tall, brought their rifles, and the girls an extra pair of shoes for a dance. Some of the girls were handsome, but bold looking, and with very fine figures. They actually took possession of the hall, and danced half the day; and then the young men went down to a level meadow and passed an hour shooting at a mark at fifty and eighty yards; and excellent marksmen, I am told, these Tennesseans are. They are brave men too! There is a look of quiet resolution about them that gives indications of that martial spirit which the trumpet of war so readily awakes in their bosoms. General Jackson was not so much *one individual* as he was the representative man of Tennessee. All true born Tennesseans are more or less like him in aspect, build, courage, and indomitable resolution. They take a pride in him! They teach their children to imitate him! His name was the most stirring war-cry used by the Tennessee legions in Mexico. Not long since Isabel was at a party where, during the evening, the bust of General Jackson was brought out and placed upon a pedestal in the hall. It was hailed with three cheers by the lads, and crowned with flowers by the girls, who hand in hand danced around it, and sang with spirit,

"Hail to the Chief!"

The days at the Springs are passed pretty much alike; —the three meals being the most important points of interest. What, with bowling and quaffing the waters, dancing and walking, sleeping and talking, dressing and eating, fighting the mosquitoes, and watching what others do, we manage to kill each day, but are half killed in our turn. To-morrow we leave. All is excitement among our party. Dickon is in ecstasies, and when he runs he turns a somerset at every third step. Charles looks happy. Philip's serene face shows his content. Edith expresses herself heartily tired of the place, albeit she has been the belle here. Do not think, Mr. ——, that the "darker shades" of our party do not find "reliefs." Probably there are here two hundred servants, belonging to the various families. Now as people generally travel with their body servants, which are of a caste superior to the rest, of course at the Springs they enjoy the *elite* of the best society of Darkeydom.

The position of each colored individual is indisputably fixed by that of his master. A servant of the President of the United States, would of course be recognized as "fuss class airystokrasy" by his fellow servants. The richer and more respectable the master, the more respectable the man or maid. Hence our colored circle is exceedingly recherché. "It is," as Edith says, "ob de highest exstinction."

If you would take your stand near the spring when they come down after pitchers of water, you would witness practical politeness. The courtesy of Samuel, the coachman of Dr. W—— to Mary, the maid of Mrs. Col. ——, as he solicits the honor of filling her pitcher for her, and placing it on the polished mahogany veneering of her rounded shoulders of the brightest brown tint, would edify you. The polite salaams of Jacob to Rachel, the dressing woman, and of Isaac, the footman, to Rebecca, the nursery maid, would charm you. But you should see the aristocracy of the shades dining. After the masters and mistresses have left the dining hall, the long table is relaid, and they who whilom served are now feasted.

I have been twice in to look at them. Not less than one hundred Ethiopian and Nubian ladies and gemmen were seated in the places occupied an hour before by their masters and mistresses. The *entrees* were conducted *comme il faut*. There were servants of "de lower klass," scullions and ostlers, boot-blacks and idlers, to wait on them. The order, courtesy, civility, and propriety that were observed at the table, could not have been surpassed at a dinner at Windsor Castle: on the contrary, they were more polite than people at a Royal dinner. The bowing and handing across the table to the ladies—the "Shall I help you to a piece of de tender loin; Missee Cinderella?" "Will you take a purtatur, Mistress Betty?" "Thank you, Mister Thomas, I will if you pleases." "Here is a nice slice of the bres' of de turkey for you, Missy Arabella." "Thankee! much obliged; it berry nice, Mister Napoleon Bonaparte." "Ladies and gemmen, here de health of our Massas and Missesses, and may dey nebber die till dere time come, an' den lib forebber."

This toast being drunk in the residue of claret, there was a more positive set-to upon the viands. And so these black rogues dine every day! I say to you, truthfully, Mr. ——, the slaves in this state seem to be quite as well content as their masters; in fact, are only second to them in all that they enjoy. I am becoming more and more reconciled to the system; but I don't think I could charge myself with the responsibility of *owning* a slave. Not that I think it wrong. The Bible allows it. But to feel that a human being was *mine!* that I was accountable to him for his happiness and comfort here, and to God for his soul's weal hereafter! This is, I think, one of the most responsible features of domestic servitude. "I feel," said an intelligent Christian lady to me, "I feel more deeply the weight of responsibility which the ownership of the slaves my father has left me, places upon me, than I do that of my own children. I tremble at the reflection that God will ask their soul's lives at my hands!"

The sound of the feet of the dancers has ceased, and

silence reigns in the hall so lately the scene of merriment.
Night is hushing all sounds. Here and there a star can
be seen, twinkling down through the opening in the trees.
The murmur of the brook reaches my ear like an audible
voice. Some sleepless Orpheus is now waking the silence with an ill-touched flute. Distant laughter of
young men, at cards, or wine, comes from yonder cabin.
A baby is crying in the room next to mine! I hear the
sleepy father's growl, and the patient mother's low
"hush." A mosquito sings in my ears, and another
bold wretch has bitten me on the hand. These are warn-
ings for me to retire, especially as we are to make an
early start homeward. So, good-night.

KATE.

LETTER XXVI.

OVERTON PARK.

MR. ———:

ONCE more in my own room, at my own desk and *escritoire*, with familiar objects, I resume my pen to address you. How much what one writes depends for its character upon the place in which it is penned? To write at ease, I must have everything about me that I have been accustomed to. I must have my light arranged in just such a way, so that a soft radiance, mellowing everything in the room, shall fall upon my paper, just distinctly enough for me to see, yet not strong enough to distract my attention by glare. I must have perfect quiet, too. I can write best by lamp-light, a shaded lamp, with the light thrown softly upon the paper. In a rainy day my thoughts flow freest. I must have an old-fashioned goose-quill. I cannot accustom myself to a steel pen. It trips me up, and I have an awkward way of bearing on when I write that a steel pen won't yield to with sufficient flexibility. Half the people in this country write on *ruled* paper. This is my abhorrence! I don't stop to notice lines, and so if I can't get any but ruled paper, I write as often between the lines as on them. I was taught, fortunately, to write straight at *school;* and so were all my schoolmates; and, till lately, I supposed everybody could write on unruled paper.

But when I was last in Nashville, I went to three book stores on an unsuccessful search for *unruled* letter paper. " We don't keep it—it is hardly ever called for—everybody buys the ruled," were the answers we received: but at length I have obtained some by sending away for it. The colonel says he has seen letters both from Henry Clay and Daniel Webster written on lines. This is no doubt owing to the accident of not having unruled paper by them. It is school-boyish to follow this habit. Certainly no young lady ought to be considered educated until she can write a letter on paper without ruled lines.

My last epistle left me just on the eve of departing from the Springs. Well, we did leave the following morning, taking up our line of travel, in the same imposing caravanish manner in which we had come.

Towards evening, after a cool day's ride through the forest, before described, we reached the little town of Mount Pleasant, which is situated amid the loveliest scenery possible. Here we remained all night, putting up with indifferent accommodations. This village ought to be the prettiest in the state. But its population seems to have no taste or pride. They let enormous hogs, with noses like ploughshares, turn up their streets, which the rain converts into bog holes; they neglect to paint, or, at least, white-wash their fences; they pay no attention to the neatness of their front yards; they are without passable side-walks, and destitute of shade trees. Why, if the scores of idlers we saw lounging about the shops and tavern, would go to work for a week, in earnest, they might make their town truly a Mount Pleasant, and double the value of it.

How dirty some of these Western towns are kept. I

feel as if I wanted to take up the people and show them the New England villages, as they show children London. I am told the citizens are intelligent and highly respectable; how then can they sit down in so much untidiness? Why is it that they don't know that rocks, barrel hoops, rails, old shoes, old hats, boot legs, rags, broken crockery, and such trash, disfigure a street, and would mar the finest avenue that ever ran through a village? The worst of it is, Mr. ——, Western people don't care one fig for the opinion of strangers; while Northerners live, as you may say, for the eyes of others. Hence the attention of the one to the looks of everything about his house and town, and the indifference of the other to those things.

After leaving Mount Pleasant, our road lay through a sweet valley, along the margin of a romantic stream. The scenery was charming. In the course of an hour's ride, Isabel selected fifty superb sites for villas; for she has a *penchant* for looking out pretty places to build upon; and, for that matter, so have I. But as I am not an heiress, I fear the only house I shall ever call mine, will be one of those "mansions" spoken of in the good Book.

About nine o'clock we passed Ashwood school, nestled beneath the wooded cone of Ken Hill, and were so fortunate as to meet at the gate the learned Professor of Belles Lettres, Donald McLeod, Esq., of Glasgow University,—a gentleman well known in the literary constellation of our land. He is said to possess one of the most scholarly minds in this country. How is it that all Glasgow, and Dublin, and Oxford men that I meet, are so much better educated than Harvard and Yale men? Is the American system superficial? One would think so. The most eloquent scholar I recollect ever to have seen was a graduate of the University of Dublin. I have never seen an American, even a Professor, who could converse fluently in Latin, or write Greek prose with facility; yet I have seen many from the above Universities do both. As for the young men here in the West, their education is scarcely deserving of the name. There is not a college in Tennessee of much higher rank than a New England Academy, and ambitious young men, after taking degrees at these Western "Colleges," go to Harvard, and enter Sophomore. Perhaps a senior Harvard man would have to enter low at Oxford! Who knows? The education of girls West is far beyond that of the youths. Expense is not taken into account where a daughter is to be educated; but fathers seem to think money is thrown away in educating boys. Tennessee has no common school system in operation, and in her capital, hundreds of children are growing up wholly ignorant.

Mr. McLeod was accompanied by a short, little, foreign-looking old gentleman, with gray whiskers, and a demi-military air, who was over-dressed like a French *petit maître* of the ancient school. He was mounted on a large gray horse, which he managed with a skilled hand. He was presented to us as "The Compte Neolis." He bowed to his saddle bow, and lifted his *chapeau* with dignified and smiling politeness, and said he was "*our very* humble servant."

"Neolis," said I, thoughtfully, "There was a Governor of Rome of that name, sir?"

"Yes," he answered; "that is me, at your service, Miss," he responded, bowing.

I gazed on him with curiosity, for I now recalled to mind that General Neolis of Rome, was commander of the Garde Mobile, which was composed of Knights; and that he held Rome against the Spanish troops. This warrior was then, in person, this old Knight of seventy now before me, riding by the side of the carriage, his riding whip and bridle in one hand, and his open snuff-box in the other. As we passed a cart which was discharging stone, the noise alarmed the old Count's horse, and he had an opportunity of displaying his admirable horsemanship, by skillfully restraining the fire of his animal; but in the caracolling, a paper was released from the rider's gaping coat pocket, which bursting as it fell, strewed the ground with candy and bon-bons. Then he dismounted carefully to gather them up, smiling good humoredly at the mishap, and telling us that he always carried them when he went to the school, "*pour les enfants.*" We found him social and amusing, and quite a gallant homme, and really regretted his departure when he took leave of us at the marble gate-way of Monmouth, the residence of Mr. A. Polk, where he resides. When he left us, he bowed to his horse's mane, and slowly rode up the avenue, as if he regretted to quit such good company as Isabel and me. Mr. McLeod left us previously, to call at St. John's Chapel. From the colonel I learned that the Count was an old French exile; that he was a nephew of Marshal Ney, and had been a distinguished officer under Napoleon. That he had been many years in this country, had taught at Germantown, and a few years since was invited to take the chair of Modern Languages in the Columbia Institute; but that, being now almost too old to teach, Mr.

Polk, with genuine Southern hospitality, has invited him to become an inmate of his house, where he has given him a home for life.

The Count is a man of excellent amiability, and a good deal of simplicity of character; but his friends say, as his memory of past events fails, he draws a little on his imagination, and they sometimes run him somewhat hard upon having said he was at two places on the same day, which were five hundred miles apart, doing good fighting at both. But the Count takes the quizzing in good part, shrugs his shoulders, plies his snuff, smiles ineffably, and says, "Maybe, jentilmen, I vas mistake de day. But vera good! You may laugh, I laugh next time!"

The Count is fond of children, for whom he always has his pockets full of cakes or candy; he is a good "churchman," and occasionally still teaches the French class *en amateur* at Ken Hill School. May he live a thousand years! if his generous host has no objections.

After passing the Ashwood gate and post-office, we drove rapidly into Columbia, a distance of seven miles; and by three o'clock in the afternoon, we once more beheld the roofs and chimneys of Overton Hall towering above the oaks which environ it. How delightful the sensation of realizing that one's wanderings have ceased, and that one is at home again! It is worth enduring the discomforts of a watering-place a short time, to enjoy this feeling. Every thing seems to be more beautiful here than before. And how many changes have taken place in the few weeks we have been absent! The peaches have ripened; the apples are becoming rosy red; a new set of flowers have made their appearance,

and instead of the little eggs which we left in the mocking-bird's cage are three innocent little things that look
something like mice, on the eve of feathering.   Then
the canaries were so glad to see us, sending forth the
wildest and most joyous carols from their tiny throats
for very happiness.   The rabbits frisked about us, and
all the dogs, " Tray, Blanche, and Sweetheart," acted as
if they would shake their tails off with their rough and
gyratory welcomings, running around and around us,
and then around the house, chasing each other in full
race, and tumbling and rolling over the grass, from sheer
excess of spirits.   Then the old blind war-horse pricked
up his ears, when he heard my voice, and gave three
great whisks of his heavy tail, ending with a low whine
of joy.   But you should have seen my pet deer, the
once wounded invalid.   I had no sooner entered the
green paddock where it was, then it came bounding towards me with long, graceful leaps, and would fairly
have run over me, if I had not stepped aside.   As it
was, it gave me a rough and honest-hearted welcome,
rubbing its nose against my shoulder, and almost, nay,
I very believe, the rogue tried to kiss me, but this salutation I adroitly escaped, and hugged my pet about the
neck in lieu thereof, and patted its shoulder.   But this
was too quiet a way of expressing its joy at seeing me
again ; so it broke from me, and began to caper about
the paddock, flying around it, then across it at right
angles, then from corner to corner, and then miscellaneously in every direction, all at once, and finally terminating this *mikra mania* by suddenly crouching at
my feet.

But the best welcome of all was that from the servants. They flocked around the carriage, every dark face radiant with smiles, and exhibiting ivory enough for half a mile of piano-keys placed in a row. Jenny Lind's reception in New York was a trifle compared with ours. I thought they would shake our hands off. After I had been a little while in my room, in came Aunt Winny, the fat cook, in her Sunday fix, having rigged up to welcome me, being too particular to come in, in her working dress. She seemed so glad to see me, and said it so many times, that I did not at all regret a trip, the return from which could be productive of so much simple and hearty joy. She then told me how they had all missed us, and "'specially the deer, Missy Kate," she added, "it acted just like a human a'ter you went away, and cried a'ter you like a baby, and wouldn't eat noffin' for de fuss two days, and I had to cook it someat nice, and coax it, and then 'twouldn't eat till I made Jake put on your old rainy cloak and old sun hat and come and stand by me, to make b'lieve it's you, you know, and the simple t'ing begin to eat right off!"

At the idea of seeing the black imp Jake, her long-heeled, thick-lipped son, personating me, I burst into a hearty fit of laughter, but I did not fail to compliment Aunt Winny's sagacity, and to reward her solicitude for my pet.

All is now as it was before we left. I have Isabel at her piano again before breakfast, practising Jenny Lind's songs; the colonel goes galloping a-field ere the dew is off the grass, and I am at my morning studies in German as before. There is, however, some prospect that ere long we shall make another excursion, but not to any watering-place. The colonel will have to visit New Orleans to arrange for the sale of his cotton and tobacco, in October, and he has invited us to accompany him. The trip will be a delightful one, the first two hundred miles being down the dark flowing Cumberland, which is described as one of the most beautiful of Western rivers, then on the Ohio, and thence launched upon the Mississippi, we shall keep its mighty current for a thousand miles. The idea of such a voyage in the superb steamers that float upon these western waters is pleasant, and I have no doubt that we shall greatly enjoy ourselves. Yet I sigh at the prospect of once more quitting our retreat. But in this world, says the wise man, "Nothing is in one stay." Every thing, indeed, is moving. The earth races round the sun, the moon around the earth, which rolls around itself; Mars and Jupiter chassé with Venus, and the sun itself, say the astronomers, marches at a dignified pace around some unknown centre of the universe. "Keep moving," then, being the watchword of the planets, how can we insignificant dwellers thereon but follow the example of our betters! So we shall go to New Orleans.

Whether I write you again before we are *en route*, will depend on circumstances. I promised you a letter from the Hermitage, and this you shall have, if possible, as next week we ride over there, it being but a short two hours' gallop across the country.

I am glad to find the Americans received Jenny Lind with so much enthusiasm. A love for music is common to men and angels. It allies us to them in sympathies the more we delight in song. It is a divine talent, and if we believe the Bible, it will go with us beyond the grave; for the happy beings in Paradise are represented as singing now the "Song of the Lamb," and now the

"New Song," to the sublime accompaniment of ten thousand times ten thousand angels striking their harps of gold, saying:

"Worthy is the Lamb that was slain to receive power, and riches, and wisdom, and strength, and honor, and glory, and blessing; and every creature which is on the earth, and under the earth, heard I saying, Blessing, and honor, and glory, and power be unto Him that sitteth upon the throne, and unto the Lamb forever;" and they ended this celestial chorus by casting their glittering crowns before the throne of Him who liveth forever and ever.

It is a hopeful thing for a nation to rise up as one man, and do homage to this personification of earthly music. They do not so much worship her, as recognize the existence in her of the perfection of that which belongs to humanity *en masse*, but is vouchsafed to but one in a generation. To see them doing homage to her kindles hope for the elevation of our country, just as following in the chariot-wheels of a conqueror, with his garments rolled in blood, would darken hopes of the advancement of humanity. One thing only is wanting to complete the halo of glory which encircles the modest brow of Jenny Lind. It is to consecrate her voice by singing therewith one *Hymn* to the Being who endowed her with it. Let her pour forth in the sacred chaunts of the princely David, or the queenly Miriam, that thrilling voice, and our souls would soar on wings of her songs to the very gates of Paradise. Then, indeed, would she be able to prove to the world that music is a "gift of God wherewith to praise Him."

Yours respectfully,
KATE.

LETTER XXVII.

MR. ———— :

DEAR SIR,—A residence on a large plantation is to a Northerner rich with subjects of interest. Every thing is so different from what he has been accustomed to, his curiosity is continually excited by the novelties which are brought before him, or which he is running his face against. First, there is the slave himself, his condition, his cabin, his dress, his manners, his labors, his amusements, his religion, his domestic relations; then there is the plantation, with fences a mile apart, presenting in one broad enclosure land enough to make a score of Yankee *pastures;* then there is the cotton-plant, with its rich, pure, white, fleecy treasures, hanging to the gathering hand; then there is the tobacco-plant, with its beautiful, tender, green leaf in spring, and its broad, palmetto-looking leaf in autumn, green lined with brown; then there is the cotton-gin, with the negroes at work in it, the snowy cotton flying from the wind-fans in fleecy showers that mock a December snow-storm! then there is the baling and screwing, the roping and marking with planter's name, all objects of interest to witness; then there is the planter himself, so different in his manners, tastes, education, prejudices, notions, bearing, feelings, and associations, from the New England man; then there is his lady, accustomed to have slaves attend upon the

glance of her eye from childhood, commanding and directing her large domestic establishment, where the food,
clothing, comfort, and health sometimes of a hundred
slaves depend upon her managing care; then there is
the son, who is raised half-hunter, half-rustic, with as
much book learning as his pastimes in the field and wood
will allow him to turn his attention to—the idol of the
old negroes and the hope of the younger ones—who has
never seen a city, but may one day walk Broadway, or
Chestnut street, " a fine young Southern blood," with a
fortune to spend, high-spirited, chivalrous, quick to re-
sent an insult, too proud to give one, ready to fight for
his lady-love or his country! prone to high living and
horse-racing, but at home courteous and hospitable as
becomes a true country gentleman; then there is the
daughter of the house, too, a lovely girl, with beautiful
hands, for she has never used them at harder work than
tuning her harp, (and hardly at this, if she can trust her
maid,) who rides like Di Vernon, is not afraid of a gun,
nor, eke! a pistol, is inclined to be indolent, loves to
write letters, to read the late poets, is in love with Byron,
sings Jenny Lind's songs with great taste and sweetness,
has taken her diploma at the Columbia Institute, or some
other conservatory of hot-house plants, knows enough
French to guess at it when she comes across it in an
English book, and of Italian to pronounce the names of
her opera songs! she has ma's carriage at her command
to go and come at her pleasure in the neighborhood, receives long forenoon visits from young gentlemen who
come on horseback, flirts at evening promenades on the
piazza with others, and is married at sixteen without
being courted!

The manners and customs thus enumerated are quite different from those at the North. Let me describe some of the more striking differences a little in detail. Who ever sees an old gray-headed gentleman, mounted on horseback, and a spirited horse at that, galloping along the road with a cigar in his mouth, in New England? Yet we never ride out that we don't meet one or more gray-headed planters, booted and spurred,—sometimes with a cloth cap on when the day is windy,—trotting to or from town at a slapping pace; and followed by one or more dogs. You might ride all over the state of Connecticut or Massachusetts without seeing the like. There they drive about in chaises, or buggies, or carryalls. Where at the north would we meet elegant coaches with plaited harness, and all the appointments rich and complete, drawn by a pair of mules? Yet here it is an every day occurrence to see them, for mules here are highly esteemed. Where in the North would fashionable ladies ride mules? Yet here it is by no means uncommon for a handsome mule to be preferred, especially by timid persons. To what rural church on the Sabbath would every family come in its own carriage? Yet a private carriage stands outside of our church for every family in it.

The customs, too, are different in respect to the license given to daughters. In the North the young lady is left alone with her beaux, and pa and her ma retire. In the South it is deemed indecorous for them to be left alone by themselves, and the mother or some member of the family is always in the room; and if none of these, a female slave is seated on the rug at the door. This is a relic of the Spanish duenna system. Young girls are kept in very strict bounds by mammas in this respect; and I was told by a married gentleman, a few days since, that his wife never took his arm till she took it to be led to church on her wedding day; and that he never had an opportunity of kissing her but twice while he was addressing her, (they were six months engaged!) and in both cases by means of a stratagem he resorted to of drugging a peach with laudanum which he gave to the attending servant, and thereby put her into a sound sleep. To this custom is to be attributed so many runaway matches. If the girls were confided in by their mothers, and suffered to see and become acquainted with those who address them, they would hardly elope. Freedom of intercourse would put an end to these clandestine marriages. I like, of the two customs, the Northern best; but both of them are carried too near the extreme. I know several young ladies in this vicinity who have told me that they were never for two hours out of sight of their mammas.

This watchfulness, by and by, defeats its own aim. The lover is piqued, and begins to regard the whole matter as a fair field for strategy; and instead of looking upon the mother of his future wife with respect and affection, he beholds in her an enemy, whom it would be a victory to circumvent. The daughter soon begins to look at it in the same view, and away they fly together to some Gretna Green.

But runaway matches seem to be marked with Divine displeasure. I have never heard of a happy one. Not far from us resides a widow lady, who eloped from an excellent mother, when she was young, with a worthless young man. She is now the mother of three grown daughters, every one of which has eloped and left her, the youngest only last June, at fifteen years of age, and she is left desolate and broken-hearted! Thus is the example of the mother followed by the children; and whom can she blame but herself? But the worst remains to be told. The eldest has already been deserted by her husband, who has gone to California, and she last week had to seek shelter in the home of her childhood; the second daughter is suing for a divorce, though she has not been thirteen months married. Ah, girls! never in an evil hour place your hand in that of the young man who would counsel you to desert your paternal home! It is cruel to deprive those who have nourished you, and with sweet hope looked forward to the happy day of your honorable marriage beneath their own roof; it is cruel to rob them of the enjoyment of this happiness. It is *their* right to give you to him who is the choice of your heart. It is their blessed privilege to bless your union, and witness your and your husband's joy. How can you then rob them of their participation in that joyous bridal, towards which they have been so many years looking forward? Daughters who elope, wrest from their parents that crowning joy of a father's and a mother's life—the gratification of seeing their daughter married at their own fireside! A bridal elsewhere is unnatural, and God's blessing will not follow it.

There is a custom here of kissing when ladies meet, that seems to me quite a waste of the "raw material," as some envious gentleman has remarked, doubtless some bachelor editor. You might see in Boston the meeting of one hundred pair of young ladies during the day, and not seven couple would salute each other on the lips. Yet in Tennessee all females kiss, old and young, even if they see each other as often as every day. I am acquainted with a teacher of young ladies here, who says that his scholars all kiss when they meet in the morning; and he has seen them when they enter late, in going past several girls to their seats, kiss every pair of lips they pass *en route*. At church doors of a Sunday there is quite a *fusilade* of this small arms. There is a warmth of feeling, a heartiness of affection, a tenderness of sympathy in the Southern ladies, that is the cause of all this. The Northern ladies are cold, without question. They are also better scholars where mere "book" is concerned. They have more comprehensive minds, and are more intellectually clever. Southern girls, from all accounts, make but poor book students. They have, however, so much imagination and feeling, that they converse with brilliancy, appear well and under an indefinable grace, peculiar to them, can veil every scholastic defect.

It is only when a lady takes up her pen that her real deficiencies of education are perceptible. If I were asked to judge of the acquirements of a young lady, I would say, "Let me see one of her letters!" I know a beautiful girl who confessed to Isabel the reason she did not answer a letter that she wrote to her from the Springs was, that "she did not know how to write a letter fit to be seen!" The truth is, the young lady was always indulged at home; went or staid from school at her will; reached fourteen without being able to spell correctly; was then mortified to have her defects made known to her schoolmates, and refused to go to school longer. Her father is the Honorable Mr. ——, and she is exceedingly beautiful and interesting, and now eighteen years of age. The pen is all that will discern her deficiencies, and this she will probably never take in her hands! Being brought up in a family of intelligent persons, she talks well! Poor girl! what mortifications are before her! If she is engaged to an intelligent man, and he should address her a letter during an absence, what excuse can she offer for not replying? If she marry him, and he discover her imperfect education, how mortified will he be! How humiliated she! Yet it is her own fault; and scores of girls in this country are walking in the same path.

Last night, we were seated in the drawing room, listening to Mr. Sargeant's fine song to Jenny Lind, sung by Isabel, and also set to music by her, when there was a sudden commotion among two or three young ladies present, and dodging, and screaming, and throwing handkerchiefs over their heads! A *bat* was in the room! Isabel was too much occupied to know it, and kept on playing, while the velvet-winged bird of dusk darted in elegant curves through the upper air of the room with arrowy swiftness. It was almost impossible to follow his gyrations with the eye. Two young gentlemen present sat very stiffly as if they expected to be hit; and at last the bat darted directly across the piece of music before Isabel's eyes. In an instant she was in the middle of the room, with a handkerchief thrown over her hair, and uttering exclamations of slight terror. Here then were four ladies with their heads picturesquely covered with their lace kerchiefs, and two of the number hiding behind chairs, and a third behind the harp.

"Bless me!" cried the colonel, "is it possible, girls, you are afraid of this bat?"

"To be sure! Do call some one to drive it out!"

At this moment a second bat made its *entreé*, and between the two, I thought the girls would go wild. Isabel, seeing her parasol, caught it, and opening it quietly sat down under it upon a low stool, awaiting the issue.

"They are harmless!" cried the colonel. "They do not fly in here to eat you, but mosquitoes, which they feed on!"

"Oh, sir, they light upon the head," said the pretty brunette, behind the harp; "and if they once get in the hair, it all has to be cut off before it can be detached from it!"

"They have barbs all over their wings and claws, colonel, indeed they have," said a blue-eyed girl, who was concealed under the piano cover;—"and if they— ah-h-h!" she shrieked out, as one of the bats swept past her forehead; and she quickly drew in her face, without waiting to finish what she was saying.

"Where were *you*, Kate?" I hear you ask, Mr. Inquisitive.

I had been reading a story in the Knickerbocker Magazine, before Bel commenced singing; and still held the book on my lap; but I neither ran, screamed, nor covered my head; for I had frequently received in my room such twilight visitors, and at first was a little nervous, as I had heard such terrible accounts of their lodging in the hair, and never being got out till the hair was cut off; but as I never take marvelous stories on hearsay, I one evening, seeing that they did not harm me, watched the motions of three bats that were together disporting themselves in my chamber. I saw, after a few minutes' observation, that their movements, instead of being erratic and uncertain, and aimed to annoy me, were governed by some direct object in view. A little closer scrutiny enabled me to see that they were in pursuit of mosquitoes, which flew about the room, and that every time they made a dart they caught one in their mouse-shaped jaws. I was greatly relieved from personal apprehension when I had achieved this discovery; and I continued my writing as if they were not there, and soon forgot their presence. At length, when I had completed the letter I was writing to my midshipman brother in the Mediterranean, I looked for my "birds," and found that they had quietly disappeared. Since then I am a philosopher when a bat is in a room.

The young ladies, however, being convinced that bats are animated combs flying about for a head to fasten in, would not be persuaded of the innocency of their intentions. The colonel, therefore, had to call in two or three servants, to drive them out, with brooms, riding-whips, and what not! But this only made the matter worse. The poor things, interrupted in their mosquito hawking, became terrified at these belligerent manifestations, and sailed low to avoid the blows aimed at them in the air. In these escapades they darted under the piano, as a shriek from the blue-eyed hider testified; and even beneath Isabel's parasol, as a sudden scream from her bore witness. The girls were now in despair. The colonel and I sat laughing and looking on. At length it was resolved, as bats are said to follow lights, to take the two astral lamps out upon the piazza. The drawing-room was darkened in vain. It was the mosquitoes, not the lamps, that attracted them, and, if any thing, the idea of their flying about in there in the dark, only increased the terror of the terrified girls. Stir out them-

selves the girls would not. The young gentlemen, in
the meanwhile, were using their hats to try and knock
the enemy down. Twice in the dark I felt the wind of
their noiseless wings upon my cheek. The lamps were
ordered back, and with a hard battle two of the enemy
were laid low, and the residue driven forth.

"Now," said the colonel, after the girls had been
twelve times assured that the bats were *hors du combat*,
and incapable of acting as combs, either fine or coarse,
side comb or back comb, and holding up to the lamp one
of the dead mosquito hunters,—"I wish to convince
you that these delicately-winged animals are not after
you, and could do you no harm."

Here he held up a bat to the light by its extended
wings. The sight of it made blue eyes crawl, and the
brunette utter an expression of detestation. It was both
ugly and pretty—its wings being transparent, and elegantly constructed, and its body like that of an over-fed
mole. Its head was small, like a mouse's, and the
colonel, opening its jaws, showed its sharp teeth, and a
little pile of mosquitoes under its tongue. "You see
what its food is!" he said. "The teeth are sharp, but
the mouth is so small it couldn't bite even a child's finger.
Now look at its claws. They are sharp and curved, to
cling by; but the curve instead of being barbed, is a half
circle; and whatever the claw grasps can easily be released from it."

"But its wings. Look at the horrid thing's wings!"
exclaimed blue eyes.

"Well, let us examine its wings," said the colonel
smiling. "You see that each angle where the joints
articulate, is defended by a small hook—one on each

wing. These hooks are but the curve of three quarters of a circle; and if a bat should light upon any one of your heads, and hang there by these two hooks, he could easily be disengaged without sacrificing one silken strand thereof. Let me try it, Bel!"

But Isabel fled, and so did the rest. A negro boy's wooly caput being at hand, the colonel placed the bat upon his crispy poll, and having made the wings take their strongest hold, he showed us how easily the hold could be removed, even from such tangled locks. "The use of these hooks," he added, " is for the bats to hang to each other by in winter, when they swarm together like a cluster of bees, and in huge masses, many feet in circumference, remain in torpid suspension until spring."

The young ladies at length professed themselves satisfied, and the colonel made each one pledge herself never to run from a bat, or cover her head again if a bat came into the room.

Mr. Sargeant's beautiful and patriotic song was then resumed and finished, and many others, and the evening, which had been so ludicrously interrupted, passed off without further incidents.

Yours respectfully,

KATE.

LETTER XXVIII.

MR. ———:

My Dear Sir,—As you were so kind as to express
a wish that I should write for you a series of traveling
letters on my route South, and during my sojourn in the
land of "mocking-birds and sunny skies," I commence
then my first letter, which like all "first letters" and
prefaces, I fear will be wofully dull. It having been
decided at the Park, some weeks ago, in full council assembled in the colonel's library, that we should all go to
New Orleans, preparations were forthwith set on foot.

You must know, that the colonel takes a trip every
year to this great Southern emporium to look after the
sales of his cotton and tobacco, which generally precedes
him some days, but he usually goes alone. On this occasion, however, there was to be an attraction in New
Orleans, such as it or any other city could have but once
in an age. Jenny Lind was to be there in February!
Therefore, Isabel won her father's consent by dint of
coaxing and pretty teazing, and, as I am never left out
of any party of pleasure, "Kate must go too."

It was a propitious morning when the family coach
drove up to the portico of the mansion to receive us,
and, I was going to add, "our baggage." But that was
so enormous in magnitude, the baggage of two girls,
that old black Peter with two mules harnessed into his

red wagon, took it to town in advance of us—having started at the peep of day. All the house servants came out and gathered round the carriage to see us off. The colonel shook hands with all the old ones, and Isabel kissed Aunt Nannie, her old African nurse, and also her mother's nurse before her, while tears filled the beautiful eyes of the maiden, at the genuine grief of the old woman at parting with her.

"Take good keer o' your dear blessed self, Miss Bella," she said, sobbing as if her ebony heart would break in two, "an' don't forget old aunty what lub you better dan she lub de life in her own ol' body. Don't fall into de ribber, and may de Lord bring you and massa and Missy Katy all back to us safe an' sound!"

There was an interesting parting aside, between Charles, the colonel's body servant, who was mounted on a fine horse to follow us, and his young wife Mary; and also a tender leave-taking between Isabel's dressing maid, Clara, and a dark Romeo, to whom she was betrothed, and for her marriage with whom Isabel had promised to purchase her a wedding dress in New Orleans.

After the parting with the servants was over, George, the coachman, at a signal from his master, flourished his long lash over his horses' ears, and away we went rolling rapidly from the door along the smoothly-graveled avenue. The very birds seemed to sing us "good bye" as we trotted down the glades of old trees which were vocal with their notes. The last thing I caught sight of was my pet-deer thrusting his meek face over the paddock, looking wistfully after the carriage, and evidently having an intelligent understanding of the whole matter, that I was going away to leave him for a long time.

Perhaps, however, I had fully made him to comprehend this before I got into the carriage; for the first thing in the morning I went round and took a ceremonious and touching leave, (don't you be so hard-hearted as to smile, Mr. ——), of all my pets. I said a few kind words to my squirrels, fed and patted my rabbits, embraced the shaggy neck of, and almost kissed, old Bruin, a famous large black dog, with an eye and a gravity like Daniel Webster, and a voice like a lion; and the deer I *did* kiss, and I do believe that the poor, gentle-hearted animal's large brown eyes filled with tears at the farewell tones of my voice. He seemed to comprehend as clearly as if he had been a human being, that I came to say good-bye. He rubbed his white face against my shoulder, and followed me to the gate, and when I shut it against him, there was a look of sorrow in his eyes that deeply moved me.

What a mystery a brute creature is! Have you not seen a horse, or a deer, or a dog, act as if a human soul were within its body, and all that was wanted was the gift of speech to express its love, and hands to embrace you with all the tenderness of friendship?—nay, only a human form to be your faithful, true, and loving friend and companion. I cannot believe that the souls of brutes perish forever! God must doubtless have for them a paradise fitted for their enjoyment, and adapted to their highest capability of happiness. The Bible has certainly said, "God shall save both man and beast."

Are there not among the countless worlds of stars, and in the boundless space of the illimitable universe, place and space for all God's creatures to live and be happy in? Shall not the noble horse, doomed to the lash and dray all his life, have compensation in a universe ruled by a God of equity? Wise men say that this earth, and all things thereon, from man down to the lowest form of life, is a type of Heaven. If, then, in the world to come, there are "spirits of men," there must be "souls of brutes," and a spiritual form of everything material. But this is too profound a theme for a young woman's pen, Mr. ——; but if my words here written will only cause some to look more kindly upon brutes, I shall be glad that I have given my ideas "shapes and sentences."

I have already written of the beautiful scenery which spreads away, on either hand, from the turnpike that conducts to the city; of the pleasant villas, noble, natural parks in all their aboriginal grandeur, and sweet cottages here and there embowered in foliage by the roadside. I have, also, in a former letter, spoken of Nashville, of its architectural elegance, of the beauty of its females, the bevies of lovely school-misses that throng the streets, the chivalry of the gentlemen, and the hospitality of all. I shall, therefore, not detain you there, Mr. ——, but drive you at once to the superb steamer "America," which, on our arrival in town, was lying at the upper landing, awaiting her passengers. If you have never seen a Western boat, you have yet to behold the most majestic and comfortable river-steamer afloat. They are constructed and arranged on a plan entirely different from the boats on the Eastern waters. They are all, also, high pressure; and our steamer was, at intervals, bellowing and roaring from her escape pipe with a muttering and condensed power, which showed how terrible is the strength of pent up steam. Having

reached the quay, which was covered with enormous hogs-
heads of tobacco and cotton-bales, which the negroes, in
getting them on board, handled with great dexterity by
means of iron hooks,—making our way through this uproar of commerce, for commerce is very noisy, all the
world over, with its thundering wheels and "heave-o-
yeo!" we gained the stage which led on board. We were
met at the landing by a polite and handsome clerk,
who, with the utmost courtesy, escorted our party to the
cabin. This was the first large steamer I had been
on board of, and my surprise at its vastness and splendor
was no doubt visible in my face. We first entered
the boat, not as in the East, near the stern, but at the
bows!

We were then conducted up a broad flight of stairs to
the upper deck, which was a spacious portico or vestibule
to the forward saloon. This portico, or "forward guard,"
as it is called, is a fine spacious promenade, and has,
withal, room enough in the centre of it to accommodate
a parapet of trunks, which rose like a wall, dividing it
in halves. We thence entered the saloon, and passed a
glittering "bar" on one side, and a range of state-rooms
for the captain and his clerks, on the other, all fitted
up with elegance and taste. Beyond this, for a vast distance, extended the main cabin, which, as we traversed
it, seemed to be endless. On either side were handsome
doors, placed at regular intervals, leading into state-rooms.
The whole was richly carpeted, hung with superb chandeliers, and adorned with the most costly furniture.
After we had walked about a hundred feet, as I should
guess, we, at length, through a suit of lofty folding doors,
reached the ladies' cabin, which was full one-third the

length of the main cabin, and more tastefully adorned. Sofas, a piano, lounges, rocking-chairs, marble tables, chandeliers, and candelabras, made up the several details of the whole. Still farther beyond were doors opening upon a noble verandah, the breadth of the whole stern of the boat, and overhanging the water.

This verandah, as I afterwards saw, extended quite around the boat, on both sides, and uniting with the portico on the bow, made a continuous and delightful promenade, broad and roomy, for several hundred feet, entirely around the whole extent of the boat. It is these verandahs which add such comfort to the Western boats, and make traveling on them so delightful. In descending the rivers, one can sit or lounge on them all day, watching the scenery, instead of being enclosed in the cabins.

There is another agreeable peculiarity of these boats, which, as we are to travel together some days on one, I wish you to understand: it is that the cabins are all above the main deck, raised on double rows of columns high above all the freight, and all the "disagreeables" of those parts of the boat where the hands and the emigrants stay.

There are properly on this upper deck *three* distinct cabins, all on the same floor, opening one into the other by folding doors; the forward one, "the Social Hall," or smoking cabin, where the card-playing, wine-drinking, and politics, go on. The next is the main cabin. used as a drawing-room and dining-room; and the third is the Ladies' cabin. In the day time, these three cabins are thrown into one, by rolling back the broad leaves of the suits of doors, and the *coup d' œil* from one end to the other is very fine; and so distant is the view, that one can hardly recognize an acquaintance who is at the romote extremity.

The interior of our cabin is painted white, enamelled, and polished as marble. The sides are ornamented by rows of pilasters with gilded capitals, between every two of which is a richly ornamented door, leading into a state-room. Every state-room has a door, not only from the cabin into it, but a door that opens out upon the broad verandah, or guard, that environs the boat. This arrangement is very convenient, both for comfort and in case of danger. At evening it was pleasant, as one walked up and down the long verandah, to see the occupants of the state-rooms sitting in their doors, conversing or looking at the scenery, like dwellers on a fashionable street.

Besides this extensive walk, there are stairs that give access to the "hurricane deck," which is the *roof* of the whole boat, and as it is but very slightly convex, and wholly unobstructed by freight, and covered with a water-proof composition, which is sanded, it forms one of the most desirable and charming twilight promenades one can well imagine; and what is more, a promenade in full motion, and under weigh, passing every moment new features in the landscape.

You will thus perceive that, so far as accommodations and comforts, to say nothing of luxury, is concerned, one of these first class Western steamers affords the very perfection of interior voyaging. I have not yet spoken of our state-rooms, which were not so much state-rooms as superb apartments with broad-curtained beds, and marble and mahogany furniture, and as complete as rooms in a "first rate" hotel.

It was on board this floating palace that our party took passage for New Orleans, usually a six or seven days' voyage, the distance being about fifteen hundred miles. It was late in the day when the last passenger, the last bell, the last clerk, and the last plank, came on board, and the dashing of the monster wheels, as they revolved in starting, took the place of the muttering thunder of the suppressed steam, and the signal tolling of the heavy bell, which for an hour had risen above, yet mingling with all the other sounds and uproars of the quay. We are now fairly under weigh, and I bid you "good night."

Respectfully, yours,

KATE.

LETTER XXIX.

My Dear Mr. ———— :

THIS is our third day *en voyage*. How delightful this mode of traveling, surrounded by all the enchantments of an elegant home, as we are in this floating palace! The manner in which we pass our time is more like that of so many guests in a nobleman's villa, could you imagine one floating down the *Belle Riviere*, as the French missionaries, who first launched their light canoes upon its tide, picturesquely designated the Ohio. But I have learned the true Indian name for the river, which is far prettier than that given by the good father Hennepin. It is Ohi-o-lee-pee-chinn, or, put together, Ohio-lepechin. It sounds sweetly and musically, and it means exactly what the French name does, "River of Beauty."

Not far above us is the celebrated Pirate's Cave on the bank, its dark mouth half-concealed by over-hanging trees. It is a romantic spot, and with the adjacent scenery of cliff, woodland, and river, would form a picture, if justice were done it, striking enough to hold no mean rank in the galleries of your Art Union, that enormous Beaux Arts Lottery.

This cavern had in former times a very naughty reputation. Some romantic fellow, with a score of reckless followers, held possession of it for many months before the introduction of steamers on the river, and levied black mail on all the descending and ascending trading boats. Many a tale of hard contests between the parties is told in the vicinity, and some of these legends are sufficiently stirring and wild, to have captivated even the magical pen of Cooper.

The shores of the river are varied as we descend from the Cumberland, by rock and woodland, and many a lonely nook where one would love to dwell in some sweet cottage was presented to the eye as we steamed past. Towards noon we approached the mouth of the Ohio. The river now widened and expanded its bosom every league, as if it would give the Father of Waters, as it neared him, a false idea of its greatness, as small men always stretch up and stand on tip-toe when they talk with a tall man.

" You've never sailed down this river afore, Miss, I guess," said, respectfully, an elderly man, with long, gray hair floating over the shaggy collar of his coarse, blue overcoat, who was standing near me on the upper deck, as I was gazing upon the shores, and straining my vision to behold the distant Mississippi.

" This is the first time, sir," I answered.

" So I thought the way you look at every thing, Miss," he answered. " I have been up and down too often to find any thing new in the 'Hio, or Mississippi either, for that matter. The first time I was on this river was in eighteen hundred and three."

" So long ago !" I repeated. " This was before the time of steamboats."

" Lor' bless you, Miss, steamboats wasn't then thought on. We used to go in them days in keelboats and flats;

and a pesky long voyage it was to Orleens then, and as
for coming up, I've done in six days in a steamboat what
thirty years agone it took me six months to do; that is,
come up from Orleens to Louisville. Steam is a mighty
'vention, marm, but it blows up a mighty sight o' people!"

Here the old pilot, for such he was, took a flat cake
of tobacco from his pocket, wrapped up in a dingy piece
of oil-cloth, "to keep the strength in," as he said, tore a
flake of it off with his thumb and forefinger with a skillful but indescribable movement of the hand, thrust it
into his jaws, and deliberately returned the cake to his
huge pocket.

"It must have been safe and pleasant voyaging in
those days," I remarked.

"Yes, Miss, it was tol'rable. But it was mighty
slow. Then we had our dangers to run. Thar was the
snags, agen which our boat would sometimes run and
get turned over or sunk; there was the bars we'd get
onto, and lay there till the boat rotted; there was the
wild Indians, as sometimes used to shoot us off when we
ran too near the shore, and then down in the low country there was them Spanish and French desperattys, as
used to dart out of the creeks and bayous, twenty black-
lookin' chaps in a long snakish-looking boat, all armed,
and attack us and rob us if we didn't fight hard to save
our plunder. Then a'ter a three months' voyage down,
we'd be took with the yaller fever in Orleens an' die, or
we'd lose all our money a gamblin', for we boatmen them
days played cards dreadful bad, and lost a mint o' money in Orleens."

"You must prefer steamboating, then, to this old way
of trading," I said.

"Wall, I don't know 'bout that, Miss! I like both on 'em, but if had my choice I'd rather keelboat it. Old times, to my notion, is the best times. I don't see as men or the world is any better for steamboats, and railroads, and the telegraphy, and such things. One thing I know, it's a mighty deal wickeder world than when I was a boy!"

Here we passed a few houses forming a hamlet, and landing, on the right bank. Upon asking my communicative friend what place it was, he answered:

"That, marm, is Trinity, six miles from the mouth. Do you see that tall sycamore, the tree with the bark white as your handkerchief eenamost, that stands just under that bank?"

"Yes; it is a very large and noble monarch of the forest," I answered, as I gazed upon one of the most magnificent trees I have ever seen, beneath the shade of which a regiment might have reposed.

"I don't know about monarchs, Miss! This is a free country, and we don't 'llow even our trees to have kings. There is a grave beneath that tree!" he added, impressively. "You can't see it, nor I nuther, for it's all smoothed and over-growed long ago; but right under it lies buried a young woman, which I never see that tree without thinking of her, and wonderin' who she was. She was not more nor twenty, but she had seen sorrow and trouble enough for a lifetime. We took her on board forty years ago it will be next month, at Louisville. She was dressed as a young lad, but none of us guessed she was a woman. She spoke broken English, said she wanted to work her way to Orleens. So we put her to cookin'. She was so gentle and kind-spoken

we all liked him, I mean *her*. But one morning when
the day broke, just as we were floating down about here,
we found her lying dead on the front part of the boat,
with a dagger buried in her heart. It was a small dagger, with a silver hilt, sich as I had seen in Orleens
among them pesky Spaniards. We didn't know who did
it. But we buried her there. I dug the grave myself.
There was foul play somewhere. One of our people
said he had heard something swimming about the boat
in the dark, but supposed it was a deer crossing the
river, as they often did in them days, and there was
prints of a man's wet feet upon the boards of the deck,
and I always believed some enemy had followed her
down the river, and swum off and murdered her. But
it's always been a mystery to me; but no doubt it'll all
turn up, marm, at judgment-day!"

Here the boat rounded to for the purpose of taking on
board some passengers, and the pilot left me; but I stood
and gazed long and silently and sadly upon the green
grave of the beautiful stranger, whose secret, as the pilot
had said, was locked up with God. It was a quiet,
shaded spot. A wild grape vine had festooned itself
above the grassy bed of the wanderer, and a few wild
flowers grew upon it. Ah! indeed, how many secrets
will the judgment day reveal!

How profoundly the unknown slept! The hoarse roar
of the escaping steam, the shouts of the voices of the
crew, the oaths of the mate, the dashing of the huge
wheels into the water, the hurry, bustle, and confusion—
how they all contrasted with the unbroken stillness of that
green spot, which death had made sacred! As our boat
resumed her way, I lingered with my eyes upon the

grave, above which, perched upon the grape vine, a robin had alighted and was singing. Sweet sufferer of a former day! Though forty years have passed, thou art not forgotten! Thy memory, cherished in the rough bosom of the old pilot, shall live in many hearts to whom my feeble pen shall relate thy brief, sad history. Many a loving heart and sympathizing bosom shall feel and beat in kindly sympathy for thee, as thou reposest in thy lonely grave beside the murmuring tide of the River of Beauty.

At this moment, while I was still gazing on the snowy-armed sycamore, a fashionable young gentleman, who had been made acquainted with us, approached me, and said, with a glance of contempt towards the old pilot:

"What rude fellar was that, Miss Conyngham, that presumed to address you without an introduction, as I presume you had not the honor of his acquaintance? You must pardon the ignorance of these Western men! They are quite beyond all forms of good society! Didn't he annoy you excessively?"

"On the contrary, I was much interested in his conversation," I answered, with some point in my tones. "He has *ideas.*"

"Ah! ideas?" repeated the exquisite, who had sense enough to comprehend what I wished him to apprehend, "you are inclined to be severe, Miss Conyngham. But, Miss Isabel says you are a wit."

"Indeed! You should be obliged to her for giving you the information, for you know wits are very dangerous people to some folks."

"Yes, I'm afraid of witty people," he answered, fingering his glossy whiskers, and then smoothing the glossy silk of his hat. "Do you know, Miss Conyngham, that there is a new style of hat coming into fashion? The brim is to be an inch wider than this—which is the latest style, and it is to turn up slightly, just the least bit in the world, all round, even in front! And the band is to be full two inches wide. You see what an effect this will produce! This band is but an inch and a quarter. And then the hat is to bell out full at the top! It strikes me that it will be a superb affair. But more than all, it is made of such material as to contract or expand to the head of the wearer, fitting each bump perfectly, so as to give no uneasiness; but, so far as that is concerned, I never experienced any uneasiness from this: my head is nicely balanced. Dr. —— Dr. —— what's his name? —once passed his fingers over my head, and pronounced it a model of equilibrium. If I have one bump, Miss, more prominent than another, I conceive that it is—is combativeness. Yes, I have a great belligerent propensity. But it is kept in check by an equal amount of prudence; otherwise, I have no doubt, I should have fought not one less than forty duels in my life! I see, Miss, you are admiring my watch seal," (which the exquisite was twirling and trying to make me notice). "It is of California gold, solid! So is the chain. Had it made to order!—This massive ring, too, is—"

Here the old pilot returned, and said abruptly, without taking any notice of the person talking to me,

"You see, Miss, that little clump of trees on that knoll to the left?" and he pointed with his large, brown hand.

The fop looked daggers at him! But there was a calm self-possession—a certain native dignity about the rough-coated old pilot, that commanded his respect and ever-

awed his combativeness, or I don't know what horrid
scene might have ensued, unless the bump of "prudence"
should come in to counteract the predisposition to combativeness.   Prudence *did* its duty!   The exquisite,
after trying to annihilate the old river Neptune with a
look which was lost on him, turned away with an equal
contempt in his equally-balanced mind both for me and
the pilot.

"Ill-bred! Vulgar tastes!" I heard him mutter, as
he moved off,—terms of his indignation, which were
doubtless intended to be divided equally between my
friend in the shaggy pilot coat and myself.

The clump of trees were peculiar and marked by their
isolated position, standing in advance of the rest of the
shore, quite down into the water.

"I see them, sir!" I answered.

"There is a different story I could tell you about
them;" he said, as if alluding mentally to what he had
narrated about the sycamore tree.

"I should like to hear it!" I replied.

"It ain't a long one.   Few words and to the point,"
he answered, as he pulled off a fresh flake of tobacco
from the diminished mass which he carried wrapped up in
the oilskin.   "I saw three men shot by the shortest of
them trees; under that ere limb that hangs partly over
the water."

"Shot!" I repeated, with horror.

"Nothing less, Miss; it was during the war with the
English. Some troops were going to New Orleans to
help Jackson, and three of 'em deserted and were caught,
tried, and shot there, all in one hour, by Col. Mead, the

officer who commanded the fleet of boats. They were
buried under that red bank thar! One of 'em was a
mere lad! He prayed for his widowed mother, that the
Great God above would give her strength to bear the
news, and then, while the tears shone on his cheeks, he
bared his white breast to the guns, and the next moment,
six bullets were tearing up the tender flesh and crashing
into his body. He fell dead! But one of the others
leaped his height into the air with a fearful oath, and
then ran for the river to jump in: but he fell dead on
the grass. Ah, Miss, still and quiet as that pretty little
clump of trees looks now, with the birds a singing in it,
it has witnessed scenes you'd hardly have guessed if you
hadn't been told. Jist so it is, marm, with human natur.
You see a man walking quiet-like, and with a steady lip
and eye among his fellows; but if he should tell you what
he had gone through in his day, you would see that,
though there are pleasant groves like in his heart, and
the birds sing in them, scenes have passed there that
would make us sad if they were told us.

"But, Miss, here we are close at the mouth of the
Ohio, and in a few minutes will be in the Mississippi.
If you'd like to get a better look of the grand sight of
the meetin' of the two greatest rivers in America, you'd
better go forward, and up into the pilot house, for it is
the highest part of the boat, and you can see wider and
farther."

I thanked my new friend, and sending for Isabel and
the colonel, I was escorted by the hardy old river man,
with a politeness that exquisites might imitate, to the
elevated throne, standing upon which the helmsman go-

verns the movements and directs the course of our mighty steamer.

In my next, I shall endeavor to give you my impressions of "The Meeting of the Waters."

Yours,

KATE.

LETTER XXX.

Dear Mr.———:

How shall I describe to you the profound impression of sublimity, so that you may have some adequate conception of it, which the sight of the "meeting of the waters" had upon me yesterday ? To see the union of the Mississippi and Ohio is worth a voyage thus far. It is one of the sublimest spectacles a traveler chances to meet with.

Everything was propitious to present to our view the junction in all its grandest features. Both rivers were of equal height: the Mississippi dark and turbid, the Ohio clear and of a green tint. As our steamer entered upon the last mile of the Ohio, I could see with a glass, with which my good friend, the pilot, provided me, the line which marked the boundary between the two waters. As we drew nearer and nearer, and at length passed out from between the arms of the Ohio into the bosom of the Father of Waters, I was surprised and delighted to find that we still were borne on the tide of the former, although fairly within the shores of the latter.

For nearly two miles after we had entered the Mississippi, we kept in the green waters of the Belle Riviere, which, pushing and compressing the murky flood of the other to half its breadth, contested the right of way to the mile-broad channel with it. The line between the waters that flowed from the Alleghanies and those which had come from the Rocky Mountains was distinctly preserved for a long distance by their different hues; and in order to gratify Isabel, the helmsman, at one time, steered so that we sailed directly on the line of demarkation—the green tinted waves of the Ohio being on our left, and the muddy, brown waves of the Mississippi being on the right—the keel of our steamer dividing them equally.

But after we had descended about two miles, the superior strength of the Mississippi began to show itself. The old Father of Rivers, as if he had merely out of courtesy suffered the Belle Ohio to occupy his channel for a little while, now began to assert his claims to the whole breadth between the banks. Here and there the turbid under current would force itself up to the surface of the waters of the Ohio, and exhibit everywhere great circular patches of floating mud. These soon flowed together and commingled; and at length the green current of the Belle Riviere became all muddy and turbid, lost its individuality, and was absorbed in the mighty rolling flood, whose domain it fain would have held in copartnership. It was full a league below the mouth before the union was so complete that we lost the last trace of the peculiar tint of the lesser and clearer stream. It was wonderful to see how completely one vast river had been swallowed up by another; and yet neither had the huge gormandizer grown larger, widened his banks, or deepened his channels; and so this mammoth of rivers goes on to the sea, a thousand miles southward, taking in a score of rivers at a yawn, and never showing signs of his voraciousness!

"Now, Miss," said the old pilot, who seemed greatly

to enjoy my admiration of the spectacle, "now we are
fairly on the Mississippi! You'll find it a wild water,
marm; and the shores al'ays keep the same as you see
'em now,—forests, and nothing else. Five hundred
miles farther down you'll see no difference. A picture
of the river taken here, and one after we 've sailed on
it three days more, will look both exactly alike; it would
take a man pretty well used to the river, if he was taken
up from one place, and put in another a hundred miles
farther down, to know he'd changed places."

The sun set with a splendor that I have never before
beheld. The river at the time was flowing west for full
five miles in a straight line, and the whole distance,
illumined redly by the sun at the end of the vista, shone
like a burnished lake of gold; while the black forests on
either shore formed a fine frame to the whole. These
"reaches" and bends of the river, which it forms every
few leagues as it flows now west, now east, now doubling
back northwardly, gives the Mississippi the character of
a chain of lakes, each from three to seven miles long,
and always the unvarying breadth of about four thousand feet.

There is something terrific, as well as majestic in this
vast moving flood. Its surface is never quiet. Repose
it knows not. It is agitated by myriads of whirlpools,
and here and there rushes along without any apparent
cause, with additional velocity, and a roar like rapids;
yet there are nothing like rocks in its bed, and its depth
is fearful everywhere. I had heard that a person falling
into it, would never rise again. I therefore questioned
my friend the pilot upon this interesting point.

"They do say so, Miss," politely answered a hale old

man who was steering, and removing his quid from his
mouth out of respect to me, and thrusting it for safe
keeping into the cuff of his drab jacket, the stained look
of which showed that it was an ordinary reception place
for such things; "but it an't al'ays true, 'cept in high
top floods. Then I'd be sorry to fall overboard. Most
usual there is an under current as sucks a man right
down, and before he can battle agen it and get up to the
top, its all over with him. Besides, the water is al'ays
so muddy, it chokes up a man 'mazin' quick. But in
low water, why a man can swim tolerable fair in this
river; but its better to keep on board if he can, and not
tempt it; for old Massassap is a mighty ugly customer to
trust oneself to, at any time,—'mazin' treacherous and
oncertain!"

Although the evening shades fell, and the supper bell
rung, I could not leave the deck. The western sky was
a paradise of glory, a heaven tinted with every hue of
beauty. Amid a clear space of pure *green*, the evening
star hung like an amethyst set in emerald. The waters
shone like living gold. The gloomy shores grew darker
and more mysterious. The stars came out overhead.
From our two tall black chimneys rolled, billow on billow, sable clouds of smoke mixed with sparks, which, as
they covered the skies over us, gave one an idea of the
heavens on fire, and the stars loosened from their spheres.
The regular boom of the breathing engine echoing from
shore to shore, the dash of the monstrous wheels creating
a continual foaming cataract, which, mingling astern,
formed a mad wake of whirlpools—the onward, life-like,
ever-pressing-forward motion of the swift steamer, which
carried me with two hundred other souls through all this

scene of novel beauty and strange grandeur, bound me
to the deck, and forbade my thoughts and soul turning
to anything else.

At length night, in all the glittering glory of her
starry beauty, reigned. Leaning upon the arm of the
colonel, while Isabel hung upon the other, I walked the
upper deck till a late hour. Showers of sparks were
sailing away in the air every moment, and some of them,
keeping their brightness longer than others, we loved to
imagine shooting stars, which they closely resembled.
Many would descend in graceful curves to the surface of
the river far astern, and, lighting upon it, be at once
extinguished. Others would ascend and move in a
spiral path higher and higher, as if they fain would scale
heaven, and take their place among the fixed stars,
which looked no bigger than they. We also amused
ourselves in watching the woodmen's lights on the shore
—large fires built at the points where wood for steamers was to be found. These signal fires, which were
visible on both sides from a mile to a league apart,
had a fine effect upon the imagination. It seemed as if
our midnight way was voluntarily lighted by some kind
beings of the main who wished us "good luck" on our
voyage, and desired that we should prosecute it in safety.
The pilot related to the colonel a very remarkable use
which he once made of these lights on the shore.

"We were coming up from Orleans in a thick fog,"
said he. "The night was dark as pitch. We could not
land in safety, as it blew hard. Our only chance was to
keep in the middle of the stream and run for it. These
woodmen at that time did not light their signal fires till
they heard a boat ring her bell, as a token that it wanted

wood. You would then see a score of fires kindled along a stretch of four miles or so. We could discern no fires to guide us, or tell us where either shore was; so I rang the bell as a signal for wooding. The next minute a fire blazed up through the fog on the left bank, quarter of a mile ahead; and a half a mile above upon the other shore, shone another like a star in the dog-days. By these we were enabled to steer; and every quarter of an hour I tolled my bell, as I ascended the river, and fire after fire would blaze up, one on this shore, one on that. In this way we ran all night, full a hundred miles, lighted by these signal fires, which we made these poor fellows kindle, supposing we were coming in to take in wood; but the rogues ought to have done us this service, as they live and get rich by steamboats.''

It was late when we left the deck to return to our state-rooms. During the night I was awakened by the noise of a steamer passing us. Looking from my state-room door, I saw its red-mouthed furnaces glare through the gloom, lighting up half the river's breadth, the dark figures of the firemen looking like so many demons as they cast the fuel into them. It was a magnificent sight, and a fearful one, to see the huge, roaring, dashing, booming, thundering monster go past, with noise enough to awake the Seven Sleepers, while the shores and the sides of our vessel re-echoed and redoubled the sublime uproar. The next moment she was past, and darkness and a rocking motion succeeded. I observed at the bow of the boat two fiery red lanterns, elevated on high, which serve as guides to the pilot, and to show the posi-sition of the boat to other pilots in the night. Our boat has a blue and a crimson one. Unaccustomed to the motion and working of the machinery, it was long past midnight ere I was able to fall to sleep.

This morning we found ourselves at New Madrid, once the capital of the Spanish empire of the West, but now a hamlet of a few houses. The place has been destroyed by an earthquake, and what remains of it is falling into the river by detachments. Street after street has broken off and gone, until but one remains. The whole country is deeply fissured by the shocks which occur every few weeks. We learn that ten days ago there was so severe a one that an acre of the front of the town fell into the river, and chairs and tables in houses were thrown down. Such, however, is the force of habit, and "getting accustomed to shaking," as the man said who had the ague twenty-four years, that the citizens do not mind these shocks; but take them as they come, as they do the storms and wind, and the other ordinary phenomena of nature.

We had a very amusing scene occur this morning, just before day! There is a young bear on board, belonging to a Missourian, who is taking him down to Arkansas, to his sweetheart, he told me. The "exquisite" had evinced some apprehension about him, and expressed it to me more than once, that he feared he might "get loose and perpetrate some mischief."

Well, sure enough, at daylight this morning, the whole cabin was aroused by such an uproar and screaming as you never heard! "The bear! the bear! the bear is in my state-room!" was shrieked in tones of mortal horror.

Upon flying to the scene of terror and to the rescue, it proved to be, that a gentleman, who from a paralytic stroke has not for several years been able to speak, was now on his way to the Hot Springs to endeavor to effect a cure. But there are times when, if he attempts to laugh he sends forth the most appalling spasmodic sounds, between a yell and a howl, with a sprinkling of awful groans, all mixed up together in one,—sounds unearthly and terrific, and therefore enough to alarm anybody of stout nerves. This poor gentleman was put into the lower berth of the state-room, which my exquisite occupied. Towards morning, the paralytic being awake, heard his neighbor in the next state-room, in stepping out of bed, put his foot into his wash-pitcher, and at the accident swear so oddly that it excited his risibles to an un-governable extent. The result was a laugh that was a compound of the roar of a bear, the howl of a wolf, and the yell of a hyena, which, the more he tried to suppress it, the worse it became. The young fop was positive the bear had got into his room, and calling on him, in his best vernacular, to prepare to be eaten up.

When the facts became known there was a good hearty laugh at the young man's expense, but the paralytic gentleman being, as the colonel observed, maliciously tempted by the enemy of our race to join in it, produced a second and improved edition of his vocal performances, that filled all who heard him with consternation.

To morrow, we expect to be at Memphis.

Yours,
KATE.

LETTER XXXI.

DEAR MR. ——— :

WE have at length reached Natchez, and I write once more from a plantation, but one situated in Mississippi instead of Tennessee, and in the bosom of the most opulent and cultivated portion of the South. I have already spoken of the town of Natchez, which possesses all the charming features of a tropical city. Its streets lined with the Pride of China tree, now in full flower, its verandah-ornamented residences, with their wide, airy halls and piazzas; the sweet gardens that fill all the atmosphere, even in the business streets, with the perfume of flowers; the quiet repose and comfort of the whole place; the indolent luxury of the nothing-to-do air of the citizens, who like all Southerners, never *bustle* about; the half foreign air descended to it from the old Spaniards, who first dwelt here, give to Natchez a *tout ensemble*, wholly different from a Northern town.

Then there are the handsome suburban villas embedded amid flower gardens, their white columns glancing here and there, from openings in the foliage of the umbrageous trees that shade them.

Many of the more wealthy cotton planters, whose estates lie on the river where it is unhealthy to reside, live in the vicinity of Natchez, in country houses, on which they lavish taste and expense without limit. There is, therefore, a beautiful wilderness of architectural and horticultural elegance around the city. The pleasant drives carry you winding along among these tasteful homes now rolling over a graveled lawn-road, now traversing hedges enclosing gardens that contain nearly all the tropical plants; now catching sight of a summer-house, now of statuary, and on all sides beauty.

It is in these homes, which extend a league or more around the town, that are to be found the families that have given to the society of Natchez so much celebrity. Here are to be found persons who have traveled abroad, and cultivated their tastes by European discipline. Their parlors are adorned with pictures from pencils of the first masters. Their halls are not deficient in fine statuary. Their private libraries are often large and well chosen. The furniture, equipages, and style of living are all in keeping.

In Natchez itself there are but few wealthy persons; but the society is exceedingly good, and every stranger, who has enjoyed its hospitality, will have a grateful recollection of their tasteful and pleasant homes.

Natchez is the diocesan residence of Bishop Green, the Bishop of Mississippi, and also of Bishop Chance, the Roman Catholic Prelate. The Cathedral is a noble building, in the Gothic style of architecture, and its tall white spire can be seen for many miles around. Although I am more than two leagues distant from it, I have it in sight, visible over a rich undulating country, with here and there the chimneys of a villa rising above the sea of foliage. The Episcopal Church in Natchez is said to have the most opulent parish in the South-western country, which is doubtless the case. The Roman Catholics are not numerous here, yet they have a Female Boarding-school or Nunnery, under the charge of Mad'lle Marcellus, a lady formerly from Baltimore, and who, in her infancy, with her mother, was one of the few who escaped the massacre of St. Domingo. This school is supported mainly by Protestant pupils, who in almost every instance leave the school with a decided bias towards the Roman Church, if not actually Romanists.

The appearance of the country from the plantation where I am now sojourning for a few days, is very beautiful, diversified as it is to the eye with woodlands, broad cotton fields, and country seats in the centre of surrounding estates. The magnolia is here the pride and glory of all trees. Within sight is a ridge that is thickly forested with them, and such a spectacle of green magnificence I have never beheld. When the sun at a certain angle glances upon the polished surface of the large leaves, every tree seems as if encased in emerald armor. Then the grand, huge flowers, that glitter here and there amid the masses of foliage like large silver stars, fill all the air around with their fragrance. Some of these trees rise to the height of ninety feet—tall, proud cones of beauty that seem to be conscious of their elegance.

The Southern ladies are all natural gardeners. The taste with which they lay out and arrange their parterres would delight and surprise a Northern eye. The garden of this house where we are now visiting, though by no means regarded as the finest in this vicinity, I will describe, and it will give you some idea of others here. But first let me describe our drive hither from town.

After we had driven half an hour amid the most luxuriant hedge rows, which extended miles further, we came to a white gateway, set in the hedge. It was the entrance to the estate. Passing through it, we rode a quarter of a mile beneath the majestic branches of a fine old forest, and then emerged into an open road, which was bounded on both sides by cotton fields, in which gangs of slaves in their white and blue cotton dresses were at work, under the eye of a mounted overseer.

The villa, or "great house," was visible half a mile off, fairly embowered in an island of the deepest verdure, for an island it seemed, surrounded by the ploughed, brown fields of the plantation. As we advanced, we could catch sight of a column between the trees, then of a wing, and get a glimpse of the portico. At length, after two or three times losing sight of it as we wound round the undulations of the fields, we emerged full in front of its handsome arched gateway. The enclosure was many acres, entirely shut in by a hedge that was spangled with snow white flowers. A slave opened the gate for our carriage. We drove through, and found ourselves within a horticultural paradise. The softest lawns, the loveliest groups of trees of the richest leaf, the prettiest walks, the brightest little lakes, with swans upon their bosoms, the most romantic vistas, met our enraptured gaze. Through this lovely place we drove over a smooth avenue, at one time almost in complete darkness from the overarching limbs interlaced above; at another rolling in sunlight upon the open sward.

At length we drew near the mansion, which was an

Italian villa of the purest style, elevated so as to be ascended by a broad flight of steps. There were immense vases, three feet tall, standing in front, just where the eye of taste would have them, containing West Indian plants, with gorgeous leaves, and flowering splendidly, the names of which I do not know. The color of the edifice was a shade under the lemon tint, which relieved finely the foliage about it. In the centre were broad folding doors, which were thrown open, and presented a prospect, through a noble central hall with a polished oak floor, of the garden in the rear of the house. Standing in the door of this hall, we could command the main avenue of the garden, which descended in a succession of terraces to a small lake glittering at the extremity. This lake lay in deep seclusion beneath a grove of overhanging oaks and sycamores, of magnolia trees, elms, and orange trees. The south piazza commanded the whole garden, which was a labyrinth of beauty and floral magnificence. Upon descending into the garden, one passed through an avenue of tropical plants, many of which I had never seen, nor could have believed they ever existed, their loveliness and grandeur were so novel and extraordinary. In some of the flowers it seemed as if "the Angel of flowers" had tried to see how beautiful a thing it could make. Such exquisite forms and colors! Ah me! how beautiful, thought I, as I gazed on them, must things in Heaven be, if things, their shadows on earth, are so lovely!

Which way soever one turns her steps in wandering through this magical garden, new and ever varied scenes open upon the eye. If I should particularize, I would but give you a catalogue and description of the plants. A bed of violets, sixty feet square, as blue and brilliant as a paved floor of turquoise, and fragrant as all Araby; bordering one side of a walk, a bank of verbenas, one hundred feet in length and seven feet broad, composed of every shade of the varied color of this flower, looked like a mosaic aisle, surpassing description for its gorgeous brilliancy. There were strange looking flowers, the leaves of which appeared as if they had been cut out of crimson silk velvet, while fringes of golden flowers seemed to hang pendant from them.

In the winter months, the large galleries of the house are shut in with glass casements, and the rarest flowers removed from the garden thither; so that one can look from the parlor windows upon flowers, or, opening them, promenade among them in a pleasant atmosphere; for these winter conservatories are kept at an equal temperature by furnaces beneath.

Many of the tropical plants require in this climate this protection from the first of December to the first of April; though all the winter the gardens look green and beautiful, so numerous are the plants that can remain out. Our charming hostess told me she used formerly to bring in the Agave Americana every winter, not thinking it would live otherwise, till at length some of them grew too large and heavy to be removed, even by four men; and she sorrowfully let them remain, supposing the winter would kill them, when, lo, to her surprise, they were not touched; and many of the *cacti* that are usually sheltered, will endure the winter abroad. I was shown by her a night-blooming cereus, preserved in

alcohol, which she cut off in the height of its bloom.
This is probably one of the most delicate and beautiful
flowers created by the hand of Him who made this world
of beauty. It is the custom here, when a lady has one
of these plants on the eve of blooming, to send a servant
to all her friends on the surrounding estates, inviting
them to the spectacle. The gathering at such times is
a pleasant one. Carriages roll, and saddle horses come
galloping up the avenue, bearing youths and maidens,
and gray heads, and children; and a merry frolic it is,
with a fine supper at the close, and an exciting gallopade
back *a cheval* by moonlight, or star-beams.

There is here a touching custom of having burying
grounds on the estates. Nearly all plantations have a
private cemetery. These places of buried affection,
where hope and faith wait the resurrection, are often
gems of funereal beauty. Some secluded but sweet
spot, not too remote from the mansion, is selected. It
is enclosed by a snow-white paling, or a massive wall of
brick; ivy is taught to grow over it; elms, willows, and
cypresses are planted within the inclosure. White marble tombs glisten among the foliage. Perhaps over all,
towers a group of ancient oaks, subduing the light beneath, and lending to the hallowed spot a mournful
shade, a soft twilight even in the sultry noontide's
glare.

Such is the family burial-place on this estate. Not
far from it, in a place scarcely less picturesque, is the
cemetery for the slaves, enclosed by a neat white-washed
wall. The affection of the poor Africans has planted the
rose and the lily, the violet and verbena, upon many

of the graves. I was struck with the inscription upon a slab at the head of one of the green mounds of earth:

"TO THE MEMORY

OF

GOOD OLD PETER,

A FAITHFUL SERVANT,

AGED 97 YEARS,

"Well done good and faithful servant, enter thou into the joy of thy Lord."

ERECTED BY HIS MASTER.

I learned that he had been in the family three generations, and that for the last thirty years of his life he had been exempt from all duties, except such as he chose voluntarily to perform. He had served faithfully the father and grandfather of our present host, who had raised this tribute to his memory.

"A faithful servant," mused I, as I fixed my gaze on those three words. Who can ask for greater commendation? In his narrow and humble sphere he served faithfully, and has entered into his rest. Oh! that I, also, may have it inscribed upon my tomb, that I have been "a faithful servant" in my sphere wherein my Maker has placed me. It is praise enough for a king; for, monarch or slave, we are all servants to "one Master, who is in heaven." I left the grave of "good old Peter' with a healthy lesson impressed upon my heart.

Yours,

KATHARINE CONYNGHAM.

LETTER XXXII.

DEAR MR. ———:

THIS will be the last letter I shall address you from this state, as to-morrow we re-embark at Natchez on our voyage to New Orleans. In this letter I shall touch upon an interesting subject, suggested by a visit which we all made yesterday to a neighboring estate to dine. It was at the residence of one of the old families, whose American origin dates back to the Spanish times. Everything was in the most unexceptionable style. But there was one thing which I did not like, and will tell you frankly what it was. I knew that in the family was a young lady of great mental accomplishments and personal beauty, from the North, who was a governess, or, as it is termed here, "teacher" in the family, and having known her in New England, I was anticipating no little pleasure in meeting her on this occasion. Not seeing her at dinner, upon inquiring of the lady of the mansion for her, she answered me that "she was in her study-room, and that she never came to the table when guests were present. She at such times takes her meals in her room."

Here then I found an educated girl of twenty, whose grandfather has left a glorious name on the page of American history, whose father has been a member of Congress, treated as an inferior, placed on a level with a housekeeper, because left a destitute orphan, she chose rather to teach than be dependent on relatives.

"I will send a servant for her if you wish to see her," added the lady coldly.

"No," I said, " I will see her in her room."

I was escorted by a servant across a noble hall hung with fine pictures, and supported by corinthian columns, to a wing of the villa. He knocked at a polished walnut door. It was opened by my lovely friend, who, on recognizing me, almost shrieked with joy, and clasped me to her heart. The door was closed, and we were soon engaged in conversation. Upon my expressing my regret at the false position which she held there, she smiled, (sadly, I thought,) and replied—

"It is not altogether disagreeable, as I do not wish to mingle in society where the ladies, however polite, would regard me as not their full equal; so I prefer dining in my room: though to tell you the truth, I am never invited at the dinner parties; nor when invitations are sent for the family am I included; and if I go, it is expected I shall keep an eye on my two sweet little pupils. Teaching here is by some families looked upon as beneath 'position,' as the phrase is. But I am content to endure all this neglect for the emoluments, which are seven hundred dollars per annum, which enable me to send four hundred dollars yearly to my mother, who has need of all the aid I can render her. With the balance, save what I absolutely require for my own use, I am paying a debt left by my father. For these advantages I am content to hold an apparently inferior position. I have no pride, dear Kate. Reverses have made me humble." Such is the true position, Mr. ——, of the governess in the more fashionable Southern families. But in some she is regarded as an equal. Usually she holds a place midway between the lady of the mansion, and the overseer's wife. Too far above one to be her companion, and too much beneath the other, she has an isolated position, under which the spirits of the most cheerful girl will by and by give way. Even her pupils feel themselves her superiors. She can never marry here; for the gentleman would not address "a teacher," and with her education and refinement she can marry no one beneath a gentleman. This line of distinction between the governess and the mother of the young children she teaches is more strongly defined in the older and more aristocratic families. Indeed it is in some of them quite as distinct as in the families of the nobility in England, where, all readers of romance have learned, the governess never associates on terms of equality with the family. But there are many families of planters who do not live in so much style and exclusiveness, where a teacher would feel at home, and be treated with affection and respect; but she is the "teacher" still, in the eyes of the neighborhood. A plain planter's family is the best to teach in, let me say to such aspirants for places as governesses as may read this letter. To be sure the *eclat* of being in a very rich, stylish family, in a large, superbly-furnished mansion, is a temptation that ensnares the inexperienced; but let me tell such that, the higher the fashion of the family, the lower will be the station of the governess, and the more she will be made to *feel* her position. Much, however, depends on the young lady herself. True refinement will always find respect; while vulgarity or brusqueness of manner will meet its level.

There are, however, in all pursuits and avocations "disagreeables." No condition of industry is free from them; and this is one of the privations and disagreeables those young ladies who seek situations in Southern families must take with the situation. Teaching here is looked upon as a trade, both in males and females. For a Southern lady to teach as a governess, she loses caste with many, though not, of course, with the sensible and right minded. I know a lady with two grown daughters who has a school not far from Vicksburg, who will not let her daughters assist her in teaching, lest it should be an obstacle in the way of their marrying *en regle*. · This woman understands the character of the people. Now in New England, teaching is regarded directly the reverse. Our teachers there are a part of the " respectability" of society. Our professors are aristocrats. Some of our first ladies have been teachers when girls. In a word, a New England mind can scarcely comprehend how teaching youth can be looked upon as a lowering vocation.

The gentlemen who teach in the South as private tutors, are placed exactly in the same position as the governesses. I am told that a gentleman, who has since left a brilliant name for genius behind him, was tutor for two years in a distinguished private family near New Orleans, and in all that time was never an invited guest at any dinner party in the house. When the planter has furnished him a room, a horse, and his meals, and paid him his salary, all obligations are considered discharged towards the "teacher." Professors in colleges

in the South are often called "teachers," and the wife
of a president is but the "teacher's wife." In a word,
no body is really aristocratic but the wealthy cotton-
planter.

The number of private tutors of both sexes throughout
the South is very great. The distance at which planters
dwell from towns renders it incumbent on them to employ
teachers at home. The situation is pleasant or unpleasant according to the family and the disposition of the
tutor. If he or she, for the sake of laying up something,
is willing to endure privation, and even "to lose position,"
for a year or two, why these trifles can be borne. The
usual salary for a young lady is four hundred and fifty to
five and six hundred dollars with board. Some receive
more, especially as in the case of my fair friend, if music
and French be included. Latin is sometimes required,
but not often. In general, the planters keep their daughters under governesses till they are fourteen, and then
send them to some celebrated school, North or South,
to remain a year or two to graduate. The sons, also,
at eighteen, and often earlier, are dispatched to Northern
colleges. Few daughters "finish off" at home. Since
the recent agitation upon the slavery question, the Mis-
sissippians are disposed to be shy of Northern teachers,
and fewer will be employed.

In one county here, at a public meeting, resolutions
were passed that no teacher should be employed who was
not born South, or was not a Northern man with Southern principles. The good people of New England have
contributed to close an avenue to preferment, South, for
their educated sons and daughters, by their injudicious

interposition between Southerners and their institution.*
It will be difficult, indeed, to find Southern born young
ladies and gentlemen who will teach, and thus prevent
the necessity of depending on the North; but there will
be, for a long time, a reluctance to employ New England
teachers; and thousands, who would have found employment on the ten thousand Southern plantations, will be
excluded. It will be one benefit to the South. Its youth
will prepare themselves to be teachers, and this despised
vocation will become honorable.

In my own case, I have not felt the sense of inferior-
ity attached to a governess. The family in which I have
so long dwelt at Overton Park have too much refinement, education, and good sense to think any less of me
for being a teacher. Indeed, I am as agreeably situated
as if I were an honored relative, and feel like a daughter
rather than a governess. If the situation of all who
teach in families was like mine, teaching would be the
most delightful occupation one could choose.

Great attention is paid here to the manly education
of boys. They are taught to ride fearlessly and sit a
horse well. The two sons of the gentleman, eleven and
thirteen years old, where we are now visiting, ride up to
Natchez three times a week, to take fencing lessons, box-
ing lessons, and lessons in dancing. They are also taught
pistol and rifle shooting. The eldest son, who has just
turned his nineteenth year, has displayed to me for my
amusement, some surprising exhibitions of his skill. With
a pistol, I saw him shoot three humble-bees on the wing,
at six paces distant. He will do this all day without
scarcely missing a shot. With a double-barreled shot-gun,

* Written in 1853.

I have seen him repeatedly, to-day, hit two oranges which he threw into the air together, firing right and left, and putting balls through both before they touched the ground.   He has an old gun which he calls "Sharp's rifle," with which I saw him shoot and bring to the ground, a vulture that was flying so high, it seemed no bigger than a sparrow.   I was admiring the plumage of a beautiful red bird which was perched on the top of an oak, when he sent in for his rifle, and before I could prevent him he had taken its head off with a rifle ball and brought it to me saying, quietly, "There it is—you see it is a cardinal."   If he goes out shooting, he disdains to kill birds at rest; but first starts them up and assuredly brings them down on the wing.   This evening, he threw up two quarter-of-a-dollar pieces, and hit them both in the air with a double-barreled pistol.   Yet this thorough-bred marksman is an intellectual, pale, oval-faced young man, with long, flowing hair, a slight moustache, and the elegant, indolent manners of a Chestnut street lounger.   His eye is quiet, and his demeanor gentle, and one would hardly suppose, to look at his almost effeminate form, that it would be certain death to stand before him in a hostile *rencontre*. It is this training which won for the immortal Mississippi Rifles, in Mexico, their great celebrity ; when a corps of three hundred of them checked the advance of six thousand Mexican cavalry, and turned the tide of battle.

I have just seen an Indian chief.   He came to the house, bringing five wild turkeys which he had shot.   He is a Choctaw, and yet bears in his independent carriage some traces of his former free and wild life.   He was grave in aspect, and said but little.   His rifle was tied upon the stock with thongs of deer's hide; and had

a rusty flint lock.   He had a powder-horn and shot-bag
of deerskin slung at his side; wore fringed leggings, moccasins, and a blue hunting shirt.   His black, coarse hair
was bound by an old red sash.   He seemed to listen with
deep attention to the piano, but no change of countenance
betrayed emotion.   He was much taken with my young
friend's "Sharp's rifle," which he examined with great
care; and then made him a sign to shoot with it.   Two
hundred and fifty yards distant, a crow was perched
upon a dead limb.   The young man leveled his gun :
the Indian watched the result eagerly, yet with a slight
smile of incredulity.   The crow fell to the earth simultaneously with the report.   The Indian clapped the rifle
on the barrel with a grunt of praise, and, taking the
marksman's hand, pressed it in token of fellowship in
hunter's skill.   He fairly fell in love with the rifle, and
finally putting it down, walked away sadly towards the
forest where he had his camp.

I was then told by our host a very striking and touching incident associated with him.   A chapel was about
to be erected on a neighboring estate.   The walls were
commenced, but the work of the first day was pulled
down in the night by an unknown hand.   They were
recommenced, and the same thing occurred thrice.   This
chief confessed that it was his act.

"You have covered with your prayer-house the grave
of my wife!" was the abrupt and touching reason he
gave.   He was threatened if he interfered again.   But
a fourth time the walls were destroyed, and, at length,
the sensibilities of the Indian were respected, and the
church erected a few feet farther south, when the devoted
husband gave no further molestations.   What a subject

for a poem from the pen of Amelia, or some of our female poetesses, or Prentice, or Park Benjamin!

My next letter will be written *en voyage* on our way to New Orleans, where we hope to be by the day after to-morrow. Till then, adieu.

Yours respectfully,
KATE.

LETTER XXXIII.

DEAR MR. ———— :

It is with a certain misgiving and want of cardinal faith in mail-bags, that I sit down to my purple, velvet-topped writing-desk and take up my jeweled gold pen (a New Year's gift from the colonel) to commence burnishing up a "Needle" for you. One paper of six shining needles, sharp as thorns—I mean the thorns that guard rose-buds—I sent to you last May, nicely sealed, and addressed to you in a plain, fair hand, that could not be mistaken for any thing else.

I placed the package carefully in the hands of the village post-master of the rural town near which I was then visiting, in Mississippi. I was on horseback, and riding up to the door with the parcel in my hand, I placed it in his possession, saying, "Parson," (for he is an ex-Methodist preacher, with gray locks, and a venerable, General Jackson-like aspect, with his wiry hair brushed hard back from his knotty forehead,) "my dear, good parson," said I, in my most entreating tones, "I entrust to you this little package, to go by mail to Philadelphia. I wish you would see that it is certainly mailed."

"Yes, Miss, it shall go to-night. Is there any money in it?" he asked, looking at its four corners, peering at the seal, and balancing it on his two fingers, as if to test its avoirdupois.

"They are needles," I said, smiling, "and they mustn't get wet."

"Needles! Miss, then; I'm 'fraid its hardly mailable matter," and he held the parcel more lightly in his grasp, as if he were apprehensive of pricking his fingers, should any of the sharp points penetrate the paper.

"Weigh it, sir, and charge postage accordingly: it will be paid in Philadelphia," I answered; and receiving a renewed promise from the snowy-headed old postmaster, who is known by no other title or name than "Parson," in all the town, I rode away at full canter, to rejoin Isabel and the handsome young planter, Edward, who were slowly walking their horses along the green path that wound by the brook which flowed past the village.

This package you received in due time, just as you were on the eve of departure for Europe, Mr. ——, as I learn from a letter, and after your departure it appears to have vanished. Doubtless, in their humility, they modestly withdrew themselves into some obscure corner of your domicilium, to give way to the glittering silver needles with which you were about to favor your readers from the lands of the rising sun over the blue water. This is the true secret of their invisibility, and I have no doubt, that by a diligent search beneath the bundles and packages of old MSS., which fills the corners and crevices of your editorial room, the missing, modest, retiring, eclipsed needles will be brought to light.

But, I fear, so long a burial in obscurity will have rusted them and rendered them unfit for use; so, whether found or lost, they are to be regarded among the things "that were."

Not seeing any of them make their appearance in your

columns, which shone steadily with the lustre of your own lively epistles, I came to the conclusion that they had been disgraced—had been quietly sent to that bourne of all rejected communications—"the tomb of the Capulets."

"Requiescat in pace," I sighed, as I thought of the parcel, and submissively bowed to your better judgment. I heard of its loss in this way. A letter from your editor pro-tem, asking me for more letters, came acquainting me with the fact of the "mysterious disappearance" of the six I had sent. Upon reading this, I remained a moment quite stupefied. If a poor hen had seen a wicked hawk at one swoop dart into the height of the clouds with six of her little, golden-colored chickens in his talons, and disappear with them forever from sight, she could not have been more confounded than I was at this intelligence of the disappearance of my six epistles. At length a heavy sigh relieved my heart; and half a dozen tears (one for each needle) fell pattering upon the letter I was reading. I could not help weeping, I was vexed, and angry, and grievously sorry. I thought of all the thoughts which I had drawn from my heart, or kindled at my brain, interwoven in their lines! It was as if they, like Noah's dove, had gone forth from the ark of my mind, seeking rest in other hearts and minds, (those of your dear readers, my many friends, for whom I wrote them all in sweet, though unseen, communion with them,) and were driven back, ruffled, wing-wounded, to rest in my own soul again—the ark from which they so hopefully went forth!

None but an author can sympathize with me. None but the author who writes—*coining his heart* as he writes

—who writes with all his intellectuality active—and *with large love for all those unknown ones*, the good, and wise, and beautiful, for whom he writes—and whom, as his pen flows over the spotless page, he sees a noble and appreciating audience assembled before him—none but an author who writes thus can feel all I felt. To such among your readers, those dear friends, whom having not seen I love, I look for that sympathy which can only atone for the loss of *so much of myself*, which I had poured out from the full fountain of my being into theirs —at least, which I believed I was pouring into theirs, but which has only been poured out upon the earth and air.

It is true, the lost MS. was but sixty pages of letter paper; but it is not the abundance, but that it is ourself, a part of *ourself* that is gone, that makes the loss. One would grieve for a finger amputated, as well as for an arm. Until now, I knew not the maternal love which an authoress cherishes for her literary offspring. Perhaps, if I am to be an author, it was best I should pass through all an author's phases, and experience all an author's experiences. I therefore made up my mind patiently to endure the loss; but I felt like a blind orator, who has been eloquently and touchingly addressing for an hour a large audience supposed to be before him, when he is afterwards told that he had been cruelly deceived, and had been pouring out his heart, soul, and spirit to empty seats—to an unpeopled void!

The end of a writer is the mind of the reader; and while writing, in imagination beholding his readers, reading his thoughts and lines of fire and love, he has his reward, though he never sees to his dying day one

of them.   But when he is told that his thoughts reached
no living mind, that they were addressed to a peopleless
void—by the destruction of his MS., before it reaches
the press,—he feels an aching void—a tumultuous backward ebb into his soul of all that had gone forth, coming
like an overwhelming torrent, at first to prostrate with
despair; but not finally destroy his energies.   If he possesses true genius, he will rally, and he will try once
more; but he can never again put forth the same
thoughts.   Their freshness is gone, their force lamed,
their beauty impaired by repetition.   He will seek a
new field, and what is lost, is lost irrevocably.   Such is
the nature of that sort of genius of which authors are
made, Mr. ——, and such is authorship in one of its
phases.

Well, I went to work again, but I did not, oh, I could
not write over the same letters, and so I let them go,
and resumed where the last of the missing ones had
ended.   The six lost, described our voyage down the
Cumberland from Nashville; adventures on the Ohio;
scenes and incidents upon the Mississippi; life on the
river; habits of the boatmen; wooding by torchlight; a
tornado; a collision; a shipwrecked steamer; an earthquake; the city of Memphis; its population, habits, and
manners; the city of Vicksburg; the city of Natchez,
and many things too numerous to mention.   Dear me!
what a loss!   And this is not all.   Another package of
a new series is gone.

The seventh letter of the new series was dated at a
plantation near Natchez, where I was sojourning a few
weeks.   It, and five more, described society in the country, in the town; deer hunting, fox hunting; a visit to

an Indian village and temple; a love scene; a confession;
a wounded cavalier; a journey to the prairie; an Indian
maid, and an adventure replete with romance. The
twelfth letter closed as we were in the prairies encamped,
and written while the gentlemen of our party were dressing a deer for dinner. These letters were put into the
mail in two parcels at the next post-office.

The postmaster was a young man with a savage mustache, a black, stiletto-like eye, and he kept his office in
a log-cabin that was half-grocery. He was terrifically
polite, and as he extended his hand to take the parcels,
he betrayed the butt of a bowie-knife in his gaping vest.
He said the stage would pass in a few minutes, and indeed, I saw it come up, a sort of dry-goods box on two
wheels, driven by a yellow-faced youth of seventeen, his
forehead and eyes buried in a monstrous buffalo-cap, as
large as a huzzar's, while his feet were bare, and over
his shoulders he wore a green blanket with a hole in the
centre, through which he had thrust his head. In this
box was a leathern mail-bag, into which I did see my
parcel safely deposited and locked up, the postmaster
with the mustache returning the key to his own pocket.
They were the only letters that went that day; and now
after four months you have received neither, Mr. ——.
It is a shame, and enough to try the patience of any
body to be so peculiarly unfortunate. I suppose they
have added ere this fuel to the flames of the hecatomb
of wandering epistles that monthly blazes in the court-
yard of the General Post-office, at Washington. It is
said they save only letters with money! Ah, young
gentlemen, or you good gentlemen with gray hair, who
superintend this dreadful fire which destroys so much

that sprung from immortal minds and loving hearts, if you had known the *value* of my two parcels, which, doubtless, passed through your hands, you would have had mercy upon them; I feel that you would have spared them from the flames, and sent them safely to Mr. —— ; and if this should be so unfortunate as to fall into your power, O grand Inquisitor of the Dread Inquisition of Letters, called *dead*, yet being filled with thoughts, can never die—spare, oh spare this, my poor epistle,* and all others that come after it, and send it on its way rejoicing, and, as in duty bound, I ever will pray for your happiness, health, and peace forevermore.

Your humble petitioner,

KATE CONYNGHAM.

* By a late law, the words " To be preserved," written around the seal, insures the preservation of the letter at the Dead Letter office.

The letters $\frac{\text{G. P. O.}}{\text{pres.}}$ will secure the return to the writer of all MSS., which are equal to *money* to author and publisher.

EDITOR.

LETTER XXXIV.

CHATEAU DE CLERY, LA.

My Dear Mr. ———— :

My last letter, dated from this beautiful villa, a
sugar estate, eleven miles above the city of New Orleans,
detailed to you my grief at the loss of the round dozen
"Needles," and my reluctance to rewrite; indeed, my
inability to write them a second time. I, therefore, must
briefly state in this that the space covered by the twelve
letters was three months, and that the twelfth found me
on the prairies near the capital of Mississippi, traveling
in a sort of caravan-fashion with the colonel and a large
party, going to look at some Indian lands which they
had purchased. We soon returned to the hospital mansion near Natchez, where we had been a few weeks sojourning, and the following week embarked for New
Orleans. From this embarkation I resume my letters,
aided by copious notes which I took while descending the
river. The city of Natchez has a romantic site, being
situated, like Quebec, upon an elevated table, which on
the verge of the river forms a perpendicular bluff of
nearly two hundred feet. Along the edge of this preci-
pice is a green mall, or promenade, with seats sociably
placed underneath the trees, upon which idlers can sit
enjoying the fresh breeze from the river, watching the
ascending and descending steamers that pass a score

a-day, or looking at the horsemen cantering through the
level streets of the opposite village of Concordia.   On
our way to the landing we stopped a few moments to
admire the wide view.   It was grand and ocean-like, so
plane and illimitable is the level sea of foliage that
recedes westward to the even horizon.   Four miles above
the city the mighty Father of Waters emerges from this
great valley of vast forests, and expands before us like
a lake, and flows sweeping past with the aspect of irresistible power, and, five miles below, loses himself again
in the bosom of this cypress desert-sea.

Our boat was not yet in sight, but a tall column of
smoke, in form like that which went before Israel, was
pointed out to me, full twelve miles northwardly, rising
skyward from the level surface of the emerald ocean of
forest.   The river itself and the steamer borne upon it,
were invisible, being hidden within the heart of the savannah; but we could trace the unseen course and tortuous windings of the flood by the onward motion of the
column of smoke.   At length, after watching it half an
hour above the trees, and seeing it come nearer, the
column, the steamer, and the river simultaneously shot
out from the embracing trees a league off.   Oh! it was
a grand sight to behold the noble steamer plough its
powerful prow through the turbid flood, turning aside
like straws in its path, floating trees that would have
made masts for line-of-battle ships, while the rushing
of the waters cleaved by her bow, and torn up by her
wheels, mingling with the hoarse double-note of her two
escape-pipes, loudly reached our ears.   As she drew
nearer, she fired a gun from her bow, and the report
echoed from the cliff, and re-echoed from Fort Rosalie,

a fine old ruin, overhanging the lower town, sunk growling away among the hills.

We were soon on board, and in possession of luxurious state-rooms, richly carpeted, and containing elegant beds, superbly hung with drapery, marble laver stands, velvet-colored lounges, and every luxury that taste could invent. I don't wonder now that the people travel so much here. The boat is a regular packet between Vicksburg and New Orleans, and being always filled with wealth and fashion—for the travel up and down the river of the planters and their families is immense—the saloons of a steamer are like a continual Levée.

But we did not long delay in our gorgeous state-rooms, inviting as they were;—Isabel and I, taking the colonel's arms, and making him a secure prisoner—he surrendering his liberty gracefully—went to the upper deck, to take a farewell view of Natchez, that hospitable, wealthy, and polished town, which has so often been spoken of by travelers, as the most charming place in the sunny South —a testimony to which I freely add my own. We had left dear friends there, and we could see some of them waving their handkerchiefs or hats from carriage-windows or on horseback, which signals of friendship we answered as long as we could distinguish the flutter of a handkerchief.

We were delighted with the scenery—with the fine old hills, broken into precipices of the most romantic shapes and wildest beauty. The spires and towers of the city appeared with striking effect above the cliff; but the most prominent object of all was the green parapet and glacis of Fort Panmure, or Rosalie, as the French anciently termed it.

This truly picturesque fort has been the scene of many a thrilling romance. The pens of Griffith, of Monette, of Dupee, have invested its site with associations of the deepest interest. Above its now verdant embrasures has floated the golden-hued flag of Spain, the lily of France, the double-cross and blood-red ensign of England, and more lately the cheerful stars and stripes of my own country; and it is my patriotic prayer that no *fifth* banner wave above it, till "time shall be no longer."

Twenty miles below Natchez, we passed a congeries of precipices frowning above the river, called the "White Cliffs." They are broken and cloven by the sapping of the river into the hundreds of fantastic shapes; and as the strata are varied by the most brilliantly-tinted argillaceous soils, the appearance of their lofty faces is extremely beautiful. A rainbow seemed to have been driven against it by the winds, and left fragments of every dye staining its sides. One of the cliffs stands alone, and from the shape of its summit, which seems to be crested with a battlement, it is called "The Castle."

It was proposed by Isabel, that it should henceforth be named "Castle Kossuth," which suggestion was carried by acclamation. Please, therefore, Mr. ——, make the whole world and "the rest of mankind" advised of this addition. Isabel is quite carried away with the great Magyar, and has named fifty things after him; and I fear, if he were a single gentleman, she would not hesitate the turning of a silver three-cent piece to be herself also named after him. I wonder Madame Kossuth isn't jealous! I wouldn't like my husband—but no matter. In my next I will tell you what I think about Mr. Kossuth; for one lady's opinion of one of the other sex, Mr.

——, is worth that of fifty men. We women see and understand instinctively. You men cogitate, reason, hem, and haw, and then—judge wrong always. Ah, if gentlemen in business would ask their wives' opinions of such and such men they deal with, be sure they would save them a great deal of loss and vexation. The good old Bible term, "help meet," means vastly more than the "lords matrimonial" ever guessed at. But, dear me —One of the cliffs is divided, leaving a pair of pinnacles. From one to the other an Indian girl, pursued by a vengeful lover, leaped, and saved her life. It was a fearful gulf across which she bounded; and only wings of fear could have compassed it in safety. The incident has drawn from the graceful pen of John T. Griffith, Esq., a planter in the vicinity, a charming story, called "The Fawn's Leap."

It was first published in one of the earliest, if not the earliest numbers of the old "Atlantic Souvenir." I read it when a child with great delight. I wish you would discover it and republish it. Mr. Griffith is a native of Princeton, N. J., and cousin of Commodore Stockton, and in him one of the first American writers has been spoiled by opulence in estate. If Mr. G. had been *compelled* to write as an author, he would, now in his fiftieth year, have stood at the head of American writers.

As evening drew near, we descended from our elevated promenade to the ladies' cabin. It was lighted by clusters of chandeliers of the richest description, resplendent with a thousand trembling prisms. Six chandeliers at equal distances revealed a series of connected saloons, with the intervening folding doors thrown back, fully two hundred feet in length. Along the centre, extended for eighty feet, stood a table for supper, that, in its perfect and sumptuous arrangements, rivaled that at the "Irving," "Girard," or any first rate hotel. Indeed, the first class steamers now are *first class hotels floating!* I am not surprised at the gentleman, who, for three or four trips, retained his stateroom, never going on shore at either port, until, being suspected of being some mysterious character who had designs forbidden by the eighth Commandment, he was questioned by the captain. In reply, he said :

"My dear sir, I find your boat so comfortable, your table so luxurious, your officers so polite, your servants so attentive, and such varied company enliven your cabins, that, being a person of leisure and fortune, I prefer residing with you, at least till the St. Charles is rebuilt. I trust you will have no objection to a permanent passenger!"

The vanity of the gallant captain took the place of his apprehensions, and, bowing politely, he left this gentleman of good taste to enjoy himself as he pleased—a privilege which I will now allow to all my good friends who have read thus far in this poor letter, which I misgivingly tend to the tender mercies of all post-masters, mail-carriers, and mail-bags on the route between this place and your fair city.

Very respectfully,

I am your friend,

KATE.

LETTER XXXV.

My dear Mr.————:

My last "Needle" left me a voyager upon the Mississippi, on my way to New Orleans, on board one of the elegant packets that ply between that city and Natchez. If you have never been a guest on one of these noble vessels that constantly plow the bosom of the monarch of waters, you can form no idea of the variety of interest and entertainment to be drawn from a trip on one of them. Let me describe the interior scenes of our cabin the first evening after leaving Natchez. In one corner of the superbly-lighted saloon was a group composed of three lovely, dark-eyed Southern girls, a handsome young man, and an elderly gentleman, with a fine, General Washington head, who was dressed in a blue coat, white vest with gilt buttons, and drab pantaloons, terminating in polished boots—a real fine old Southern gentleman, with princely manners. They are all engaged in seemingly very interesting conversation, and the girls laugh a great deal and merrily, and seem to refer everything with a charming familiarity, yet respectful affection, to the snowy headed gentleman, who seems to be in the most admirable humor. His full, hearty, cheery laugh does one good to hear, especially when one sees his fine face lighted up with benevolence and kindliness.

The three girls seem to be teazing him to consent to

some request, while the handsome young man looks on
and enjoys the scene.   I don't hear a word they say, but
I know they are all happy, and I sympathize with their
joy.   Oh! how many ten thousands of happy groups
there are in all the world as happy, whose voices I not
only do not hear, but whom I do not see, and never shall
see, nor know, (until I get to Heaven,) that they ever
existed!   Every hour there is a world full of joy felt by
millions, whose hearts beat like mine, and if all the happy
laughter that at this moment, while I write this line,
could be heard at once thrilling through the air, we
should think all the stars of God were shouting for joy,
and all the music of Heaven to be floating around the
earth!   Indeed, this world is a happy world, and if tens
of thousands of hearts in it daily beat

> "Funeral marches to the grave,"

tens of thousands of other hearts bound with all the
delight of joyous life.

I have often thought, when I reflected upon the sweet
and gentle characters of the dear friends I find wherever
I go, and learn to love ere I part from them, that there
must be in this God's good world, in thousands of places
where I never have been, nor ever shall be, glorious
armies of as sweet and gentle, of as intellectual and
loveable ones, whom, if I knew them, one and all, I
should love, and they would love me.   I sigh to think
that I live on the same green earth, a life long with a
legion of loving spirits congenial with mine, and never
see them face to face, and that all of us will go down to
the shades of death, ignorant that the others had been
created.   But, when I begin to regret this, Christianity

unfolds to my eye of faith, the world of undying life beyond the tomb; and I console myself with the thought
that *" There* I shall see them and know them all, and be
known and loved of them! There the veil which separates us congenial ones in this life will be removed, and
I shall see and know them all; *not one of us all will be lost
to the others there!"* But my pen is a great truant, Mr.
——. It will not so much follow facts as wander after
thoughts. It is like the "busy bee,"

> " Gathering honey all the day,
> From every opening flower."

In the opposite corner of the saloon sits, or rather inclines a little out of the shade of the chandelier, yet so
that the light falls in soft transparent shadow upon her
transparent features, an invalid lady of thirty years!
Kneeling by her footstool is an Africaness, with a scarlet
kerchief bound about her crispy brow, who looks up into
the pure intelligent face of the lady with watchful solicitude, while with a gorgeous fan of peacock's feathers,
she slowly and gently creates a zephyr-like air about
her. There is something in the countenance of the invalid that is touchingly beautiful. It is a face that looks
as if it were spiritualized by suffering. Her dark, intelligent eyes, unnaturally large and bright, uneasily wander
about the saloon. The presence of strangers seems to
alarm and distress her. Yet her looks are peaceful,
calm, and resigned, like one whom sorrow hath chas-
tened, and who hath learned to say to pain, "Thou art
my sister!"

I feel a deep interest in her, and will approach her,

and speak gently to her, and offer my services; for she seems to be alone, save her faithful attendant.

Hark! pulse-leaping music rolls from a grand piano through the noble saloon. A tall, graceful, blue-eyed lady, whom, with her husband, we took on board at a wood-yard an hour ago, has seated herself at the instrument, at the solicitation of several gentlemen and ladies, who seem to know her, for on these Southern boats everybody seems to know everybody, and feels as much at home as on their own plantations. What superb melody her magic fingers draw from the ivory keys! I cease writing in my note-book to listen at a perfect April-shower of harmony—sun-shine, rainbows, thunder, singing birds, and ringing rain drops, all bewilderingly and joyously heard together! The "fine old Southern gentleman" first pricked up his ears, and then rose and advanced; the three graces forgot to tease him, and hung breathlessly over the piano. The lady commenced singing Casta Diva. The invalid raised her gloriously bright eyes, and her pearl-hued cheek flushed with a tint as delicate as the reflections of a rose-leaf; and with parted lips she seemed to drink in the melodious waves of air, and receive them into her very soul. How seraphically she smiles as she listens! Oh, music is heaven-born! Music can reach the soul of the dying when it is deaf to the voice of earthly love! Once I watched at midnight by the bedside of a loved and dying maiden, whose brow the day before had been blessed with the waters of baptism.

"Sing to me, dearest Kate,—sing to me," she whispered. "I am dying. Sing to me, and let me hear your voice the last sound of earth! I feel that my soul is going *alone*. Alone, into the vast void that stretches between time and eternity. Oh, sing to me as you find my spirit departing, that my wandering soul may have some sound of earth to cling to as it launches into that dread unknown!"

So I sang to her, and her soul took flight on the wings of the sweet words,

> " I would not live alway—no, welcome the tomb;
> Since Jesus *hath lain there*, I dread not its gloom.
> There sweet be my rest, till he bid me arise,
> To hail him in triumph descending the skies."

The graceful stranger who had taken her seat at the piano, soon gathered about her not only all the ladies and gentlemen in our cabin, but the gentlemen in the great saloon left their politics to advance and listen, others laid down their books and newspapers, and even parties rose from their cards to come nigh her! There was a perfect jam about the cabin entrance—tiers of heads beyond tiers of heads! I myself was perfectly entranced by the syren. Without apparent effort she would pour and pour, and pour forth from her superbly-shaped throat, liquid globules of melody, that intoxicated the ear of the listener with hitherto unknown pleasure. She brought tears into many eyes by the tenderest pathos, and again dispelled the tears by successive outbursts of the liveliest strains of wild, rich, song. Now she would fill all the saloon with a storm of notes, gorgeous and grand, and unearthly beyond conception; torrents of music, music, music, loud, wild, and terrible, seemed to be roaring around us in one continuous overwhelming cataract; and when we could bear no more, a sudden and instantaneous cessation of keys and voice would be succeeded by a soft gentle, loving air, as simple and clear as that of a bird. This bird-like air warbled in her throat, would seem to ascend and ascend, and mount and soar, and still ascend far upwards, rise higher and higher, higher and higher, growing sweeter and fainter, ascending, and still ascending, until, breathless with enchantment, we listened till we lost the far off voice of the lark-like notes in the skies—dying away at length into a sacred silence. Every heart suspended its beating! With lips parted, eyes raised upwards, and ears intent, stood every one of the eager and bewitched listeners, as if an angel had gone singing up into heaven, out of their sight.

A sudden crash of music startles the silence, as if thunder had burst from the skies upon our heads! It is one grand sweep of the fingers of the charmer over every key of the instrument, in an overpowering finale, when, rising from her seat, she seeks blushingly and modestly her husband's eye and arm, amid the most rapturous and prolonged applause.

"Who can she be? It must be Jenny Lind! or it is certainly Kate Hayes!" said fifty voices. But it was *neither* of these! All musical talent, Mr. ——, is not displayed in concert rooms. In private life, among American ladies, especially among the highly-educated Southerners, to whom music is a native air, there is as much talent as is possessed by Miss Lind, or Miss Hayes, or Madame Parodi. This sweet stranger and noble performer was a Mrs. W——h, a young married lady, whose husband's plantation was near the point where they embarked, not many leagues below Natchez, of which she is a native. Miss Cole, formerly of New Rochelle, Miss

Watson, of Nashville, and many others, I can name, sing Casta Diva and a score of other operatic pieces, with as much effect and feeling as any cantatrice that ever appeared before a public assembly. America has more musical talent and skill buried in the retirement of her Southern plantations, or adorning her Northern drawing-rooms, than Sweden, Italy, or Germany possess, in all their valleys and amid all their romantic scenery.

Should circumstances call them to make use of their talent and genius as a means of support, our ladies could "beat" Europe in operatic music as our gentlemen have lately done in yachting. Biscaccianti—withal her Italian husband's name substituted for her own—is an American girl, with whom I once met in her school! This intellectual and soul-full Biscaccianti has not at present her equal in opera song. She has the *key* to our *joys* and *tears*. I learn that she has lately sailed for California, to awaken there the echoes of the "Golden Gate." Should it "grate harsh thunder" before her approach, at the sound of this songstress' silvery voice, it will swing wide, like Milton's Celestial portal

"On harmonious hinges turning."

Yours,
KATE.

P. S. I have dated this and two preceding letters from "Chateau de Clery." This is the sugar estate of a French gentleman of this name, where I am sojourning for a few weeks, and from which I shall write you some accounts of life in the villas of the opulent Louisianaises.

LETTER XXXVI.

My Dear Mr. ———:

How shall my feeble pen describe to you the beauty of the scenery of the Lower Mississippi! If the northern portion of this mighty flood, as it rolls forever and ever amid its dark wildernesses, is gloomy and awe inspiring, the southern arm is infinitely more beautiful. One or two of my last letters have been devoted to a sketch of our trip from Natchez towards New Orleans. It is at Natchez that the wild forest-like character of the Mississippi begins to assume the more cheerful features of varied scenery, and cultivated savannahs.

Natchez itself sits like a queen crowning a fortress-looking cliff, and extending her sceptre over the verdant plains and smiling valleys of Louisiana. Then twenty miles below this city frown down upon the voyager the craggy peaks and tower-like walls of "Ellis Cliffs." From that point till Baton Rouge comes in sight, the shores become more open, and the banks more interesting with cliff, upland, and many a green spot of rustic loveliness, where the blue smoke curling upwards amid deep foliage, betrays the secluded home of the planter.

A few leagues above Baton Rouge, the cotton fields cease, and for these snow-white acres is beheld the tall, straight sugar-cane waving to the breeze for many a league. Until I came in sight of the first sugar estate,

I was not aware of the distinctness with which the lines of climate that mark the locality of our country's different staples can be discerned. In descending the Upper Mississippi, the last wheat field was taken leave of at the same moment the first cotton plantation was pointed out to me; and after sailing eight degrees through the cotton latitudes, the last cotton plantation and the first sugar estate meet not far above Baton Rouge. Thus the advance with majestic progression on one of these mammoth steamers down through the latitudes, has in it something of the sublime. But I regret to leave the pure, white plains of spotless cotton fleece, than which nothing can be more charming to the eye. I shall never forget when one morning as I rose from breakfast, at Lake Providence, the gentleman, at whose house we were guests, cried,

"Come, Miss Kate, ride with me, and I will show you a sight worth going across the ocean to see, and which beats all John Bull has got in the Crystal Palace."

After twenty minutes' gallop along the arrowy shores of the lake, we drew rein on the verge of a cotton-field.

"Now hold by that branch, and stand upright in your saddle, Kate, and look before you," he said.

I did so, and beheld a level expanse, containing eleven hundred acres in cotton, without fence or ridge to break the beautiful spectacle. The plant was in full boll, hanging to the hand of the picker in the richest luxuriance. A small army of slaves, whose black faces contrasted oddly with the white fields, were marching onward through it gathering the white wreaths, and heaping therewith their baskets, while the loud musical chorus of their leader's voice, to which their own kept tune, as he sang "the picker's song," fell cheerfully on my ears.

"That field alone," said the major, with a sparkling eye, "is worth $60,000."

Oh, the wealth of these cotton-planters, Mr. —— !

But if *they* are rich, what shall be said of the owners of the sugar estates, which are far more profitable to cultivate than cotton plantations! Our New England farmers have no conception of the riches of these Southern people. Let me give you an instance of the manner in which money accumulates here. A young gentleman, whom I know near Natchez, received, at twenty-one years of age, thirty slaves from his father, and fourteen hundred acres of wild forest land on the Mississippi. He took his hands there, and commenced clearing. Thirty axes do vast execution in a wood. As he cleared he piled up the cloven timber into fire-wood length, and sold it to passing steamers at $2 50 a cord. The first year he took $12,000 in cash for wood alone. The second year he raised 80 bales of cotton, which he sold at $50 a bale, and he also sold wood to the amount of $14,000 more. The third year he sold 150 bales of cotton, and cleared by wood $10,000, which, with $8,000 his cotton sold for, brought him an income of $18,000. Out of this the expense for feeding and clothing his thirty slaves per annum was less than $1,800. The young man, not yet twenty-nine, is now a rich planter, with a hundred slaves, and is making 500 bales of cotton at a crop. Excuse these business-looking figures, Mr. ——, but in these days ladies are expected to know about such things, you know, and if I have learned such facts it is no harm for me to write them. If I were writing from Lapland,

I should, perhaps, tell you how many reindeer's skins went to make a young girl's marriage portion.

It was half an hour before sunset when we came in sight of Baton Rouge, the capital of Louisiana. The state-house, large and white, loomed grandly up, and overtowering the town belittled it so that its best houses seemed no bigger than cottages. The place is small, but flanked by United States Barracks on one side, and by the Capitol on the other. The star-spangled banner was flying at the top of the government flag-staff, and flaunted saucily in the breeze.

"There is General Taylor's house," cried the captain of our steamer, who, by-the-way, is a great lady's man, and the civilest spoken gentleman to be a rough, wea-ther-beaten Mississippi commander I ever knew.

He directed my gaze to a small, white dwelling on the verge of the parade-ground, with its garden descending to the water-side. It was an humble home, and would not have been too fine for the sergeant to live in. I gazed upon the spot with those indescribable emotions with which we always gaze upon localities with which eminent men have once been associated.

"From that unpretending abode he went forth to the conquest of Mexico," said Colonel Peyton, addressing Isabel and me, "and from it a second time he was called to preside over the destinies of the Union."

"His body lies buried beneath the trees there," said one of the passengers.

"No, answered our captain, "his remains were taken to Kentucky."

"There is old Whitey," exclaimed a beautiful young girl near me, one of those who had come on board at

Natchez. "Dear old Whitey; he deserves that the girls of Baton Rouge should every day crown him with flowers, and interwreath his mane with the gayest ribbons."

Sure enough I saw the ancient war-horse himself. He was grazing quietly on the slope of the parade-ground; but at the noise of our passing boat, he raised his aged head to regard us philosophically! He looks venerable, but has not lost his symmetry; and they say that at the sound of the morning and evening gun he pricks up his ears, tosses his head, flings his gray mane abroad, and canters into the smoke, snuffing it up, and neighing like a trumpet.

I walked through the four or five pretty streets that constitute Baton Rouge. It is a French looking town yet, though French manners with the language have given way to a highly-polished American population. The streets are prettily shaded; the houses have verandahs; ladies were in the balconies; beautiful olive-cheeked children, with hair dressed *a la Suisse*, promenaded the sidewalks; servants were indolently occupying the door-sides, and a few carriages drive through the streets. I was on the whole agreeably impressed with Baton Rouge, and think it would be a charming residence. It is one hundred and thirty miles above New Orleans; and from this point begins the superb scenery of that part of the river called "the Coast."* The moon was up when

---

* "The portion of the river Mississippi, which lies towards the Mexican Gulf, for a distance of two hundred and fifty miles above its mouth, has been called the 'Coast,' from the earliest settlement of the country. The reason why this misnomer has been thus given to the banks of the Southern Mississippi, is unknown."—*History of Louisiana.*

we left Baton Rouge, after an hour's delay, and with the addition to our passengers of some forty members of the Legislature, most of them with French physiognomies, we resumed our voyage down the stream.

Wishing you, Mr. ——, a safe voyage down the stream of life, I remain,

Your faithful friend,
KATE.

LETTER XXXVII.

My Dear Mr. ———:

If you see a report going the rounds of certain barbarous journals that I am married, I forbid your copying it, and *command* you to contradict it. It is a shame how some of these bachelor editors will make use of a young lady's name. If one protests, they say, "It is only a paragraph," and each one scissors away and sets up his type, without caring who is hurt, so that his paper is "racy." I am not married; and when I am, I desire it to be properly announced, under the head of Marriages, like those of other people, and not blazoned *en paragraphe* in an editor's column. Why, the bare idea of being thus paragraphed, is enough to prevent any modest young man from proposing, much less marrying, at such a venture.

So, please, Mr. ———, don't paragraph my marriage, even should you hear of it; and if you catch that ugly, little paragraph about me going the rounds of those everlasting echoing country papers, put your finger upon it, and annihilate it. It originated somewhere in Oktibbehaw county, in a paper called the Independent Rifle Ranger, the editor of which is the intelligent gentleman who took a telegraph wire, stretched across the country, to be the Tropic of Cancer.

In my last we were just quitting Baton Rouge, the rural and Franco-American capital of Louisiana. The name of this place (Red Pole) originated in a very pretty buccaneering custom of the olden times of this romantic corner of the New World.

"You see, ma'am," said our old pilot, who told me the story,—for these ancient river-gods of the Mississippi are tremendous story-tellers, (I don't mean fibbers, Mr. ——,) and they always have a grand, great story about every bend, point, island, bluff, and pass in the river,— "you see, ma'am, in them old Frenchified times, folks didn't care 'mazin much 'bout law, nor gospel neither. If a man killed another, why, if there was any relative of the killed man, he'd take it up, and shoot the other; and so it went, every man his own lawyer. Well, there was no steamboats them days, and keelers used to float down from up country, filled with peltry and sich goods for the Orleans market. There wasn't many men on board to man 'em—pr'aps seven or nine; but they kept well out in the middle o' the stream, at long shot from the Indian's arrers, and the Frenchman's gun. But there was a regular band o' pirates lived on the river where Baton Rouge now is, and they had a captain, and numbered fifty men or more—awful rascals; every one on 'em—had done enough murder to hang seven honest Christians. This captain was the essence on 'em, all biled down for deviltry and wickedness; and yet they say he was young, almost a boy, plaguy handsome fellow, with an eye like a woman, and a smile like a hyena; and his men were as afraid of him as death.

"Well, he lived in a sort of castle of his own, over on the little rise you see, near the town, and people said he had, begging your pardon, ma'am, as many wives as old Captain Bluebeard, and killed 'em as easy. Well, he had a lookout kept on the point just in the bend, and there had a red pole raised to hoist a flag on. When his men saw a boat coming in sight, they'd hoist a green flag to the top o' the pole, and in the night a green lantern; for he was a great friend to green color, and wore green velvet himself like a foreign lord.

"When he'd see the light or the flag, he'd wind his silver bugle and collect his men to the boats, and when the keeler would get nearly opposite, he'd shout like twenty heathens, and dart out with his seven barges upon the descending craft. It was short work they made then. A rush, and leaping on board, a few pistol shots and cutlass blows, and the crew were dead or overboard. The prize was then towed into the cove beneath the castle, and plundered, and set on fire. Them were rough and bloody times, Miss!"

The pilot, finding his cigar had gone out, drew a loco-foco match from his vest pocket, ignited it by drawing it across his horny thumb-nail, relighted his cigar, and began to scan the appearance of the sky, which looked fitful. But I was too much interested in my Green Corsair of the Rouge Baton to let his story end there; so I said:

"Please tell me, Mr. Bedlow, what became of this man and his crew?"

"Some say he was shot in the Public Plaza, in New Orleans, by the Spanish Governor; but I heard an old pilot say, that he was assassinated by a young woman he had captured; and that is likely by all accounts."

" How was it ?" I inquired, seeing that the old man's eye looked communicative.

" On one of the craft captured there was a young girl, the skipper's wife, who had been married only the day afore the keeler left Pittsburgh, and Major Washington (afterwards General) they say was at the weddin', and gave away the bride; for she was mighty pretty, and General Washington, like a true soldier, always had an eye to a handsome face. Well, this pirate took the craft, and killed or driv' overboard all hands, and he made the bride prisoner. He took her to his castle, and was dreadful in love with her. But she saw only her husband's blood on his hands, and, taking a pistol from his belt, she shot him dead, and escaped in a boat to New Orleans, where the Governor gave her a thousand crowns, and afterwards married her. They say he took her to Spain, and presented her to court, and that she became one o' the greatest ladies in the Spanish land. That's the story I hearn, ma'am, but I won't vouch for its Bible truth, for it's mighty hard reckoning up things happening so long ago."

So the old pilot left me, being called to the wheel, while I pondered on the story I had heard, and gazed on the shores about Baton Rouge with deeper interest—so wonderfully do associations fling charms about locality.

What a nice story some writer of imagination might make out of this rough-hewn narrative of the old pilot! Cooper is dead, Simms a Senator, Kennedy a politician, Mrs. Lee Hentz an editress. Who shall we get to write it? All the old novelists have left the field, and if we do not have more new ones come into it, there will be no more novels. Perhaps the world would be wiser and better. Who knows yes? Who knows no?

Among the passengers who came on board at Baton Rouge was the newly elected Senator from Louisiana to Congress, Mr. Benjamin. Having heard much of him, I scanned him closely. He is a small man, but made with a certain compactness and dignity, that makes one forget his stature in his bearing. His face is very fine, dark, healthy, full, and pleasing. He resembles General G. P. Morris, as this latter gentleman was some years ago; he has the same smiling eyes, agreeable mouth, and *bonhomie* air. His eyes are dark and expressive, and his whole face indicates rather good-natured repose and amiable indolence than that high order of talent which has won for him, at little above thirty years of age, the high distinction of representing the proud state of Louisiana in the U. S. Senate.

The more I looked at Mr. Benjamin, the more I was puzzled to divine why he should have been chosen to this high position. I could see in his face only qualities that would attach him to his friends, make him a loving father, and a husband greatly beloved by whatever lady might be so happy as to hold the holy relations of wife to him; but I saw no indications of that ruling and marked mind, which I took it for granted he ought from his fame and rank to possess. While I was observing him, as he sat reading, some gentlemen approached and entered into conversation with him, upon the subject of the annexation of the suburban town of Lafayette to New Orleans. His opinion was referred to. His eyes opened and lighted. His face changed its whole character, and for half an hour I listened to his conversation with increasing delight and fascination. I saw and heard the man of talent! I discovered in his close reasoning, his acute manner of analysis, his calm self-command, his thorough knowledge of his subject, his fluent and graceful speech, the causes of his elevation above the men about him.

His voice is not good, and his size is against him; and when he shall first appear in the American Senate he will not attract any eye, save the glance of wonder at his youthful appearance, for he does not look above twenty-five. But they will find him their equal—an eagle among eagles. His eloquence, wisdom, and knowledge of affairs will make him tell in the Senatorial Hall. It was Mr. Benjamin, who, in speaking of the progress of the age, gave utterance to this fine sentiment in one of his speeches in the Legislature of Louisiana:— "The whistle of the locomotive is finer music than the clarion of war, and the thunder of its wheel, than the roar of artillery."

Mr. Benjamin is an Israelite. His election, therefore, is a practical illustration of the free institutions of our happy land, where theological disabilities are not known. It is surprising how the Jews, I mean the educated and talented, place themselves in the highest rank of society always. There is inherent in them an element of greatness that irresistibly finds its noble level. We see in them the blood of David and Isaiah, of Abraham and Solomon, of Joseph and the Maccabees; their princely lineage is not extinct. How odd it would be if we should have a Jew to be President of the United States. And why not? Mr. Benjamin is a Senator. He is a rising man. He may one day hold the highest office in the

gift of the nation.   Would any man refuse to vote for
him *because* he is a Jew?   But I am adventuring beyond
my depth—so, good night, Mr.——.

Yours truly,
KATE.

LETTER XXXVIII.

CHATEAU DE CLERY.

MY DEAR MR. ———

THIS will be the last letter I shall write you from this plantation, where I have been passing a few weeks in the most agreeable society. Our party landed here early on the morning after leaving Baton Rouge; for M. de Clery, the proprietor of this noble sugar estate, is a relative of the Colonel's, and the two gentlemen are great friends.

But before I say any thing about my present abode, let me describe to you the scenery of the "coast" between Baton Rouge and New Orleans. Present to your mind's eye a moving lake of dark, oak-tinted water, rolling onward nearly a broad mile wide, and winding league after league through an illimitable valley, as level as a billiard table, and as even all around the horizon as is the edge of the sky-meeting ocean. Behold both banks lined with wide sugar plantations extending rearward, from a mile to a league, green with the corn-like leaves of the young cane, and bordered in the rear by impenetrable forests.

In the bosom of each of these estates you see a stately villa, its chateau-like roof towering above a grove, and surrounded by colonnades, which are hedged in by orange and lemon trees, the rich, golden fruit hanging within

reach of the hand from the drawing-room windows.   On
one side of these chateaux, or else in the rear, glitter the
white walls of a score or two of African cottages, which
compose the village of the slaves, each with its little
garden plot, and shaded by a roof-tree.   In the midst
of this neat and pretty Ethiopian village, rises a tower,
on the summit of which is swung a plantation bell, which
at day dawn rings up the slaves to commence their labor,
rings them to their meals through the day, and to their
quarters at night.   Not far from this negro village,
standing massive and alone in the midst of the sugar
fields, rise the high brick walls and tall, steeple-like
chimneys of the *sucrérie*, or sugar-house, where the cane
is ground up, and goes through its various processes,
from gross molasses to the purest white crystalization.
Some of these sucréries are of great size, looking like
universities, or some public edifice; and they cost so much,
that, with the other expense of establishing a sugar
estate, it is common to say that a "man must be a rich
cotton planter before he can commence as a poor sugar
planter," the expense of starting a cotton plantation
being very small compared with that for the latter; but
the sugar planter has the advantage of striding on to
opulence in proportion to his outlay.

This description which I have given of a sugar estate,
with its vast, level fields, like emerald plains, its stately
sucrérie, its snow-white negro village, its elegant chateau half buried in trees, will answer for that of the
hundreds that continuously line the two shores of the
Mississippi, between Baton Rouge and New Orleans.
The steamer, therefore, as she moves down, seems as if
passing through a majestic canal, with a street of villas

on either shore. A few yards from the water runs a beautiful road, level and smooth, bordered on one side by gardens and houses, and on the other by the river. This road is always enlivened by carriages, horsemen, or foot-passengers; for the whole line of shore, for the one hundred and fifty miles, is a continued unbroken street. When our steamer ran near one shore or the other, we could look in upon the inmates of the houses, and see them at their meals, and as we sailed past by moonlight, the voice of song, the thrum of the guitar, or the soft cadence of the flute, would float off to us from the piazzas or lawns, or some bower buried in the shadows of the garden. The atmosphere was laden with the fragrance of flowers, and the mocking-bird's joyous and varied melody filled the branches, to our imagination, with a whole aviary of singing birds. Ah, it was perfect enchantment, Mr. ——, sailing through these lovely scenes beneath the broad shield of the moon casting its radiance of burnished silver over all. The very river, usually in its mildest mood, champing and growling like a chained lion, flowed almost unruffled, like a moving glass surface, mirroring the light with dazzling brilliancy. Below us, and above us, the red and green signal lights of other boats, ascending and descending, added to the changing beauty of all, while the bright flames kept burning all night at the wood stations, along the shores, casting their long, blood-red columns far along the surface of the stream, added a certain wildness to the general features of the whole.

I remained on deck to a late hour, wrapped well in my shawl, to guard against the dews, and enjoyed the novelty of the time and place, with emotions that were

new and delightful. Occasionally the sombre tower of
a Roman chapel, or the gray walls of a convent, (for we
were passing through the heart of a Roman Catholic
population,) came into view. One called the Convent
of the Sacred Heart, "Le Sacre Cœur," was one of the
most lovely objects I ever beheld, lighted up as its long
corridors were by moonlight, casting half its front alternately into light and shade.

This, I am told, is a remarkably good school of education, and many of the "first families" in the South have
their daughters educated there, or at the Ursuline Convent in New Orleans—Convent des Ursulines.

There is no doubt, Mr. ——, that these Roman Catholic schools for girls are among the best we have. I
have seen, in the South, several estimable ladies who
were educated at this Convent, and certainly I never
met with more intelligent, well-informed, interesting
persons, more thoroughly accomplished ladies.

"Ah, yes," you say objectingly, "but they are in
danger of becoming Roman Catholics."

Of these ladies but one is a Roman Catholic, and she
is not very strongly grounded in that faith, usually
attending the Episcopal church with her husband, and
bringing up her children in this church. The danger,
if girls are well instructed first at home, is very slight
of their being won over to the Roman faith in these
schools. There is a certain romantic fascination connected with this religion, which, for a time, has its influence on an imaginative temperament, but it soon wears off.
I know and love an interesting lady, who, from her thir-
teenth to her seventeenth year, was a pupil at the Ursuline Convent. She came out a romantic Roman Catholic,

but is now a communicant of the Presbyterian church.
She says she "dearly loved the kind good nuns; that
they were gentle and devoted, and she used to love to
sit up with one old nun, Ursula, at her vigils, about
Christmas times, and listen to her tales of wonderful
miracles performed by saints and the Blessed Virgin; in
all of which good dame Ursula had faith. She stoutly
and piously believed "how the Virgin once came down
and touched her cheek with her finger, and cured her
toothache;" how St. Ursula, their patroness, pinched
one of the sisters on the arm for sleeping at her post,
so that the mark, in the shape of a cross, remained there
at this hour; how she had seen the blood from the hands
of the picture of Christ crucified, over the altar, and
fall in great drops to the floor, and one of these drops,
which she caught on her 'kerchief, she showed me, first
crossing herself and me with the signs of the cross made
backwards and forwards! But the story that most captivated me was how (as she was watching before the altar
one Good Friday eve) she saw the infant boy Jesus leave
the arms of his blessed mother, there in the picture, and
fly with golden wings to the great picture of Christ crucified, on the right of the altar, and, with tears, wipe
the blood from His hands, and feet, and side, and tried
to stop its flowing, with many lamentations! All this,"
added the intelligent lady, "I firmly believed, but they
produced upon me no religious impression; I listened
to them just as I read Mrs. Radcliffe's horrible tales of
dungeons and bleeding nuns. Our education was not
committed to this good, credulous dame, do not suppose,
but there were ladies in the Convent of the most elegant
manners, of the most accurate education, and minds

every way accomplished; ladies of rank, who had left the brilliant society of European cities to devote them-selves to heaven. My chief teacher was Sister Therése, who had been in France the Countess de ——, and who is said to have loved Napoleon, the King of Rome, and at his death had retired from the world. All the nuns were French ladies."

When I asked this lady if she still felt attached to the nuns, she answered, "Oh, yes; I never visit New Orleans that I do not go and see them and they receive me in the most affectionate manner! If I should ever meet with a reverse of fortune, and lose my husband and child, I should, I have no doubt, seek the calm repose and holy shelter of that home of my childhood; for, when I left them, the Superior said, as she wept on my shoulder, "Daughter, if the world is adverse to thee, remember thou hast here always a shelter from its storms."

I am not advocating, Mr. ——, the habit of educating Protestant girls in Roman nunneries; all I can say in their favor is, that they *do* bestow *thorough* educations upon their pupils; and if the Roman Catholics would only give up their wicked additions to Christianity, their worship of Mary, their prayers to Peter and Paul, their confessional, their idolatry of the mass, their merchan-dize of sins, and their other excrescences, which they have heaped upon the Gospel, till it is almost lost sight of, they would be the best teachers of youth in the world. But holding on to these errors, they will always keep at a distance the many who would patronize them.

The Episcopalians are now taking the place once so prominently occupied by the Roman Catholics, as teachers of youth; and the female schools kept by Episcopal clergymen, are acknowledged, even by other denominations, to be the best schools in the United States.

I forgot to say that my intelligent friend informed me, that good old Aunt Ursula always knelt down with the soles of her bare feet turned up to the fire, when she said her prayers, in order that they might, while she was praying and telling her beads, get nice and warm before she jumped into bed. I have heard that "prayers and provender hinder no man's journey;" but Aunt Ursula knew that to say one's prayers, and warm one's toes the whilst, hindered not a holy nun's devotions.

Yours respectfully,
KATE.

LETTER XXXIX.

MY DEAR MR. ———:

As these letters have been mainly descriptive of scenes and voyaging before I reached here, this will be mainly descriptive of the scenery at the Chateau. It will give you some idea of the domestic arrangements of the opulent French planters, than which nothing can be more agreeable. No people know so well how to enjoy this world as the French; and *par excellence* their descendants in Louisiana, which offers to their pleasure the climate of Eden with all its fruits,—with the "tree of knowledge of good and evil," I fear; for with much luxury, there is much evil in the world; and, unfortunately, one cannot live magnificently, indulging all the goods of the earth, without "sin."

> "Luxury and sin
> In Eden did begin."

The Chateau de Clery, where Talleyrand, Louis Phillippe, and Jackson have been guests, is a large, imposing, French-looking mansion, with almost an acre of roof, situated on the banks of the Mississippi, and embowered in a grove of magnolia trees, interspersed with live-oaks and orange trees. The house is vast in width, and made very long, with piazzaed wings, and all around it runs a

broad colonnade supported by columns entwined by flowering plants.

The view from the upper balcony, on which all the
parlors open by Venetian windows, is very beautiful, and
to the eye of a person born in sight of mountains, novel
in the extreme. There extend to the right and left, as
far as the eye can see, level sugar-fields, waving at this
season with the green billows of the breeze-tossed cane-
leaves. The appearance of a cane-field in this month
being very similar to that of a field of corn in the green
leaf, before it begins to display its tassels. Turning the
gaze from the vast savannahs of Southern wealth, the
lawn in front of the villa fills the eye with its shady,
live-oak trees, its groves of orange trees, and long aisles
of lemon and magnolias. From the broad steps of the
entrance to the portico to the river side extends a noble
carriage-way, bordered on each side by live-oaks. A
fringe of orange trees runs all around a magnificent garden on the left, but the severe frosts of last winter
have rendered them leafless; and there they stand, gray
and fruitless, wholly destitute of foliage, striking contrasts
to the rich vegetation everywhere visible around them.
The majestic Mississippi flows past in front of the lawn
a furlong distant, and confined to its banks by the green
levee, inside of which runs smoothly the carriage-road
down to New Orleans, and along which horsemen or carriages are constantly passing up and down. There is
scarcely an hour in the day in which a steamer is not
visible, ploughing its huge path along, with the deep roar
of its escape-pipes and comet-like trails of black smoke
rolling along the air astern, darkening the waves beneath,
like the passing thunder-cloud. The opposite shore a

mile off, is visible, with its pretty villas, its groves and parks, and its African villages white as snow, and the imposing turreted sugar-houses beyond, with their tall towers.

I am perfectly charmed with the scenery of this region. Once I fancied that no landscape could be pretty without hills or mountains in the distance; but the beautiful shores of Louisiana have led me to change my opinion; and, although I was born in sight of the White Hills, I can see much to admire in the richness of these scenes, where there is not an eminence of any sort—not a mole hill. All is one vast ocean-like level; but so diversified by cultivation, so ornamented by taste and art, so decked with noble seats, so enriched by groves, gardens, fine roads, and avenues, so variegated by the countless world of flowers, and the splendor of the foliage, and gracefulness of the forms of the forest trees, its atmosphere so colored by the purity of the azure and golden heavens of morning and evening, with the ever changing glory of the moving river, that I forget the absence of mountains, and give my heart up to the full enjoyment of the paradise around me.

You will never behold the finest portion of the Union, Mr.——, until you have visited the "coast of Sunny Louisiana." The people, too, whose lot is cast in the midst of this mighty Eden of a hundred miles in extent, can appreciate the charms of their scenery. Vast wealth has begotten education and taste; and refinement, and mental accomplishments adorn most of the elegant mansions that border the river.

There are seventeen rooms in the Chateau de Clery, most of them of a magnificent description. There are two parlors, a large drawing-room, a vast hall, larger than any room in the house, and which is the general rendezvous of the family after dinner and tea; a sitting room for the ladies; a nursery, several bath rooms, a library, and a study room near it, for the governess and children; besides numerous bed-rooms and dressing-rooms. These rooms, the parlors and all, open out into the piazza, which encircles the whole mansion. They are all upon one floor, and every window is a glass door, opening with leaves. The whole edifice is raised ten feet from the ground, on brick pillars, leaving beneath the pile numerous servants and store-rooms, concealed from the eye of persons approaching the house by a lattice-work, covering the whole front of the lower area.

The house is stuccoed, and tinted lemon color, while the numerous columns are painted white, and being usually enwreathed by vines, the whole effect is very fine. Carriage ways, strewn with shells, surround the mansion, and terminate at the stables—which are handsome edifices, beneath the shade of two enormous live-oaks. From the rear of the gallery is visible the snowy houses of the African village, sixty-eight in number, forming a long street, bordered by trees, with a small garden in the rear of each dwelling. In the centre of this picturesque village, every house in which is the exact pattern of the other, rises the taller roof of the overseer's mansion, above which still rises the tower of the plantation bell, which peals out many times a day to call to work and to meals.

Beyond this attractive village for slaves, where neatness and comfort prevail, rise the tall walls of the sucrérie, or sugar house, half a mile off, towards the centre of the estate. It has the aspect of a huge manufactory. It is two hundred feet long, has three vast chimneys, one of which is seventy feet in height, and twenty feet broad at the base. The whole structure is white, and looks from the house, as Isabel describes it, like some handsome convent. From the villa, a smooth road (of course level as a floor) runs to it, and indeed, passing it, extends to the cypress forest two miles beyond it. This road is lined with hedges of the flowering Cherokee rose, and is our favorite morning gallop, as the Levee road, along the banks of the Father of Waters, is our favorite evening drive.

To-morrow we leave this lovely place for the city; and I will tell you a secret, Mr. ——, which you mustn't breathe for the world. The eldest son of M. De Clery, who has only last year returned from Paris, has fallen in love with Isabel, and they are to be married. We go to the city to select the bridal apparel and gifts, &c.

The young gentleman is extremely handsome, four-and-twenty years old, with a cultivated mind, and a good heart, and unexceptionable temper. This last qualification is the most important. If a husband is not amiable, dear me! what a wretched woman his bride must be! Girls should see if their suitor is *good tempered*, and if he is not, have nothing to say to him. If a man is bad tempered to his sister or mother, be *sure* he will be still more so to his wife, because his wife is more completely in his power. As a young man treats his mother and his sister, he will treat his wife. Young ladies! take this as an unfailing test, from your friend, Kate.

M. de Clery has a fine temper; and as he is also very rich, and a sincere believer in Christianity, Isabel will make a good match, and doubtless be very happy in the dangerous lottery of matrimony. But I am in tears as I write, at the thought of losing her; and the dear colonel looks through tearful eyes upon her, and kissing her, bids "God's blessing on her." It is a hard struggle for the father, though he desires the union.

The marriage of Isabel will change all our plans for the summer. The whole wedding party will proceed, soon after the nuptials, to the North, and the bridegroom and bride will embark for Europe. You ask what will become of me? A very sensible question, good Mr. ——. With Isabel's engagement yesterday, my vocation as governess went. The future is all before me where to choose. But the question of the future remains to be settled after we return from the city, where, as I said, we go to-morrow, to be absent a week. It is probable I shall accompany the bridal party North, and take the opportunity of visiting the humble home of my childhood, amid the green hills of New England—for, with all my attachment to the South, and the warmhearted Southern people, my heart,

"Dear New England, turns ever to thee."

P. S. My next letter will be from New Orleans, from which I hope to write you something interesting.

KATE.

LETTER XL.

MY DEAR MR. ———:

THIS is the first moment which I can call "my own," since I arrived in this splendid bedlam of a city, the diurnal roar of which, although it is nearly eleven o'clock at night, has not yet ceased. Carriages are swiftly rattling past, over the rocky streets, taking theatre and party-goers home; the night-policeman's staff echoes hollowly on the banquette, as he signalizes to his fellow-guardians of the city; the wild song of a group of bacchanals swells not unmusically up into the air, and penetrates my open window; while from an opposite drawing-room comes the rich soprano voice of some maiden singing at the piano—perhaps to a late-lingering lover.

Fatigued with the sweet excitement of the day in choosing her bridal attire, Isabel sleeps softly within the snowy folds of the lace musquito bar (which guards every bed in this climate); and as excitement always renders me wakeful, I embrace the hour till midnight to give you some idea of this great city of the South—this magnificent key of the Mississippi, which stands, as Constantinople at the entrance of the Bosphorus, the gate of a commercial interior, the value of which "no man can number."

In my last letter, dated at the sugar estate of M. de Clery, I briefly stated the happy engagement of my dear pupil Isabel to young Isdiore, his son, and that we were to come to the city to make preparations for the wedding.

At first it was determined that we should go down in one of the handsome packets that daily descend the river; but it was finally decided that we should take the carriages, and drive down by the Levee road, the distance being easily accomplished in two or three hours. At six o'clock in the morning, therefore, the horses were at the door, and as we had breakfast early, in order to take advantage of the cool air of the early day, we were soon on our way, rolling smoothly along over one of the most delightful of roads.

I have already mentioned the novelty and beauty of both of the green shores of the Mississippi,—how a verdant embankment five feet high borders each side, to prevent overflows; and how within this embankment is the river-road, following in and out every curve of the embanked shore, and level as a race-course track. Thus, one riding along this road has constantly the green bank, or Levee, on one side, with the mile-wide river flowing majestically by, bearing huge steamers past on its tawny bosom. On the other hand are hedges separating gardens, lawns, cottages, villas, and emerald cane-fields, with groups of live-oaks, magnolias, lemon, and banana trees interspersed. For miles, all the day long, the traveler can ride through a scene of beauty and ever lively interest. At no moment is he out of sight of the water, with its moving fleets, and the opposite shore beautiful with residences, groves, and gardens; at no moment is he not passing the tasteful abode and grounds of some planter, bordering the road-side.

If this drive is so attractive to one on the land, what must the scenery appear to the eyes of the passengers on steamers sailing from sunrise to sunset through it? But I cannot attempt to convey to you a just conception of these gorgeous river coasts of Louisiana. It is not the charming landscape alone that lends them their attraction to a northern eye, but the delicious climate, which bathes every thing, and in which every object seems to float.

You may judge that our ride towards the city was greatly enjoyed by me. I could not help, at the time, feeling a sensation of awe steal over me, as I looked from the carriage window and saw the level of the river higher than we were; for we had to rise up in the carriage as we rode along to *overlook* the Levee, when we could see that the river was within a foot even with it on the outer side, while the road over which our wheels rolled was four feet lower than its surface on the inner side; in a word, we were riding with a wall of water, kept from overwhelming us, and the fields, villas, and whole country, only by the interposing bank of the Levee, from four to six feet in height, and yet this guard of heaped earth was for hundreds of leagues enough to confine the monarch of waters within his bounds, so that the people dwelt in security upon his borders.

There are, however, times of terror, when the vast river, swelling to unwonted height, presses with irresistible power against some weaker part of this barrier, and forces a passage into the road beneath. At first, the breach may not be larger than a stream of water from a hose, and can easily be stopped with cotton-bales, or bags of earth, if at once applied. But when at night one of these crevices (which they call here " crevasses," when they become large) begins to form unseen by any watchful eye, it rapidly enlarges, till what at first could have been stopped by a schoolboy's dam, in half an hour becomes strong enough to turn a wheel, and in an hour plunges a roaring cataract twenty yards wide, rushing like a mill-race, and deluging road, gardens, fields, and pastures. The thunder of its fall, at length, awakes the planter or his sleepy slaves; the alarm-bell is rung out, as if for fire, and the whole coast is soon awake and alive.

One plantation bell after another takes up the note of terror, and for miles is heard their affrighted clamor, accompanied by the shouts of hundreds of slaves, hastening from all quarters to the scene of danger; for the peril of a crevasse is a *common peril to all,* for only stopping the incipient Niagara can save the whole region down to the Gulf, for a thousand square miles, from overflowing and ruinous devastation.

The scene at the stopping of a crevasse is only equalled by that at putting out a conflagration. The constant arrival, spurring at mad speed, of planters, followed by gangs of half-naked Africans, armed with spades and gunny-bags filled with dirt, the loud commands, the louder response, the tramp of hoofs and of men's feet, the darkness of the night, the glare of torches, and the roar of the ceaselessly plunging and enlarging torrent, as described to me by Isidore de Clery, must be both sublime and fearful. Imagine the reservoir on Fairmount to burst its sides some fine night, and the scenes that would follow in the neighborhood of the path its wild waters would make, in the efforts of the people to stop them, and you will be able to form some picture in your mind of a *crevasse,* and its destructive effects in the level country of Louisiana.

Not long ago a crevasse opened in the Levee not far from New Orleans, and became so alarming that steamers, laden with hundreds of men, sailed from the city for the place, and it was not finally stopped until fifty leagues square of the richest portion of the country had become submerged, and a hundred sugar planters ruined.

Nevertheless, in the face of all these facts, we rode calmly and securely on, with the river wall four feet higher than our road, thinking of any thing but crevasses, and enjoying the scenery that was ever changing its features, and increasing in beauty at every change.

Our cortége consisted of two carriages, in one of which rode the colonel, Isabel, and the senior M. de Clery, and Mademoiselle Marie Victoire La Blanche, his niece, a beautiful, olive-cheeked, dark-eyed Louisianaise, who was to be one of Isabel's bridesmaids. In another carriage, which was an open phæton, was Isidore, the happy and handsome affiancé and Miss Conyngham. Why they placed this young gentleman under my charge, separating him for the drive from Isabel, I can't tell; unless it was a pretty piece of tyranny, allowable, perhaps. At any rate, it was the plan of M. de Clery, the senior, who said, "The young folks will be enough in each other's society after they are married, so let them ride in different carriages now. Miss Kate will be so kind as to keep the young gentleman in proper decorum."

Dear me! I—a young, giddy girl of twenty scarcely, to be selected by two gray-headed gentlemen—to be the guardian of a young gentleman of three-and-twenty, as handsome as Adonis! So, what with answering Isidore's hundred and one questions, all about what I knew of Isabel ever since I had known her, and looking at the scenery, I was kept very busy,—for the scenery constantly challenged my attention, and the lover would constantly talk of Belle. By the time we reached the city I was half in love with him myself; and I then recollected how that Isabel had said to me, smilingly, when I was seated in the carriage,

"Take care of your heart dear Kate!"

But I hear an awful clamor throughout the city that compels me to stop. A deep-mouthed tocsin is ringing out "Fire! fire! fire!" as plain as a human voice could utter it; and a score of lesser bells reply, even as a huge ban-dog, alarmed in the night by a prowling burglar, opens his deep-mouthed bay, while Tray, Blanche, and Sweetheart, and all the little dogs, in every key, chime in, in confused, discordant uproar; so are all the bells of the city clamoring, and the streets, which had begun to sink into midnight quiet, are once more thundering with the artillery-like wheels of engines, hastening, amid a Babel of voices, to the scene of conflagration, the light of which, reflected from an opposite tower, already glares redly and balefully into my window.

I will now say "Good Night," but not without a heartfelt prayer for those who shall be made houseless and destitute by this fire, which rages more and more terribly, lighting up all the city roofs like a burning crater.

Yours,
K. C.

LETTER XLI.

NEW ORLEANS, LA.

MY DEAR MR. ———:

THE impressions which are made upon one's mind and memory on first going into a large city, are indellible. I shall never forget mine on approaching the city in our carriage, about three hours after leaving Chateau de Clery.

New Orleans is wholly unlike any other American metropolis. Its aspect is foreign, and French decidedly. When within six miles, we entered the pretty suburbs of Carrolton, where the road is a continuous street until lost in the labyrinth of the city avenues.

Instead of continuing along this road we alighted at the railway depot, leaving our carriages to return home with the coachmen, our intention being to go back by the river. The cars run to the city every half hour, and our party had no sooner got seated than we were off like an eagle shrieking as he flies. Oh, what dreadful noises those horrid steam whistles make! So shrill and loud and terrific, that I did not wonder to see cows, horses, mules, dogs, ducks, geese, and chickens turn, scamper, fly, trot, gallop, and scatter to the right and left in consternation.

There were three Indians in the next car, one of whom, in an old scarlet frock coat, fancifully fringed, placed his hands to his mouth in rapid succession, and echoed the cry of the engine whistle almost as shrilly. We all looked into the car to see what it was. He stood up and repeated the cry, saying with an air of tipsy satisfaction—

"War-whoop! *Me* war-whoop—*he* war-whoop."

What more he might have said was abruptly cut off by the conductor pushing him by the shoulder, and thrusting him with a huge oath roughly into a car still farther forward; and driving two patient-looking Indian women laden with baskets after him. Ah, for the poor Indian!

> " Like April snows in the warm noon,
>   He melts away! Where once he trod,
>   Lord of the earth and free as air,
>   He now creeps cowering like a cur,
>   Scorned, whipped, spit upon, abused,
>   Cursed of the white man, and not where
>   To lay his head where once he reigned a king."

The Indian is every where the same from Maine to Louisiana. They look alike, their pursuits are alike, their degradation equal. These were wandering remnants of the Choctaw tribe; for many linger about the scenes of their father's deeds and resting places of their bones, and support their precarious existence by fishing and basket-making. I have seen many of them in the city since, going about selling little bundles of sassafras root or herbs gathered in the woods. The women never smile, look sickly and suffering; while the men are gaily dressed and keep in a state of lordly drunkenness, the only affinity to "nobility" left to these poor lords of the forest.

I fear America has much sin lying at her door for her neglect of her Indian children.

Our car contained a strange medley. Directly in front of me sat a handsome yellow "lady," her head surmounted by an orange and scarlet plaid handkerchief, bound about it Turkish-turban fashion; a style that prevails here among the Creole servants. She had in her ears a pair of gold ear-rings, as large as a half-dollar, plain and massive; she wore a necklace of gold beads, hanging from which was a cornelian cross, the most beautiful thing I ever saw; upon her neck was a richly-worked black lace scarf; her dress was plain colored silk, made in the costliest manner. Her olive hands, which had very tapering fingers and remarkably *oval* nails, were covered with rings, chiefly plain gold ones. In one hand she held a handsome parasol, and the other fondled a snow-white French poodle upon her lap, said poodle having the tips of its ears tied with knots of pink ribbon, and a collar of pink silk quilled, and made like a ruff, while the end of its tail was adorned with a bow of blue ribbon, in the tastiest style; and, as if his poodleship were not sufficiently decorated to be taken to the city to visit its town cousins, it had a nice bow of red satin ribbon tied about each of its four ancles. This luxurious little fellow took it quite in high dudgeon that I should scan him so closely, and putting his little pink feet upon her shoulder, he shot fire out of his deep-set black eyes, and began to yelp at me most outrageously.

"*A bas, Fidele, fi donc!*" exclaimed his mistress, in certainly one of the most musical voices in the world; and gently patting the ferocious little aristocrat on the shoulder, she tried to quell its expressions of hostility towards me. Finding that it would not be pacified, she, turning round, and fixing upon me a pair of magnificent eyes, and a face of surprising and unlooked-for beauty —a strange and indescribable sort of beauty—she said:

"Pardon, Ma'mselle! La béte s'est mal comporté envers vous. Tranquilliez vous, Fidele! Ne vous inquietez pas!"

Here she kissed her spiteful little favorite, and gradually soothed its irascibility; but it would occasionally, nevertheless, glance at me suspiciously, and utter a *petite* growl in its little white fleecy throat. The seat on my left contained a French gentleman, aged and thin, with a huge gray moustache overshadowing his large mouth. He wore a long nankin blouse (a sort of loose frock-coat) and a yellow vest with bright buttons, gray trowsers and drab gaiters—altogether a peculiar costume, especially with his hat, which had a brim so narrow that two flies could not walk arm-in-arm around it, while the gray, weather-worn crown rose upward into the air above him like a rusty stove-pipe. The intense gravity of his countenance attracted my attention. He was as grave and dignified as a whole bench of supreme judges; yet he carried in a little paste-board box, with slits cut at intervals therein, a little, half-fledged mocking-bird; carried it as tenderly as a little child would have done; watched and guarded it against the jolts of the cars, the sunshine in the window, and the draught of air when the door was left open by the conductor. His whole heart seemed to be wrapped up in that miserable little bird, which sat trembling in the cage so pitifully, that I felt like asking him to let me take it out and nestle it between the palms of my hands.   But hear him talk to it!

"Pauvre petite!   Ah, bonne, bonnette!   Vous avez bon voyage.   Voyez vous les arbres?   Voyez vous les jolis champs?   Voyez vous les bels oiseaux?"

He would then hold the little wretch up at the window and point out the trees, and fields, and flying birds to it, exactly as if it could understand every word he said, and vastly enjoyed the "bon voyage" and the sight from the window.

The cage had evidently been made by him, impromptu, with his penknife, and was a very ingenious affair; and in the top of it was stuck a small rose-bud and sprig of thistle.   The little bird was evidently his pride and joy. He had perhaps caught it in the fields, and was taking it home to his grand-children, or had purchased it for some favorite.

It was an interesting sight to see a tall, warlike, mustachioed man thus giving his whole mind to such a little thing as the poor, chirping, crying young one in the cage; but it was beautiful to contemplate the scene.   It showed a good heart and kind; that he was affectionate and domestic, and must love children and all others of God's creatures that are helpless.   I regarded him with respect.

Finding the little bird did not seem to enjoy the scenery, he took a piece of cake from his pocket and began to tempt it to eat a crumb from the end of his finger, which he thrust into the cage.   "Mangez, petite!   Mangez le bon gateau!"

In a few minutes the cars stopped at his place, and he arose, and covering the cage carefully with his handkerchief, left the cars with it; and, as we started on, I saw him approach the gate of a pretty Creole cottage, half hidden in grape vines.   Several children and their youthful mother came to meet him.   "Voyez, voyez!" he cried, with great glee, holding up the cage.   "Voila l'oiseau, mes enfants.   Nous chantons comme les anges!" and, opening the little cage, he was showing them his prize, when the prisoner made a spring from between his thumb and finger, and fluttering its little winglets, went sailing through the air four feet from the ground, and threatening to knock itself against it every minute.

One general outcry escaped the confounded group, one double deep base mingled with altissimos; and as the cars were whirling us beyond view, I saw the whole party, headed by the tall, gray-headed French grandpa, start in full cry after the hopping and flying truant.

But I reserve the rest of the ride into the city for my next.   Till then, faithfully

Yours,
KATE.

LETTER XLII.

St. Louis Hotel, New Orleans.

Dear Mr. ———:

My last I closed somewhat abruptly, as you perceived, in the midst of a description of our railroad ride
to this city. I will now resume the notes of my journey
where I broke off, as I wish you to have a distinct impression of the scenes in the entrance to New Orleans,
by the cars.

As we approached the city through a level landscape,
level as a lake, we flew past now a garden on this side,
now a Spanish-looking little villa on that, the gardens
richly foliaged with lemon and banana trees, and far
over-stretching verandahs shut in by curtains to keep
out the sun from the piazzas. Such gardens and villas
one after another in great numbers we passed for a mile
or so, when the houses grew more numerous, the gardens
narrower and narrower, and shops and small tenements
were crowding together, where once had stood the orange,
lemon, and banana tree. Side-walks of brick, as we
darted forward, now took the place of green way-side
paths by walls and fences, and stone pavements were
substituted for natural dirt roads. People began to grow
more numerous on the walks, carts laden with brick and
lumber, carts laden with vegetables and butcher's meat,
bread carts, and ice carts, and omnibuses (those un-

sightly vehicular monstrosities) rolled, gallopped, rattled, thundered, raced, and rumbled past, and cross-street wise, making it impossible almost to hear one's self speak for the noise.   Onward our car wheels bore us, deeper and deeper into the living heart of the city.   Nothing but small shops were now to be seen on either hand, with purchasing throngs going in and coming out of them, while myriads of children seemed to swarm about the doors, crawl along the curb-stones, paddle in the gutters, and yell miscellaneously everywhere.   I never saw so many children in my life.   Some were black, some not so black, some yellow, some golden skinned, some tawny, some delicate milk and gamboge color, and some pure white, at least, such spots of their faces as the dirt suffered to be visible, seemed to promise an Anglo-saxon complexion underneath.   The major part, however, were olive brown, and plainly of French extraction; and I could hear the bright black-eyed little urchins jabbering French, to a marvel of correct pronunciation that would have amazed a school girl.

At length the houses grew more stately, the streets more genteel, the crowds more elegantly attired, and the cars stopped, and we were in New Orleans!

In an instant we were besieged by a very great number of polite gentlemen with whips in their hands and eager visages thrust up to the window.

"Fiacre, madame!"   "Hack, sir!"   "Carriage, ma'am." "Will yer ladyship's bright eyes jist look at my iligant haack?" insinuated a snub-nosed son of Green Erin, with an old fur cap cocked on his head, the visor behind, giving him a superlatively impudent look.

Seeing me apparently hesitate, he added with an eloquent intonation in his rich brogue. "It is vilvit kushioned, m'im, and glass windies intirely, Miss, and I've got the naatest tame dat'll take ye where ye wist in no time at all, at all!"

At this juncture Isidore came to conduct me to a carriage with the rest of our party. As we descended the steps of the car, a Chinese, in his small tea-cup of a blue cap, presented to my irresistible temptation, as he thought, some beautiful kites made of blue, yellow, green, and crimson tissue paper in the shape of superb butter-flies. They were two feet across the wings, and ele-gantly constructed of light wire bent into the desired shape, and covered with the paper. He asked but twenty-five cents a piece, and they looked so invitingly pretty, that I was half tempted to buy one for myself, recollecting my girlish days, when I used to fly kites, fish, and play ball with my brothers; but before I made up my mind to this speculation, a slender sloe-eyed quadroon girl of sixteen, with a superb smile, offered me a delicious bouquet, from a basket filled with them, which she was adroitly balancing on her head. The rival John-China-man interposed one of his handsome kites between my eyes and the bouquet, and while I was bewildered which to choose, a Frenchman thrust nearer my face than all, his forefinger, on which was perched a splendid parrot, with a nose like the Duke of Wellington's.

"Puy de kitee, Meesee! twenty-vive cen'," eagerly urged the Chinese.

"Mussier ne veu' 'pas le bouquet pour mamsel?" softly and musically entreated the girl, of Isidore, in her Creole patois.

"Buy pretty Pollee. Achetez mon joli oiseau!"

"Polly wantee cracker," screamed the parrot in my ear.

Thanks to the carriage-step at hand, by which I was enabled to secure a flight from the scene; and Isidore laughingly handed me the bouquet, which he had purchased of the quadroon, who thanked him with a brilliant smile.

Having purchased one of the persevering Chinaman's beautiful kites to take North, as a curiosity for Yankee boys, and implored the parrot-man to take his noisy, squalling, crooked-beaked, saucy-eyed, knowing-headed bird out of my sight, the carriage, at length, moved on out of the throng; and after a few minutes' rattling through rough paved streets, narrow and foreign-looking, we reached the St. Louis hotel, an edifice that looks like a superb Parisian palace—and a palace it is, as we experience in all its internal appointments and comfortable elegances of arrangement.

Respectfully yours,
KATE.

LETTER XLIII.

HOTEL, ST. LOUIS.

DEAR SIR :—How shall I describe to you this city, so as to convey to you any thing like an adequate idea of it? It is unlike any other city in the Union, being foreign in air, in customs, and mainly in population. Level as the water level of the river, above the surface of which it is elevated but a few inches, it extends for five miles along a grand bend of the river, which, doubling on its course, sweeps at this point northward, and then southward again, forming a majestic yoke, or letter U, and hence its name Crescent City. The front of the city is defended from floods by the Levee, which is raised a few feet higher than the general plane of its site. This Levee is the grandest quay in the world. Tyre nor Carthage, Alexandria nor Genoa, those aforetime imperial metropoles of merchant princes, boasted no quay like the Levee of New Orleans.

Picture to your mind's eye an esplanade or open front, a quarter of a mile broad, shaped like a new moon, its two horns four miles apart! Behold this noble space built up on one side by blocks of lofty brick or stone-stores, warehouses, steam-presses, hotels, cotton and sugar magazines, in which the mightiest energies, talents, and riches of commerce have their fields of daily activity. Interminably, farther than the eye can follow them, in their recession in the distance, they extend, range succeeding to range. Opposite this league-front of stores lie the various vessels which are the winged servants of the princely merchants, who occupy these commercial palaces. The whole Levee bank, from horn to horn of the magnificent crescent, is lined with shipping and steamers.

First are the cotton ships, which extend three in a tier for a mile and a half in unbroken line, their intermingled masts presenting the aspect of a wintry forest stripped of its leaves. I have been along the whole Levee in a carriage, and seen all this with my own eyes, and as I gazed I wondered at the sublime spectacle. A half league mass of ships, those proud ocean eagles which swept the clouds with their snowy crests, which rose defiant to the down pressing storm, tossed the ocean spray upon their necks, as the horse of the desert flings his mane, whose path has been sublimely held amid tempests and displays of the Almighty's power, whose swiftness, glory, and beauty of motion and form mocked that of the sea-bird—to see these once free and independent creatures, (ships to me always seem living things with life in them, like the wheels in Ezekiel's vision,)—to see those superb ocean messengers stripped of their white plumage, tied by the bit to wooden wharves, like newly captured elephants to strong stakes—to see them secured and motionless, fast bound in chains of iron, prisoners and captives, all their winged swiftness and their late ocean freedom changed into captivity, made me feel sad. I gazed on them with pity and sympathy. Yet, captives as they were, tied in threes as I beheld them, divested of their white wings as they were, there was still left much of the spirit of their former grandeur.

Their dark hulls, huge and massive, rising high out of the water and overtopping the Levee houses, and which I had to gaze up at, their curving bows and tall bulwarks, their noble outlines and vast proportions still lent them a dignity which commanded respect.

"Ah, brave ships," I said, "though bound fast now in port like caged lions, the day will come again, when, laden with the silvery fleece of this sunny land, and the glittering crystals of its emerald sugar fields, ye will once more spread your broad wings to the breeze of heaven, your now motionless keels will once more cleave the blue waves of the illimitable ocean, and again you shall try your oaken strength with the tornado, and do mighty battle with the billows. Conquering and still conquering your pathway, you shall traverse the farthest seas; some of you penetrate the icy Baltic, to lay your treasures at the feet of the Russian Czar; some of you pass beneath the frowning shadow of Gibraltar, and win your way to far Egypt, and unlade your precious burden on the quay of the city, where once reigned Joseph and the Pharaohs; some of you less ambitious, shall follow the curving shores of our vast republic, and passing the Vineyard and the Capes of New England, shall fold your canvass within sound of the church bell of my mother's native town.

As we rode slowly along, gazing on the poor tied up ships, I noticed that they bore flags of every land; for a sea captain had died that morning, and all the vessels in port had their colors at half mast, a very touching expression of nautical sorrow; for a flag not completely hoisted, is, in the symbolic language of seamen, inverted, a signal of distress at sea, of sorrow in port. My

old friend, the Bengal captain, (who has gone to sea
again, and is now away off in India,) carried this half
masting idea so far, that being in mourning for a relation, with black crape on a white General Jackson hat,
he always wore the strip just half way up his hat, (half-
mast, as he called it,) with a streamer half a foot long,
floating out behind. The dear good old tease of a Bengal tiger! I wonder if he will ever write me that long
letter he promised me he would do, and tell me all about
his adventures in those far away lands and seas. If he
does keep his promise, Mr. ——, the letter is yours to
put in print.

Some of the ships were Swedish, blunt, square-bowed,
high-shouldered, buffalo-looking hulks, with white-headed
and fair-skinned men on board, in blue and red woolen
caps. Their pretty flag was a white cross on a blue
ground, with a scarlet field in the upper corner, ornamented with a small white St. Andrew's cross, (the letter X.) I thought of sweet Jenny Lind, as I looked at
the flag of her country, which I felt would have brought
tears of joy into her eyes, to have seen it here, so far
away from her home-land.

How much Sweden owes to Jenny Lind in song, Miss
Bremer in letters, and Thorwaldsen in sculpture! But
for these three gifted children of her hills, Sweden, as
before their birth, would be obscurely known to the
world. But they have placed her first in music, first in
letters, first in art; so that now she takes her proper intellectual rank with the cultivated nations of Europe.
If three persons can give glory to their native land in
the eyes of the world, how carefully ought every indi-

vidual to live, that he may peradventure reflect honor upon his own nation! No one is insignificant.

There were four Swedish ships, and two Norwegian barques, showing in their flag a large blue cross on a red ground, the flag of Ole Bull's land. A Portuguese brig, with her pretty green and white striped colors, I also saw. There were half a dozen Russian ships, with their flags striped with red, white, and blue. The most part of the vessels displayed the star-spangled banner, flashing and glittering above the Yankee decks, as saucily as though it felt itself at Lome on its own soil. The red, sanguinary-looking ensign of old England, with its double cross in one corner of a blue ground, floated proudly and gloomily above full a hundred ships; for, next to the commerce of our own ships, that of England stands confessed. The tri-colored flag of France was visible here and there, and the yellow and red colors of Spain flaunted above inferior-looking vessels.

Of the Yankee ships, nearly all were from New York, and ports north of it, the half being from New England. The handsomest ships which I saw were from Bath, Maine; and a captain, to whom the colonel spoke, told me that the best ships in the world are built on the Kennebec river in Maine. Those which I saw and admired, were certainly models of grace, majesty, and strength. They looked like peaceful frigates, tamed down, and broken into the merchant service. After leaving the long range of ships, we came to the part of the Levee where the Mississippi, Ohio, Missouri, and all Northern and interior steamers moor. For half a mile it was a grand display of snow-white hulls, round-topped wheel-houses, tall, black, iron chimneys, some belching forth

clouds of murky smoke, that rolled and rolled over the
city like threatening thunder-clouds, only more awful-
looking. I never saw anything so dreadfully sable as
these volumes of smoke, which rise from furnaces crammed
with pine knots and tar-barrels.

After the steamboats, come the small Spanish and
Creole coasters, and the Texas and Florida trading
schooners, which are very numerous, with swarthy crews
in red shirts, knife in belt, and with huge beards.   Then
we came to the Ocean steamers, those mammoth sea-dan-
dies that go steaming about the world smoking their rusty
sheet-iron cigars, and leading a very fast life, much to
the scandal of the sober-going merchantmen.   These
steamers, with their jet-black aspect, and odd-looking,
shark-headed bows and huge dimensions, have a very de-
moniacal appearance; and if I had been a timid person
at all, I should have hesitated about venturing within
their capacious power, recollecting how Jonah once came
too near a sea-monster of a similar species, and was swallowed whole.

Nevertheless we went on board; but as they were taking in coal with scores of wheel-barrows, everything was
dusty, noisy, and disagreeable; and painters being at
work in the cabin, all things were upside down, like
a New England scouring day.   So we beat a retreat, and
continued our ride two miles further, again coming upon
a chain of ships nearly as extensive as the first we had
seen; both sides of the city being flanked by these wooden
marine walls and forests of masts.

Imagine every ship engaged in lading, or unlading,
every steamer discharging, or taking in freight and passengers, and every third one letting off noisy steam and

belching smoke; while steamboats constantly arrive from the river above, and round to and land, or depart amid the roars of escape pipes, and the clamor of bells. Imagine four thousand drays aiding in loading and unloading these thousand vessels, and moving in all directions along the Levee, till its whole surface is alive with a ceaseless maelstrom of motion, accompanied by a noise of hoofs, wheels, and voices, almost deafening in their aggregated thunderings. Imagine one broad field of such commercial life, four miles in unbroken extent, and you will have some idea of the "Levee" at New Orleans. No city on earth can present such a striking scene,—and all at one glance of the eye! No quay-view anywhere could convey such an impression to the mind of the observer, of the power, and might, and action, and energy of commerce.

But as I gazed upon all this, I could not help recalling the terrible chapter in Revelations addressed to Babylon, "that great city wherein was made rich all that had ships in the sea, by reason of her costliness."

For her luxuries and sins, Babylon was terribly judged! Will this city remember God, and glorify Him "who maketh the merchants of the earth to wax rich," when they say, "What city is like unto this great city? Shall she also be made desolate, and her crown be removed and cast into the dust? God forbid! Let Religion go hand in hand with, and sanctify Commerce, and this city need not fear what otherwise it should apprehend,—the doom of all those hitherto which have forgotten from whose Hand "cometh all prosperity."

Your friend,
K. C.

LETTER XLIV.

DEAR MR. ————:

THIS is the last day we are to remain in this Franco-American Metropolis of the South. What with shopping with dear Bell, in assisting her in making bridal purchases—with riding at twilight on the magnificent "shell road," with visiting the cathedrals, and churches, and public edifices, and above all, for interest, the old cemeteries of the city, my time has been fully occupied.

Our hotel is in the French quarter of the city, and a grand, French Tuilleries' looking affair as it is. It is under the superintendance of Mr. Mudge, who is a native of New England, was formerly a dry-goods merchant in Portland, and being unsuccessful in business, came out here many years ago to make his fortune, and, unlike many who go from home for this purpose, he has eminently succeeded. From being only a salaried assistant in the office of the St. Charles, he rose by his probity, industry, talents, and genius, to become its proprietor; and now is manager temporarily of this until the St. Charles is rebuilt. He is a gentleman of fine manners, a pleasant countenance, and has a most interesting and charming family. To manage a hotel now-a-days, requires very much the sort of talent requisite in a commander of a man-of-war or a military officer, and this ability Mr. Mudge possesses. Hotel managing is a profession, and a highly honorable one. It requires training, talent, nay, genius. The first hotel started in the United States, on the modern plan, was the Tremont. Its clerks became managers of others, till now, in all the best hotels, the managers have either been educated to their office at the Tremont or Astor, (which sprung from the Tremont under Mr. Stetson,) or by gentlemen who graduated at one or the other of the "Hotel Universities." Those large establishments are now regular colleges, and should issue "diplomas" to their graduates. It is not now, as it was formerly, that a man, who is not fit for any other business, can keep a hotel.

All this knowledge I have got from hearing a conversation between the colonel and one of the proprietors of the house. Nothing can be more recherché, more superb, more in perfection, than every appointment about this noble house. It strikes me that Queen Victoria could not entertain us better in Windsor Castle, than Mr. Mudge does here.

I love to walk through the French streets, and look into the prettily fixed-up shops, or sit in the drawing-room window, and gaze out upon the streets, watching the passers-by, and the people in the neighborhood. Two-thirds of them are French, the gentlemen with mustaches, which seem to be worn universally here, and the ladies in Parisian hats, and long lace veils, with dresses very short, to exhibit their pretty feet,

> "Like little mice peeping in and out,"

as they trip along the banquette; which, by the way, is the ordinary name here for side-walk. The French are a very odd people. They don't seem to know or care

that anybody looks or listens. They talk and gesticu-
late in the most extravagantly ridiculous manner, and I
am infinitely amused a hundred times a-day at what
passes before me.

One old man comes out and sits in an arm-chair on
the banquette, and does nothing but make little paper
cigars and smoke them, and read an old torn book,
through a pair of enormous, round-eyed, iron spectacles.
No matter who goes by, what goes on around him, there
he sits, the crowd passing and repassing him, as quiet
and unconcerned as if he were alone on Robinson Cru-
soe's island. At eleven o'clock, a little negress, in a
bright red 'kerchief bound tastefully about her brows,
brings him out on a waiter a bottle of claret and a little
tumbler. He drinks three glasses, and she retires, while
he resumes his smoking and reading the old book. Once
I saw a priest stop and address him. The old man rose,
bowed politely, crossed himself, offered the priest a cigar,
which was accepted; the priest bowed and went on,
while Monsieur, crossing his breast, bowed and reseated
himself, with a half smile on his old visage, as if the
brief interview with the priest had gratified him.

Not far from this person sits from morning to night,
in a shop door, a sallow, thin lady, engaged in working
a piece of embroidery. She has her soup and garlic
brought to her by a child, and eats her dinner in face of
the world with perfect indifference.

The French seem to love "out doors." They turn
themselves, the whole population, from their doors at the
close of the afternoon, and sit on the banquette till bed-
time, talking, laughing, singing, and even eating their
suppers, if the banquette be wide enough. They are, as

all say of the French, a gay, happy people, and seem to
be quite divested of all care for the morrow. It is our
American undue care for to-morrow, that makes the to-
day always so heavy. They make it bear its own weight
and to-morrow's, a double burden which our Saviour
wisely forbade us to put upon ourselves. *A présent* is
the life of the French.

There are two distinct cities that make up New Orleans—the American and French. The former is so
much like a Northern city that I did not remain in it
much, although the most superb portion; but I took
kindly to the latter for its very novelty. In the French
part, few of the population speak English. Their language, manners, customs, are preserved; and a Parisian
would think himself in a city of France, if he did not
cross Canal street, which is the Rubicon that separates
the American quarter from it.

In walking through the French municipality, or district, I could hardly realize that I was in my native
land. French names to streets—Rue Bien-ville, Rue
Royal, Rue Chartres! French signs above the stores, and
within mustached Gallic visages of men, and dark-eyed
foreign-looking women, with smooth, raven hair dressed
a la Suisse; French architecture everywhere, and the
French tongue constantly heard by old and young, by
African and freemen! All these peculiarities made it
almost impossible for me not to fancy myself in Europe.
If I entered a shop *Des modes,* I was addressed in French
by a smiling dame, or a polite Monsieur. If I asked a
direction in the street, I was answered in the same
tongue. If I entered a book store, I found in every
volume I took up the native language of Lafayette. The

yellow fiacre-men called to their horses in a patois of the same language, and a woman at the corner of the street offered me Boston apples, with a "Mam'sel, veut elle des pommes ce matin?"

If I passed two gentleman conversing, I heard French; and the children shouted to each other in the same universal speech, much to the amazement undisguised of Edith, who attended Bell, Monsieur Isidore, and me, in our perambulations, and who could not comprehend how little barefooted wretches of six and seven years could talk the language which "Missy Bella" had been three years in learning with masters at an expense of hundreds of dollars.

It seemed to her ignorance of things quite an unequal distribution of gifts of Providence. On her return she will probably excite the wonder of the whole Ethiopian population of the plantation, by asseverating that she heard in New Orleans little children talking French. I do assure you, frankly confessing it, Mr. ——, that it made *me* quite indignant to hear the little imps so independently speaking the language without ever having looked into a horrid grammar, and being wholly innocent of dictionaries, who had never conjugated *avoir* nor *faire*, and knew no more of *être* than they did of the 119th Psalm. I felt like giving every one of them a good whipping, thinking how many wakeful hours I had spent on grammars and dictionaries, to learn what came to them, as their walking did, by nature. We found that the French spoken to us in the shops was not a little different from the Parisian pronunciation. I noticed that the Orleanois clip their words, do not speak the nasal termination so full and distinct, and have a shriller intonation throughout. I should judge that the difference in pronunciation between them and the Parisians to be greater than between New Englanders and educated Englishmen. As these are easily distinguished from one another although saying the same words, so are the Louisiana French to be easily distinguished from the Parisian.

There are a good many French gentlemen here at present who have taken prominent parts in the politics of France, and who find French soil unsafe for their feet just now. One of these expressed himself to me at table yesterday with great animation about this country and the society of New Orleans, with which, he said, he was perfectly charmed. "There is a naiveté and simple grace in the ladies," he remarked, "that we see not in France, at least not exactly like it. They are gentle, yet proud; independent, yet, like the vine, seem to look to the sterner sex for support; intelligent, yet indolent; not much learned in books, yet irresistibly captivating in conversation. They seem to combine," he added, "the splendor and haughty bearing of the Spanish women, with the tender loveliness of the Italian, the bonhomie of the French, and the discretion and repose of the English: a noble combination which would constitute a perfect national character."

I agree with Monsieur de B—— so completely that I give his description of the Louisianaise as my own.

Yesterday I had pointed out to me a large, heavy, gigantic-looking personage, in a blue frock-coat and gray trowsers, as the Prince de Wurtemburg, who is traveling in the United States. He is a fair Saxon in aspect, with a flashy countenance, blue eyes, and double chin—

a thorough heavy German. I was at once interested in him, not because he was a prince, Mr. ——, because all our young Americans of "Young America" are princes born,—but from the fact that he is a lineal descendant of that good Duke of Wurtemburg who was Luther's fast friend, and whose adhesion to the Protestant cause gave such impetus to the Reformation.

There are scores of the old noblesse of France living here in quiet and more or less competency; some as gentlemen still, others as fabricateurs of cigars, teachers, &c. Here also are to be found exiles of all nations, and men of desperate fortunes, self-expatriated. Every language of the civilized world can be heard in this city in a day's ramble through its thoroughfares.

Yours respectfully,

KATE.

LETTER XLV.

Dear Mr. ———— :

THE more I see and understand this Franco-American city, the more I am pleased with it. The novelty of its being a perfect plain, level as a chess-board, is one of its striking characteristics, in a northern eye. Next is its foreign air, then there is the magnificent *coup d'œil* of its league-long quay, the majesty of its moving river, the massive grandeur of its public edifices, in which New Orleans surpasses northern cities, and the picturesque variety of costumes in the streets. Even the water in the streets, after a heavy shower, runs *away* from the river towards the rear of the town, instead of running into the river, as it *ought* to do in all well-regulated corporations.

The cause of this latter peculiarity is that the river is higher than the level bottom on which the city stands, and from its shore the land gently inclines for a mile or two, until a dead level is reached where the waters lie immovable. Like all rivers through an alluvial region, the Mississippi flows grandly and loftily along on a ridge of its own making, and which it continues to elevate by every muddy overflow.

But I leave these matters to Sir Charles Lyell and Professor Forshay, and will write less learnedly, albeit learned ladies are now the mode, and all our female boarding-schools are transmogrified into *Collegiate* Insti-

tutes, and colleges where degrees are bestowed, asserting
that the young ladies are proficients in (making pies and
puddings, doing up preserves, churning butter, and pressing cheeses, roasting, baking, and boiling, making shirts
and mending cassimeres?) oh no! no, no, no, but in ana-
lyzing the atmosphere into globules; in explaining the
electric battery; in measuring the depth of the primary
secondary, and tertiary formations; in dissolving the
nebula trapezium in the belt of Orion into stars; in condensing vapor, and explaining the mystery of the steam-
engine, and *perfectly* familiar with the science of political
government, and can demonstrate the forty-seventh Problem of Dr. Euclid!

I have to-day passed two hours, divided between
two of the great Roman Catholic churches here, one
of which, on Place d'Armes, is a cathedral, by which
term I understand the church wherein the Bishop or
Archbishop himself preaches.

We went to the cathedral first, which fronts, with the
State government offices, a sweet public garden, adorned
with snow-white statues, and interlaced by lovely walks;
an oasis of taste in the very heart of noisy commerce,
like a gentle thought in a bad man's breast.   This square
is not large, but it is a *bon ton* of squares, for its neatness
and attractive air.   On one side the massive walls, tower,
and turrets of the cathedral look protectively down upon
it; on two other sides stand the noble ranges of edifices
called the Montalban Buildings, constructed alike, and
facing each other on opposite sides of the Plaza.   The
fourth side is open to the quay and river, at the point
where the magnificent ocean-steamers lie, to repose a
while from their stormy voyages from clime to clime.

The walks in the square were lively with nurses and children, while lazy fellows with mustaches lay asleep on the luxurious grass, or smoked cigars. This square has been for more than a century the parade-ground of the troops of the several nations which have held New Orleans: Spanish, French, English, and now Americans. It was formerly the place of public execution, and from it is fired at nine o'clock the cannon which we have heard every night at that hour shake the city, and start Isabel and me, and other unsophisticated country girls, from our propriety.

The cathedral has an imposing and costly air. It is the old cathedral, that ancient, time-honored structure, of which I have read in novels, and the very sight of which creates a romance in the imagination. But modern taste has veneered all this antiquity, and out of the old pile has produced a very elegant temple of worship. We made our way along the front of the government offices, between massive columns supporting a corridor, and a row of cabriolets, which are the "hacks" of New Orleans. The cabriolet is a handsome, chariot-shaped vehicle, that is too pretty to be confined, as it is, entirely to the hack-stand. These *cabs*, as they are called "for short," are driven by Irishmen, or by colored men, the latter of whom sat half asleep on the boxes, while the sons of Erin were alert, and extended to us very pressing and polite invitations to suffer them to have the "honor of dhrivin' our ladyship and our honors to any part of the city." The front doors of the cathedral were closed, but M. de Clery, our attendant, turned with us down a narrow avenue, which had the wall of the cathedral on our left, and a row of French-looking build-

ings on our right, which, said Isidore, are occupied by
the priests; and of this fact we had ocular proof, by
seeing two sleek and unctuous-looking gentlemen, with
pleasant visages, sitting on a balcony, one with a paper
cigar in his lips, and the other reading to him from a
small, greasy book; there was also a very young, slen-
der-looking priest in a long, black serge-gown, reaching
to his heels, who was at the door of another house, purchasing, with a smile and a jest, some superb Huston
peaches from a basket balanced on the head of a Creole
woman.

We proceeded about fifty yards down this avenue when
we came to a side door, which an elegantly shaped, veiled
female was in the act of opening to go in. Isidore politely held the door for her and us, and we passed through
a second cloth door into the interior. At our left was a
marble basin, containing consecrated water, into which the
veiled lady dipped the tip of her forefinger, and, tnrning
round to the shrine of the Virgin, crossed herself on the
forehead and bosom gracefully, at the same time bending
her head in the act of adoration. The cross is made by
touching the forehead, the breast, the left shoulder, and
lastly the right, in quick succession with the right forefinger.

The door by which we entered, brought us into the
Cathedral, close to the shrine of St. Joseph, near the
chancel. The extreme beauty of the interior; the soft,
mellow, lemon-toned tint of the ceiling and columns, the
vast height of the fresco-adorned dome; the variety of
fine architectural forms into which the walls around us
and the ceiling were shaped; the liberal air of space and
expenditure apparent everywhere; the superb altar, with

its commingled paraphernalia of splendid things, of which
I neither knew the name nor their use, fixed my admiration, and riveted me to the spot from which I first caught
a view of the rich *ensemble*.

After a few minutes, when I had comprehended the
grand outline, I began to examine details. I walked
around the immense church, from shrine to shrine, and
from picture to picture. The last are always daubs, in
all Roman churches, except the altar paintings, which
are always rich, and usually by a master's pencil.

I allude, under the term "pictures," not to the great
oil-paintings which rise above the central shrine, but to
those colored engravings, in black or rosewood frames,
that are seen in all these churches. They represent, in
a series, the events in the sufferings of Christ, from his
arrest to his ascension. These pictures are, I think, sixteen
in number, and are so hung around the church, that a vo-
tary, commencing with Jesus in the hands of His captors,
ends on the other side of the church with bowing before the
representation of His crucifixion. All good Romans
often make the "penitential journey" round the church,
saying a prayer (composed for the purpose, in their Li-
turgy) before each picture, having reference to the scene
represented by it. These pictures are always engravings,
highly-colored, and sold by the set to supply churches,
not only in this country but in Europe. Each one is
sacredly surmounted by a little black cross.

As we entered, a negress, with a little mulatto child in
her hands, was engaged devoutly making the tour of the
"Passion of Jesus." I watched her, and saw her kneel before each engraving, and mutter her prayer, the little,

black-eyed child pulled down on its knees by her side, but its shining eyes always turned around and fixed on us.

There were several confessional boxes. Seeing the skirt of a robe protruding from the alcove by the side of one, I moved in that direction, and beheld the graceful lady, whom I had for a few times lost sight of, kneeling before the lattice blind, with her mouth close to it, and pouring into the ear of the unseen priest, shut up within, her secrets and her sins!

That she was penitent, I felt sure, for there were "tears in her voice," as its slow sounds reached my heretical ears. Sorrow always commands reverence. I turned away, leaving her to her humiliating work, and wishing to say to her in the language of inspiration, "Daughter! None forgiveth sins, but God only!" Ah, this confessional! It is the secret of Roman power over the consciences of her people. "Tell me your secrets, and you are my slave," was said two thousand years ago, by a Greek writer; and it is true to-day, and Rome practically asserts its truth.

I observed that over the door of each of the confessionals was printed in gold letters, the name of the father-confessor; so that the penitent knows (possibly if no mischievous and evil-minded young priest steal in, or jealous husband unawares to priest and penitent) to whom she is unfolding the secret intents and thoughts of her heart. I should hardly be willing to tell my husband everything, (if I had one, Mr. ——,) less so to one of these jovial-eyed, good-natured, bald-headed padres! and much less to a handsome young fellow of a priest, whom I saw cross the chancel, in at one door and out of the other, half bending his knee before the crucifix on the altar, as he passed by it, not without half an eye cast upon our party! The confessional alone would frighten me from ever being a Romanist.

If you have ever been in a Roman church, you must have been struck with the *three* great altars or shrines which are invariably in all of them, at the east end of the church. The centre one is the High Altar, with the crucifix, holy, vessels, &c., and is the shrine of Jesus! On the right of this, at the same end, is the shrine of the Virgin with her altar, and the objects associated with her worship. On the left of the High Altar, at the same end, is the shrine and altar of St. Joseph, the husband of Mary.

These three altars take up the whole of the east end of all Roman churches. The three are equally worshiped, or rather the shrines; and the Virgin always has the greatest number of votaries. Her altar is heaped with the freshest flowers; and three kneel before her shrine, where one kneels before the high altar of "the Christ."

The religion of Rome is Mariolatry. The Mother of Jesus is the supreme object of the worship, homage, adoration, and supplication of Romanists. Jesus is worshiped and adored not as "the ascended Lord," but as *the infant in arms.* He is a peculiarity of the Roman worship. They are so accustomed to think of, and to behold Jesus in the arms of His Mother, that they lose sight of Him as "the MAN Christ Jesus;" and the habit of seeing Him only as an *Infant* leads them to look upon the Blessed Mother alone in the light of protectress and guardian of the Holy Child. Thus they associate with her a maternal influence and maternal power in relation to Him, which is the foundation of their whole system of "Prayers to the Virgin."

Christ in the arms is the centre of Roman worship: Christ on the cross, of Protestant. It is natural therefore that the worshiper of the babe should transfer a part of adoration to its mother.

After half an hour spent in the Cathedral, we departed as we came, and taking one of the cabriolets, drove to St. Patrick's Church; of my visit to which I will not trouble you with an account, as it interested me less than that to the Cathedral. On our way we paused at Christ Church, the richest Episcopal Church in this city. It is a low, ill-planned structure for its architectural pretensions, looking, as if the main body had sunk some six feet under ground, after being built, and the spire had sunk as many feet down into the bosom of the tower. The whole wants elevation, and up-lifting into the air.

The interior I am told is very rich; but gates and doors were locked,—for, I regret to say, the Romans are the only people who "shut not their gates" to the foot of the wayfaring worshiper, who, at all times, should be able to enter the "courts of the House of the Lord, and worship towards His holy temple."

Very respectfully,
K. C.

LETTER XLVI.

CHATEAU DE CLERY, LA.

DEAR MR. ———— :

THIS letter's date shows you that I am once more an inmate of the charming abode from which I have so frequently written you. My last was dated at New Orleans, where we had been to purchase the hundred little elegancies for Isabel's bridal, which having done to *all* our satisfactions, we returned home on Tuesday last. I see by one of your papers that I have been so *distinguished* as to find a *critic*.

Dear me! I had no idea, not the remotest, that any thing coming from my pen could be worthy of the notice of any other pen, especially such a graceful one as that of your New Orleans correspondent. If I use "Needles," her pens are pointed with gold, and sharpened with diamond dust. Present to her my most gracious compliments, and say to her that she is right in supposing I had made a mistake in giving to one railroad terminus some descriptive sentences which really belonged to the other! I thank her for the correction and especially for making it so pleasantly. But who could be expected to have their heads *perfectly* clear, Mr. ————, (I ask *you*, who are a married man, and ought to know about such matters,) when they were shopping with a bride-elect,

attended by a handsome young man, and half in love with
him myself?

I do not mean Isabel's affiancé Isidore, but a friend
of his, who escorted us; for Isidore is too diffident to go
a-shopping with Bel, on *such* an occasion.   Now, having
told you the secret, Mr. ——, you are not surprised.   I
feel confident that my head was a little giddy, and that
I mistook my notes about one railway at one end of the
city, jotted down when I came from a day's trip to Pass
Christian for those made for the other railway at the
other end; and I trust that this explanation will make
me friends with your correspondent.   And talking of
such contributors to your columns, pray *who* is "Nicolene?"   She writes with taste to be sure, and does me
great honor, in her graceful humility, to furnish such
exquisitely woven threads for my "Needles."   But I do
her injustice to call them *thread*—they are the finest
silken floss of the richest and most brilliant tints.   How
intimately one can know an *unknown* one by means of
the magic press!   This "Nicolene" and I are already
friends, stitched as closely together as twin-sisters, by
means of our "Thread and Needle."   Shall we ever
meet in this green world under the sunny blue sky, hand
in hand, and friendly eye looking into friendly eye? or
if not, and we cross one another's bright path in celestial
fields, shall we know who one another is; and shall we
then be to the other as the "thread" to the "needle:"
two but *one* in aim, and in all things?

Perhaps, too, I have many friends—many kindred
spirits, who have become acquainted with me through
my "Needles."   I sometimes love to fancy myself visiting, incognita, some of the firesides where they are read,

and where I am loved through them;* and to imagine
the dear welcome I should receive from smiling eyes and
pressing hands, when I told them who I was.   Thus, my
dear sir, my pen has become to me the key to open many
hearts, who think and speak of me, as if they had seen
and talked with me face to face.   They will continue to
be my friends, forever, and I to be theirs; so that I have
two sets of friends in the world; those whom I have seen,
and whose voices are familiar to my ear; and those
whose forms, whose faces, whose voices, whose names,
whose homes on earth, are all unknown to me! To them
I send love and greeting.   To them I send wishes of
happiness and heaven; for them my prayers ascend; towards them my pleasantest thoughts wander, when in
the still twilight I give them free wing over the shadowy,
half-star-lit world.

In this letter, dear Mr. ——, I meant to have given
you a description of the great preparations which are
making for Isabel's bridal, which takes place on Thursday morning next; but I have not time now, everybody
is hurrying everybody so; for one comes and urges me
to lay down my pen, and entwine a wreath of flowers for
some statuette; or another runs and asks me my opinion
of such an ornament for the chandeliers; Isabel sends
the pretty golden skinned slave, Emma, to ask me if she
ought to wear any rings at all during the ceremony, and
which, one or ones? and then my taste is in demand for
the best mode of dressing the chancel of the little gothic
chapel, where the ceremony is to take place; and what
with trying to keep Isidore within proper decorum, con-

* A great number of letters and poems were addressed to the
authoress.—*Editor.*

sidering he is soon to become a grave husband, and showing Aunt Chloe how to frost cake "Bosting-way," as
she calls it, I have enough to do; so good bye for this
day, good Mr. ——. In a day or two you shall have
full particulars of the wedding.

Your true friend,
KATE.

LETTER XLVII.

CHATEAU DE CLERY, LA.

DEAR MR. ———:

THE wedding of Isabel had like to have been put off
for at least a whole month, just for a point of etiquette!
And what do you suppose it was?

Why, you know, that my sweet pupil, Isabel, who for
two years past has grown into the charming grace of intellectual womanhood under my eye, had captivated the
calm, elegant, retiring Isidore de Clery, while on a visit
at his father's with her own father, Colonel Peyton.
When it was perceived that lovers they were, and married they would be, why the dear, good colonel gave his
consent, and proposed that the party should go to the
city to purchase the wedding dresses, jewelry, and ever
so many and so forths!

Of course Bel did not object; M. de Clery, senior, did
not object, but was perfectly enraptured at the prospect
of having such a lovely daughter-in-law; and Isidore did
not object by any means. So the wedding, it was decided, should take place at the Chateau de Clery.

But now, only think of the tyrannies of fashionable
propriety, Mr. ———! After we had returned from New
Orleans to the Chateau, a certain very precise, very
starch, very ancient old lady aunt, who was invited from
her sugar estate to the wedding, took it into her antiquated

head "that it was most becoming for young maidens
to be married (wheresomever they may be courted) at
their paternal mansion; and that it would not be *comme
il faut* if Isabel were married at the house of the father
of her intended husband! that the bridegroom should go
to the house of the bride elect after his bride, and take
her home!—at least that was the custom in *her* day!"
which was *entre nous*, Mr. ——, when three brothers,
named Shem, Ham, and Japhet, got their wives, I am
quite satisfied.

Now to the plain Tennessee manners of the colonel,
to the unsophisticated ignorance of poor Isabel, to the
want of *savoir faire*, pardonable in a Green Mountain
Yankee girl, this idea never occurred to us before.   The
old aunt's brocade and farthingale notions prevailed over
the better sense of the colonel, and he absolutely told
Bel that she had best be married at home, in Tennessee,
and that we would return on purpose for the next boat!

Bel came to me with her large, glorious, brown eyes,
overrunning with tears, and told me all.   I was surprised and indignant.   I wished all meddlesome antedi-
luvian aunts a league beyond sundown, and telling Bel I
would see what I could do for her, and not to spoil her
pretty eyes with crying, I left my room and went to the
colonel.   On the way, in the salon, I encountered Isidore.   His face was pale, and his whole aspect perfectly
wretched with an expression of despair.   He met me
with extended hands.

"Sweet, good Kate, you must reverse our fate!   You
can do any thing you attempt.   Influence the colonel to
change his mind.   It is absurd!   Why can we not be
married at my father's as well as at Bel's?   I wish her

aunt had been blown up ———" (no—not so bad as that,"
I said, putting my finger on his lips) "well, sunk to the
bottom of the Mississippi ere she had come here to mar
our felicity. For Bel's sake, as well as mine, do something in our behalf!"

I promised Isidore I would see what could be done,
and, followed by his blessings, I sought Colonel Peyton,
whom I found walking up and down the piazza on the
shady side of the house, looking as gloomy as if he had
the toothache.

"Well, Kate, I see you have heard the news," he said,
approaching me. "Bel will cry her eyes out, and Isidore will blow out his brains! But, bless me, what could
I do? There is my precise sister, with her old, Revolu-
tionary-War notions, says it will be 'an absolute scandal' if I suffer Bel to be married here, and that such a
thing was never heard of, and that—that—the—d——!
would generally be to pay ——."

("Fie, colonel!" I said, trying to stop the word at
the syllable, but it was no use—out it came with a heartiness that was resistless.)

"Well, Kate, it is enough to make old General Taylor
swear!"

"What does Monsieur de Clery say?" I asked.

"He, you know, is so excessively polite that he can't
gainsay a woman, so he bows, and bows, and smiles, and
outwardly acquiesces to my sister, while I very well know
he would be most happy to administer chloroform to her
for the next nine days to come. But, if scandal is to
come of it, Bel must be married at home, as I have told
her. Confound fashion, Kate."

Here the colonel gave such a petulant fling to his

cigar, that it went like a rocket through the air, and lighted upon the thick woolly pate of old Aunt Elise, igniting the unctuous crisp to the sudden consternation of the old dame, who screeched so loudly, with her apron over her head, and ran so madly, yelling "Fire!" that the colonel burst into laughter, and his anger evaporated, for he is too good-natured to hold ill-humor.

"Well, Kate, I will be guided by your good sense, and if it offends my sister we must bear the brunt. What do you propose in order to keep these lovers from dying with despair? for, I confess, that to put off a marriage a whole month, which was to take place to-morrow night, is a pretty trying affair; don't you think so?"

"I do not know any thing about such matters," I answered, very quickly; "but if the good lady is not to be pacified, I propose that you suggest to M. de Clery that he invest you with the proprietorship of Chateau de Clery for a day or so. Do you understand me, colonel?"

"Upon my word I do not, Kate," he answered, thoughtfully.

"I understand her, colonel," responded the cheery voice of M. de Clery, who overheard me, and now joined us. "It is a good idea. Bon, *bon!*"

"A *good* idea will be the most acceptable to me just now," answered the colonel, with a blank look. "What would Miss Kate be at?"

"I do not wish to offend so respectable a person as Madame, your sister," said M. de Clery, with a smile, "and as her prejudices touching where a Demoiselle should be married are not to be easily overcome, I herewith invest you, my dear colonel, for three days, with the sole proprietorship of this chateau, servants, and all it contains, and for that period, Isidore and I will have the honor of being your happy guests!"

At this the colonel burst into a hearty laugh, and, shaking M. de Clery by both hands, turned to me and kissed me, looking the uproarious picture of satisfaction and delight, and began calling for "Bel," at the top of his voice!

The matter was soon arranged. Bel smiled again, like an April sun coming out from behind showery clouds; Isidore said I deserved to be married to an emperor, and the colonel would have kissed me again, if I hadn't adroitly glided from the reach of his hospitable arm. The prim aunt was but half and half content. She somehow felt as if somebody had been whipped around the stump for her especial benefit; "she couldn't exactly see how it was, but she *hoped* it was proper."

It would have amused you, Mr. ——, to have seen how amazed the servants were when they saw the chateau so suddenly change hands. M. de Clery resigning his place at the table to the colonel, and all giving of orders. It was a merry time we had, and all was carried forward with commendable gravity, greatly to the edification of the antiquated lady, who presided at the tea-table, with inexpressible majesty.

To-night the wedding takes place. All are in a flutter and excitement. You would think every soul on the place, black and white, was going to be married, instead of the blushing, trembling, trying-to-be-composed-Isabel. Such showing of ivories, on red and black ground, from hall to kitchen, such Ethiopian merriment, such good humor and activity generally, never was before.

One servant runs to the garden to gather bouquets for
the pier-tables and mantles; another gathers ripe fruits;
another wreathes flowers; another goes by laden with
frosted cakes; another flies this way; and another that;
till all know not whether they are on their head or their
heels. For my part, I never was more excited, and don't
believe that if I were going to be married myself, I
should be half so fluttered, and my heart so tumultuous.

Yet with all my joy for Bel, there is mingled inexpressible sadness! To night she ceases to be my beloved
pupil—to night she is no longer her father's, but *another's!* The fond, paternal arms which have encircled
her for so many years in prideful affection, are to be replaced by those of a stranger. Every relation which she
has held to those she has loved, will, to-night, change!
She passes from us to revolve in another orbit, around
another sun than that which has warmed and lighted the
world of her young heart.

Ah, what a risk a young girl runs to marry! What a
lottery is wedlock! How untried, *until he is tried,* the
man for whom she so courageously and confidingly leaves
father, mother, brothers, sisters, home, and all things
familiar and fondly loved! Will *he* be to her *all* these?
Will he weigh down in life's unequal scales *even* weight
with these? But I will not moralize! Blessings be on
the pure head of dear Isabel! She is noble and worthy to
be happy; and may all that heaven loves to shower on its
favored ones fall upon her through life. Be fragrant
flowers about her path, and singing birds around her
steps, and pleasant skies above her. My blessings go
with thee, my prayers surround thee, dearest girl!

And thou, lordly Isidore! strong and manly in thy

princely beauty, take this gentle dove into thy bosom, and shelter it with thy tenderest care! The tendrils of the fragile vine, that thou hast unclasped from the paternal oak, teach kindly to enfold about thy own heart, each sustaining and binding one to the other in an imperishable union!

Good bye, Mr. ——,

KATE.

LETTER XLVII.

Dear Mr. ———:

ISABEL is married! My dear pupil is to-day hailed with the matronly and dignified title of Madame Isidore de Clery. The wedding took place yesterday evening, at 4 o'clock, in the little brick chapel, which nestles in a grove of sycamores, a mile from the chateau.

As I know you men have a great deal of curiosity about everything, though you try and hide it, as well as you can, behind the shadow of your beards, I will give you some account of the ceremony, and how it came off.

The day was as fine as if it were the first day that morning had ever broken upon, the skies were of so "heavenly a blue," as Mrs. Hemans describes the peculiar azure of the cerulean and transparent autumnal atmosphere. There was but one cloud visible, which floated over the east, like a bridal scarf, graceful and undulating, as if borne onward by a company of invisible fairies, by and by to descend and cast it over "the bride of the day." The birds, all of them, blue and gray, orange-colored and scarlet, brown and black, were all on the wing, and singing quite beside themselves, as if they well knew there was a grand holiday.

The little army of sable urchins, that always appertain to a planter's domestic establishment, were arrayed in their "Sunday best," and with great fragments of corn

bread, sweetened with molasses, in their hands, were
tumbling, rolling, somerseting, galloping over the green,
and as generally beside themselves with joy, as the birds
were.   Then all the dogs—Tray, Blanche, Sweetheart,
and old Bonus—seemed to have inhaled exhilarating gas.
Such wagging of tails short, tails long, tails shaggy, and
tails genteel! such extravagant demonstrations of joy
were never before known among the canine family of the
chateau.   Every particular dog seemed to delight himself in chasing his own tail around and around a circle,
and the whole yard seemed to be converted into a sort
of animated orrery, the orbits in which they revolved
having old Bonus for their central sun, and Bonus, like
the sun, made slow and majestic revolutions on his axis,
and, unlike the sun, would once in a while elevate his
toothless jaws, and, opening his huge mouth, send forth
towards the heavens a doleful and horrible howl.   Poor
Bonus! it was his best.   He would have yelped and
laughed, like the younger dogs, if he could; but all that
he could do towards approaching a proper expression of
the common joy were the hoarse, guttural notes, which
from time to time reached the ears of Isabel, and made
her turn pale with apprehension.   "It is an evil omen,
dear Kate," she said, trying to laugh.

"It is old Bonus' best mode age has left him to hail
your bridal day," I answered.   "You should take it as
a compliment from the old dog, Bel.   Hear him! It
does sound wofully doleful, but let it not annoy you.   I
will have him muzzled.   But pardon his unusual excitement, considering the occasion."

But Bel was troubled, and I had to order Pierre to
put a muzzle on the howling patriarch; and no sooner

had he obeyed, than all the little dogs ceased their revolutions after their tails, and came and stood around him, gazing upon him with looks of curiosity and canine sympathy, and evidently were doing their best respectfully to console the old patriarch.

Noon at length passed, and I went in the carriage to the chapel, to see if it were all dressed for the bridal. On the way I met Dr. S——, the clergyman, in his black coat and white stock, jogging along on a big, handsome mule, which was his favorite riding *horse*.

"Good day, Miss Conynghame," he said, bowing with courteous kindness. "You will find the chapel all arranged with taste, by my daughters, and several other maidens. How is Miss Peyton?"

"Well, sir," I answered. "Isidore was wishing to see you, to ask some questions about what he should say and do in the ceremony."

"Yes, yes," he said, smilingly. "Young people feel a little nervous at such times. I must drill him to the tactics for the day. Good-bye."

So he thrust his left heel thrice into the left flank of his mule "Columbus," and went pacing off up the Levee road, at an enormous gait.

I soon came in sight of the chapel. It was prettily and rurally situated, in a fine grove, a hundred and fifty rods from the road. It faced the river, and, with its little cemetery about it, glittering with white marble monuments, formed a picturesque feature in the scenery. But all was beautiful everywhere the eye fell, the whole mile from the chateau to the chapel, and for leagues below it. The river road was bordered with gardens, and villas, and lawns, and groves, on one side, and on the other was the green elevation of the Levee, with the ever-rolling tide of the dark brown flood of the Mississippi, the other side of it; while upon its broad bosom were pleasure boats, and row-boats, crossing this way and that—fishermen suspended motionless above the deep, in their light red canoes, and in the distance, the majestic forms of ascending and descending steamers marked their paths above the trees by long trains of dark, chocolate-colored smoke. All was beautiful and grand, with the splendid sun shining obliquely down on all, tesselating land and water with a mammoth mosaic of light and shadow, copying on the ground, "in shade," the forms of all things it shone upon.

The little chapel is an ancient and very small edifice, brown and ivy-grown, with signs of age in its steep, moss-covered roof, and weather-brown doors. It has two narrow painted windows, on each side, a triple-lancet window above the chancel, and a lower one oddly shaped, surmounted by a red spire, crowned by a cross, which had once been gilt, but was now bronzed by exposure. Two immense sycamores stood before the low Gothic door of the tower, and rising far in the air, spread their broad, white arms protectingly above it; while in their rear grew elms, and a majestic live-oak, that overshadowed the altar-window, and a lowly grave beneath. Shade, repose, and holy seclusion marked the spot. One might forget there, it would seem, that around, though out of sight, rolled the great wicked world, and that sin was but a dream of the past, but for the graves about, and the recollection of the fearful words, "Death came by sin."

Yes, even there, in that sweet, secluded, shut-out spot

of peace, the graves—which added to its solemn beauty, and gave it an air of repose—spoke of *sin!* No—nowhere on earth can we escape the presence of it, or of its memorials : it is only in that bright world, beyond the glittering constellations that pave the floor of the "mansions of God," that peace and sinlessness are known. " *There* shall be no more sin."

All things on earth speak of death. Its sable seal is impressed upon everything below. The flower buds, blooms, diffuses its fragrance, and withers away. This is *death*. The lordly oak decays with age, and falls to mingle with the dust from which it sprung: and *this* is death! The day fades into twilight, and loses itself in the shades of night: and *this* is death! The green spring, which blooms through all the summer, in autumn turns gray and sear, and casts its dry leaves upon the earth: and *this* is death! The new moon fulls, and wanes, and ceases to shine: and *this* is death! The stars leave their spheres, glitter for a brilliant moment, and disappear in darkness: and *this* is death!

The seal of death is truly impressed upon all things beneath the shining sun. " Nothing remains in one stay." Even the nuptial vow before the altar was echoed from the white marble monuments of the dead, that glared into the windows upon the bridal.

But, my dear sir, this is a sad conclusion for a letter upon a " wedding." But it is the reflection of the shadow upon my heart. Isabel's marriage has made me weep more than smile, for she is lost to me, and ere many days elapse, we separate—perhaps forever.

In my next, Mr. ——, I will describe the wedding, for really I have no heart to do it to-day.

LETTER XLIX.

DEAR MR. ———:

IN this letter I will redeem my promise, to write a description of the wedding at Chateau de Clery. We are now—the whole wedding-party—in this city, waiting for the Crescent City, in which we are to embark by way of Havana for New York.

The hour for the nuptials was 4 o'clock on Thursday last. At half past three, the *cortége*, in four open carriages, started from the villa for the chapel, a mile down the river-road. There were outriders, young gentlemen of the vicinity, on prancing steeds, and at least two hundred well-dressed slaves following on foot, and in the greatest glee. The scene, the Levee-road exhibited, was novel and interesting, with its varied population and gay apparel,—for the negro women invariably wore scarlet, or orange-colored, or sky-blue headkerchiefs, and the men sported red or yellow waistcoats.

Isabel and her father, Isidore and myself, rode in the first barouche. The bride looked charmingly, arrayed in the richest white, embroidered crape, with a coronet of pearls upon her brow, and bracelets, and necklace of pearls. Over her head was thrown a veil of the purest Mechlin lace, as superbly elegant as if woven of silver gossamer and lilies interwined. She looked *so* happy, and yet trembled so, that I thought one might compare marrying to being drowned in Cologne-water, or hanged with a perfumed cambric handkerchief! Isidore also looked deadly pale, and then fearfully rubicund, and said, in that short ride of a mile, more silly things than, I dare say, he will say again, if he lives to be as old as Methusaleh. Isabel kept silent, and feared to meet his eyes, which I observed he never took off of her.

How simple going to be married makes a person look! I am glad that I have yet escaped this nonsense, Mr. ———. By the way, the handsome young man whom I saw in New Orleans on our former visit, intends taking passage in the Crescent City to New York. He is certainly a very modest and unassuming person, to be so handsome and wealthy as he is;—and so intelligent and highly educated. If I ever marry, Mr.———, (dear me! what am I writing about? Oh! Isabel's wedding! People can't always keep from having wandering thoughts, though one prays never so hard against them).

As I was saying, Isabel looked very lovely and was very silent. Old Bonus suddenly was heard howling behind, trying, with all the other dogs of the family, to keep up with the carriages. This doleful sound made her look uneasy, and she glanced at me. At this moment, the coachman, in giving his long, new whip a flourish at some tame doves in the road, accidentally curled the green silken lash about the neck of one of them, and, with the backward movement of his hand, it came into the carriage and directly into Isabel's lap! It was as white as the driven snow, with a pink bill, and olive-brown eyes. It was dreadfully frightened, but Isabel, who looked upon it as a good omen against the howlings

of old Bonus, smiled, and drew it to her bosom soothingly,
stroking its cream-pure plumage with her white-gloved
hand. We all pronounced it a "good omen," and Isidore said, "he would have a cage of gold made for it,
put rings on its fingers and bells on its toes, and it should
have music wherever it goes."

We all laughed at this absurd speech of Isidore, knowing that he was too happy in his foolishness to know
what he said, and he had wits enough left to laugh, also
when he reflected a moment.

"Never mind," said the colonel, "it is his wedding
day; and the most sensible men then sometimes play the
fool."

Isidore smilingly bowed to the compliment, and we
drove up to the church, the dove being transferred to the
possession of the footman, who had instructions, both
from Isidore and Bel, to keep it with the tenderest
care, and take it to the chateau after the wedding was
over.

We found the front of the church thronged with the
guests, and in the background, the groups of curious and
happy servants, that mingle in all Southern scenes. But
how shall I describe to you the unlooked for reception
of the bride before the church!

The carriage stopped at the outer gate, fifty yards
from the entrance of the chapel. The gravel path was
lined with twenty-four young girls, dressed in pure white,
each having a wreath of white blossoms in her hair.
Each maiden carried a basket, filled with the *leaves* of
roses—heaped up. At the gate stood two tall, lovely
girls, holding aloft an arch wreathed with flowers in the
most magnificent manner.

Beneath this arch the bride and bridegroom passed, and as they moved onward, the twenty-four maidens preceded them and strewed the way with rose-leaves, so that Isabel's foot touched not the earth, only flowers from the gate to the chapel. Before the door stood two other maidens, holding a chain of flowers, and, as the bride and groom passed between them, they encircled them in one flowery bond. Within the vestibule stood a beautiful girl, who held two crowns in her hands, one of laurel-leaves, the other of orange blossoms; and with them, she preceded the bride and her twenty-four bridesmaids for all these lovely girls were Isabel's voluntary bridesmaids.

Arrived at the chancel, they knelt before the altar, in front of which stood the venerable Dr. ——, in his surplice, the prayer-book open at the place "Matrimony." The bridesmaids knelt, twelve on each side, in brilliant crescents; and above their heads the two tall graceful maidens held the arch of flowers.

The ceremony, that of the Episcopal Church, was deeply impressive; and as the colonel, who was a Presbyterian, said,

"It ties a couple together so fast and firm, that a blacksmith's hammer and anvil couldn't unrivet them."

After the ceremony, the venerable clergyman (and for venerable, very *old* clergymen it is well enough perhaps) kissed the bride; and, before Isidore could do so, I had her sweet cheek; and then her father, and then the four-and-twenty bridesmaids, "all in a row." When Isidore at length got his turn, I thought he would never have taken away his naughty lips from her pretty, ripe mouth. Dear me! what a difference just marrying makes!

I forgot to say that the maiden who held the wreath, crowned the pair as they rose from their knees. The "happy couple" had no sooner left the church, than the maidens commenced a lively chaunt; the slaves crowded round, and showered blessings on "handsome massa and missis;" the birds in the old sycamores sang more noisily and sweetly, and twenty times more lively than ever before; the little dogs scampered and yelled with joy, running under every lady's feet; old Bonus howled most appallingly in his efforts to bark his compliments; and the very horses of the carriage into which Isidore and Isabel stepped, tossed their small heads more proudly, pricked their delicate triangular ears with vanity, and arched their necks with infinite pretension.

They were but a few minutes, the beautiful stag-hoofed bays, in conveying us back to the chateau, at which the whole wedding-party alighted, just as the sun went down in a pearl-shell sky. A superb wedding-dinner, at 7 o'clock, came off, in a magnificently lighted hall, with sixty guests, planters, their wives and daughters, from the neighboring estates, two-thirds of whom were French, which language was almost wholly spoken at the table. In the evening there was a grand ball, in a true Creole style, with a great deal of dancing and imbibing of champagne. A *fusilade* of corks was kept up with great spirit till midnight; arrows were shot from black eyes into exposed hearts; and there was a great taking captive of unsophisticated youth. Every orange-bower echoed softly with the whispers of some stolen away pair; the recesses of the piazza betrayed gentle forms half encircled by a manly arm; and—but I won't tell tales, Mr. ——, for I should tell one on myself—for the elegant young French gentleman, from New Orelans, was at the wedding, and somehow or other I saw a good deal of him in the course of the evening, and we had a charming walk together on the banks of the dark, star-lit river!

Well, the third day after the wedding, we all started for New Orleans, where we are now. We embark to-morrow for New York in the Crescent City. After a brief stay there, M. Isidore de Clery and his fair bride proceed to Europe by the steamer. They have invited me to accompany them, but my mission is done. Isabel is no longer a pupil—at least not mine; how much soever she may be her husband's—(for I believe all young wives are, for the first two or three years, under tutelage, till they learn and fall into their liege lord's "ways")—I shall not undertake to say.

After they leave for Europe, I shall return to my native hills in New Hampshire, and settle down a village old maid of twenty-two, and with the reputation, among the simple folks, of being a great traveler.

Yours truly,
KATE.

LETTER L.

DEAR MR.———:

To-DAY we embark for Havana, that city towards which so many filibustering eyes are at this time directed. The bustle and hurry of packing and getting our trunks on board is over, and there are yet three hours to spare, in which quiet and a pen would be, by contrast with the turmoil of the hotel, a great luxury. But as I wrote you only yesterday, I will use my leisure and my pen for the purpose of writing a letter to my Yankee brother away in the hills of New Hampshire, those glorious snow-capped pillars of the clouds upon whose summits the intellect of Webster has enkindled a blaze that shall light the remotest posterities. Wrapped in his senatorial gown, he has laid down to rest among the mighty dead of the past, himself one of the mightiest of them all.

But my poor pen is too humble and impotent to speak of such a man. His peers only should attempt it, and where, at this day, are they to be looked for!

My little brother, of whom I speak, is my regular correspondent, or rather I write to *him* regularly, and in return I receive certain hieroglyphics in the shape of very crooked pot-hooks and trammels, crossed in various directions by bold, independent strokes, which no doubt show energy, but are quite incomprehensible. In a word, my brother is too small yet to know how to write, but he is too gallant a little fellow to leave a lady's letter unanswered, and so sends me the best fist he can achieve. As it would gratify him very much to have a *printed* letter, Mr. ——, I will just write to him through your columns, and let his sister read it to him when it reaches her.

" MY DEAR LITTLE CHARLEY :—There is some satisfaction and pleasure in writing to you, as I know you *can't write* in return, and that your little heart will dance with gladness to get a letter from your sister Kate all in *print*. You remember, Charley, I said to you, in my last letter from that French gentleman's house, Mr. De Clery, that the blue-birds had built a nest in the piazza. Now I have a story to tell you about these same birds.

" One day the sun was shining very warm, and Isabel wanted to make a grass wreath for the colonel's hat, so we walked out to gather some pretty green grass, and as I walked along what should I spy but a little, *tiny* blue-bird, that was not old enough to walk? There he lay, roasting in the hot sun, and no one near him! Poor thing! he soon would have died, but I took him up, and he nestled down in my hand just like a little baby on its mamma's lap. I thought if dear little Leila, your sister, should fall out of doors, how grateful I should be to any one who would take care of her. So I took the little bird, and laid it in the shade in some nice grass, so that its mother might see it, and know it was alive. I then went away a little distance and watched it. After a while two old blue-birds flew to the tree, and began to flutter and chirp in great trouble, and they then talked to each other, and afterwards I saw them fly down on the grass, and try and coax the poor little bird to follow them.   The father took a worm in his mouth, and hopping down, fed it, and then running away a few steps, chirped and coaxed, but the little thing could not fly. Then the old bird went away, and told his neighbors and friends of his trouble, while the good mother sat by, soothing and comforting her baby.

" In a short time, the old bird came back with troops of friends—yellow-birds, robins, mocking-birds, orioles, sparrows, and black-martins.   They all took the deepest interest in the unhappy little thing, and would fly down, around it, and over it, almost touching it with their soft wings, all the while chirping in the greatest excitement, but the little baby-bird sat quiet and trembling in the little bed of grass I had put it on, its eyes half closed. Then two young blue-birds, which, I guess, were its cousins, went and gave him a pink-colored worm, which it ate as if it were very hungry.   Such singing and talking as were now heard in the tree you have no idea, for new friends kept coming, and the sorrowful parents had to tell each new comer their pitiful tale.   I think, dear Charley, that birds can talk as well as children, though we cannot always understand them.   These birds seemed to say :

" ' Poor birdie ! you are to be pitied.   You are so little, and you have fallen out of your mother's nest, and we can't put you back.   Don't you think you can use your little wings, and fly up ?'

" ' See me,' says the yellow-bird, ' *see how I fly !*' and away it went from bush to bush.

" ' Now,' says the mother, from a little, low stump, ' just hop here.   You can soon do it, and we will get you back to the nest where you fell from.'

"Still the little bird never stirred, only lifting its eyes pitifully, and moved not a feather of its half-grown wings.

"Presently hopped along a ground-sparrow, in his neat gray coat, and said, smartly:

"'Come, little fellow, hop after me! Hop! one—two—three—right into the tree! Hop first, and then you will fly! Come, now—one hop, two hops, three hops, and then away go we!'

"And away went master sparrow, but alone by himself, for birdie moved not an inch.

"Then all the birds got on one tree near by, and held a great confab, and by the way they chattered, they seemed very much distressed that they could not, with all their coaxing, get the little bird up into the nest again. Then I went into the house, and took my little work-basket, and lined it softly with white cotton-wool, and went softly to it and laid birdie down carefully in it, as nice as bird could wish to be, for the night was coming on, and the ground was cold and damp. The birds looked on, and did not fly away, but seemed to know the little fellow had found a friend, and by their chirping, after I had done, they seemed right pleased that it was so well cared for, for I tucked the cotton in all round its sides, leaving only its little head peeping out, just as I have seen you when you were a baby, tucked into your crib under the snow-white sheets.

"When I went into the house, I told the colonel and Mr. De Clery the story. The kind, good French gentleman then got a servant to bring a step-ladder, and went up to the nest, and I reached up to him the wee birdie, to put into it with his three little brothers and sisters, who were all safe in bed, tucked under their mamma's wing. You never saw any thing so happy as the mother looked when the little runaway was nestled again under her feathers, and all the rest of the birds seemed to rejoice with her; they chirped and sang so loudly and noisily. I think the little bird was very glad to get back again into its warm nest, and will be very careful not to fall out again. I suspect he disobeyed his mother, and leaned too far over the edge, just as some little boys stretch their heads out of the window, when their mother tells them not, and then away they fall out. But little boys do not live when they fall, as they strike the hard stones and are killed; and, if that little bird had struck on a stone, instead of the soft grass. he too would have died. When you and little cousin Fred get up to the windows, remember the little blue-bird and be careful not to lean too far out.

"Now, good-bye, dear Charley, and remember the little blue-bird and his fate, and take warning, and I shall be more than repaid for writing the history of his mishap. Be a good little fellow, and kiss your ma, and my little sister, and cousin for me over and over again, and tell mamma that sister Kate will soon be at home, after her three years' absence.

"Your loving sister,

"KATE."

Now, Mr. ——, I know a letter to a child is not the wisest piece of composition that ever was penned, but Charley is a fine little fellow, and may be an editor himself one of these days; so, if you will be so good as to print the letter, I will be very much obliged to you, and send an extra paper containing it to Charley himself. The signal to embark is now heard, and I must end.

Your friend truly,

KATE.

LETTER LI.

DEAR MR. ———:

IF the penmanship of this letter be a little wavy, and old Stephen Hopkins-like, you must attribute it to the unsteadiness of the ship, which goes prancing and bounding across the great green waves like a black war-horse, breathing smoke and fire from his nostrils.

We left New Orleans day before yesterday, with a large number of passengers, and in a few hours were past the Balize on the bosom of this inland sea. The run down the one hundred and twenty miles of river was very interesting. The shores were lined for many leagues with the lemon-colored or snow-white villas of the opulent sugar planters, half hid in groves of oak, elm, and orange trees, the latter bearing still the scathing marks of the last frost, which laid their emerald and golden glories in the dust. It was pleasant, as we steamed along, to see the families upon their piazzas, watching us with spy-glasses or waving kerchiefs (the gentlemen red silk and the ladies cambric) to friends on board, who waved kerchiefs, and hands, and hats, and scarfs back again; the French people sending kisses shoreward from the tips of their fingers—a very graceful feat, and requiring some skill in archery to send them straight at the ruby lips for which they are aimed!

I amused myself, as we steamed down, in watching the fishing canoes of the negroes, and coast luggers, manned by Spaniards and by French Creoles, which were either reposing on the water or moving in all directions across the dark, buff-colored surface. The shores were constantly beautiful, and with bordering roads as level as a church aisle for leagues. The "English Turn" is a remarkable bend, in which the river doubles back upon its course, and runs northwardly for a few miles, and then as abruptly shears off southwardly towards the Gulf, as it ought to do. But great rivers must have their vagaries, Mr. ——, as well as other folks,—and the Father of Waters, considering his age and experience, may well be allowed one in his course through the world. But this one, it is said, sorely puzzled some English boats, once upon a time, ascending the stream; for when they found by compass that they were running south again, they imagined they had only been following an arm of the gulf, and so turned about, and went back the way they had come, and thus saved the then French city of New Orleans from a hostile visit. Hence the name of the place—at least so said a nautical-looking gentleman who stood near Isidore, and his bride, and myself, and kindly volunteered this piece of information; but travelers sometimes get their ears filled with strange tales, hence so many veracious Munchausens printed from year to year by authentic tourists. Dear me! If I should believe one half I *hear* in my travels, I might publish out of the selection a very interesting volume of travels, new edition, with wood-cuts, beautifully colored, and a portrait of Mr. Gulliver, jr. facing the title page.

You may depend, Mr. ——, upon all I tell you as sober

truth, even the tiger story, that some naughty person has been so uncivil as to throw doubt upon. Please tell him never to doubt a lady's word. When we had got about fifty miles below the city, we had passed the ranges of sugar estates, and the shores were in the uncultivated wildness of Nature. They were level to the horizon, and from the wheel-house, one gazed over a vast savannah of eternal green—a sea of foliage—amid which, like a huge, brown, shining serpent, the Mississippi wound and interwound its tortuous course.

It was novel to see the masts of invisible ships ascending and descending far across the green level, a league off, in another portion of the bending river, while at intervals, from the bosom of the savannah, would rise columns of black smoke, indicating the passage of a steamer, the hull of which was invisible below the level of the tree tops. The sun shone magnificently, and the air was like that of May in New England. On board, our party was in fine spirits, and Isabel seemed in her enjoyment of the trip to forget that she was a "married lady," and ought to put away such juvenilities as clapping her hands at anything striking or pretty she saw on the shores. Her extreme beauty, and the noble intelligence in all her face, caused her to be much observed and greatly admired ; while the young gentlemen looked as if they would like to throw the handsome, happy Isidore overboard.

How is it that most men always have a lurking dislike towards a man with a handsome wife? The colonel says it is so, and he ought to know I suppose. Now, if I see a lady with a perfect Adonis of a husband—poh! I don't think of feeling envious of her—not I! I only feel glad

for him—if he looks like a fine-hearted and generous
fellow—that he has got such a handsome wife.   But you
men are never half so amiable as we are.

The French gentleman from New Orleans, is on board,
a passenger, and I think he is one of the most agreeable,
modest young men I ever saw.   He has somehow read
some of my letters, and has taken quite a fancy to talk
with me.   I don't mean to say that he talks love—oh! we
are both too sensible for anything of that kind.   We
talk of literary men and women, of the literature of Germany and Spain, with which he is perfectly familiar; we
talk of nature, of the universe, and its infinite grandeur
and beauty; of the spirit world and of God, the centre
and source of all.   Though raised in the Roman faith,
he is, I have discovered, more of a philosopher than a
Christian, and seems to have a religion of his own, which
is based upon his love of the beautiful and good in the
world.   He says that if we adore nature, we adore God
who made it.   In a word, his piety is intellectual, not
moral; meditative, nothing more; and we have keen ar-
guments upon the faith of the New Testament.   He said
to me to-day,

"I understand God, but I do not understand Jesus.
I do not see the need of Him : He is an incomprehensive
enigma to me."

Ah, me!   I fear I was a poor theologian to argue with
an educated mind like his; but I did my best to show
him the true nature and design of Christ's advent; and
he listened with great attention, and has promised to
read some books I am to lend him.

Before night we came in sight of the Balize, or "Bea-
con," at the outlet of the river, and launched amid the

glories of an autumnal evening, upon the azure bosom
of the Mexican Sea; the gleaming lantern of the Pharos,
at the mouth of the pass, sending after us a long pen-
ciled line of glittering light.

And such a night upon the sea! Oh! how marvellous
the universe above, illimitable and unfathomable in its
splendid stellar mysteries! The delicious breezes blew
off land, and gently ruffled the bosom of the Gulf. There
was a strange light over all the sea, and filling the heavens and the air. There was no moon, and it must have
come from the myriads of bright stars reflected back
from the sea, multiplied in numbers by the reflection.
Earth absorbs the star-rays, but the sea seems to receive
them mirror-like, to *re*-light the sky with. It was as
light as dawn, and yet it was near midnight, as I gazed
from the deck upon the starry infinity. In the south,
Sirius hung like a great electric globe, dazzling the eye
like a lesser sun; Orion walked down the west, sword-
armed and belted, flashing like a warrior; and, above
him, Aldebaran beamed with those mystic rays which
have foretold the fate of empires to astrologers; higher
still hung the Pleiades, like a cluster of grapes, and
scintillating with a splendor truly celestial. I never before saw the stars shine so brightly.

In the north-east, I beheld Arcturus rivaling Sirius
in the south, in stellar magnificence; and around the
solitary Polar Star (in this latitude, low in the north)
paced the Great Bear with majestic strides. Ah! there
is nothing in this world so beautiful as a starry night on
the sea. Heaven above—heaven around—heaven reflected beneath. There is such a transparency in the
atmosphere, that the skies seem within the reach of the

arm. A tranquillity unspeakable reigns in the upper air, and the heart is attracted gently upward, and the thoughts irresistibly dwell on heaven and God, and the great eternity, of which the skies are a visible emblem.

Speaking of the Pleiades, was there ever a seventh? and if not, what becomes of Mrs. Heman's sweet address to the "lost Pleiad?"

I have always loved the stars—loved them more than the moon. When I was in Tennessee, I was walking with a little fellow, of four years, on the piazza, who had just recovered from the measles. He looked up, perhaps for the first time suffered to be up so late, to see the stars, and said to me naively, and as if he had made a discovery,

"Dear Miss Katy, the sties dot the measles!" "No, buddie," cried his sister, two years older, "they are only all *freckled!*"

Both words are descriptive—and the last decidedly poetical. It was the same little girl who, looking out of the window one foggy morning and seeing nothing, said—

"It looks as if there were no world!"

What can be finer than this? If the sayings of children were printed, they would make a book surpassing all others for naturalness, poetry, truth, and originality of ideas.

It is past midnight on the sea!

Good-night,

K. C.

LETTER LII.

Dear Mr. ———:

WITH the queen city of Western Ind just disappearing from sight, and the Castle of the Moro visible like a gray speck against the back-ground of the blue hills of Cuba, I retire to my state-room to collect my thoughts, and write you a few pages of a letter.

The scenery, which is yet visible from the port by which I sit, is beautiful exceedingly. The azure outline of the sunny Isle reclines in majestic repose, like a mighty lion, his form half concealed in the green bosom of the sea. About the frowning Moro floats the smoke of cannon, fired to salute an American ship-of-war, which entered as we passed out.

Around us are the white sails of full thirty vessels, ships, and brigs, and schooners, steering in all ways; though most of them, like ourselves, are just out of Havana, and are stretching away to the northward and eastwardly.

You will expect me, I dare say, to give you some account of what I saw in Havana. But the "letter writers" have filled the papers with everything, until Havana is now as well known to Americans as New York. If I spoke of my brief visit, (for it lasted but a day,) I should write of pure, soft skies of mingled gold and green—of

delightful breezes—of tall cocoa and palm trees like
kings and queens of the vegetable kingdom, standing
gloriously upon hill tops and upon the crests of cliffs, and
waving their superb feathers in the passing breeze—of a
great castle, gray and old, and dreadfully frowning,
hanging from a rock like a giant's eyebrow, with cannon
beneath, flashing like eyes—and long lines of open-
mouthed guns belching forth fire and blue smoke—of
dark visaged soldiers, dressed very much in red, and
fierce with terrific moustaches—of police-boats, boarding
us, filled with blue-coated, black-eyed Spanish officers, as
polite as French dancing-masters in bodily gesticula-
tions, but looking very dislikable and disliking out of
their eyes—of narrow streets—of half-clad Guinea
negroes crowding the pier—of guards and military display—of huge-wheeled volantes and gaudily-harnessed
mules and postillions, with boots a yard high—of small-
sized Spanish generals—of thin-visaged Spanish colonels
—and of great pomp, and show, and trumpets, and guns,
and cigar smoke, and cigar shops, everywhere—&c., &c.

The ladies rode out three on a seat, in open, odd-
looking carriages (volantes), wore no bonnets, but had
their hair superbly dressed, while they were richly attired, as if for a ball. I did not see the "Paseo" outside
of the city, where everybody rides and walks—the
"Battery" of Havana—as we had no time; but I had
pointed out to me the fortified hill "Antares," on which
the devoted Crittenden—who will yet be remembered as
the Pulaski of Cuba—with his fifty companions in arms
met his dreadful fate.   Oh! what a fearful responsibility
in taking away the life of a man which God gave!   God,
on one side, giving; man—little, insignificant man, on

the other side, taking away! To destroy what we cannot replace is a weighty matter. To destroy, when we know not what we destroy, is the act of madness and folly. Who knows what he does when he kills a man? Who knows what life is? I think all killing, whether by the assassin or by the law, equally dreadful. Why kill a man to punish him? It is no punishment to the dead. I do hope that the day is not far distant when humanity will rise superior to this relic of barbarism, "execution of wrong-doers," and that they may be permitted to live in confinement until they die " by the visitation of God."

The city of Havana has a very interesting aspect to a Yankee eye. It is *so* foreign, and unlike any thing we have in the United States. One must certainly go from home to see the world—but at Havana, one not only sees the world, but more, too!

The warlike appearance of the entrance to the harbor reminds me of a pair of bull-dogs, crouching and showing their teeth at all corners. What a grand sight a war-ship is, with its rows of cannon looking so meaningly forth from the yawning port-holes, her tall black masts, and yards, and lofty battle-walls of oak! One passed us two hours ago, and seemed to move as if she were the very empress of the sea. Over her quarter-deck floated the red flag of England, with its double-cross—a fearful-looking ensign when I recalled its associations. Once, to American eyes, that flag was the flag of the foe—and hateful and detested. Against it, Paul Jones the brave hurled his iron shot—and the gallant Preble, and Perry, and Hull, and Bainbridge, fought against and conquered it. As the insignia of conquerors, it waved above the

trees of Boston Common, floated above the Battery in
New York, flashed in the morning sun above the tower
of the old State House in Philadelphia, and even cast its
dread shadow down upon the dome of the Capitol at
Washington. I could not but watch it with interest;
but when I glanced above our own decks, and beheld the
brilliant stars and stripes waving in the upper air in folds
of beauty, I thought, too, of *its* glories, and my heart
bounded with pride, and I could not help mentally apos-
trophizing the red flag of Great Britain in this fashion:
—"Thou hast hitherto ruled the wave, Britannia, but
the day is near when these starry belts shall float, not
only over the seas of the globe, but over its broad continents, and the sceptres of the nations shall do homage
thereto."

Oh! who can predict the glory of our mighty empire
of republics, Mr. ——? ADELANTE! adelante! onward
and forward for ever is its destiny, if its rulers fear God,
and the people are virtuous and true to themselves. It
is said by some one, that history always revolves in circles; at each vast revolution of centuries bringing back
again the same or like scenes, events, circumstances, and
issues. No doubt this is true, and that the mighty circle of American history will bring round its "decay and
fall of the American Republics" in the course of time.
Southey has said finely, but I hope not truly, that "the
Republics of the United States are splendid fragments
out of which future kingdoms and empires are to be
created."

Speaking of the destiny of my country, forces upon
my mind the recollection of Clay, Calhoun, and Webster! Living, they formed a large portion of our glory

and honor as a nation before the nations. Dead, we have fallen before the nations, just so far as their great names, and deeds, and splendid fame raised us. Alas! for my native land! Who can wield the helm of state, or fill the Senate with wisdom needed, surpassing that which Rome or Greece ever knew? Who shall be Webster? who shall be Clay? who shall be Calhoun?—in the next Senate, and the Senates after? Far down the defiles of time the voice of inquiry shall pass, ere echo answers, "Behold him here!"

Has it ever occurred to you, sir, that these three mighty men—these three intellectual "Sons of Anak"—represented, personally, mentally, and in all things national, the three great divisions of the Union? New England and the North were embodied in Webster! the West was personified and incarnate in Clay! the South in Calhoun! Thus, the North, South, and West, were personated by an intellectual incarnation of its own peculiar character in these three men. Each showed the characteristics of the division of the Union from which he sprung. The South could never have produced Webster—nor the North, Calhoun—nor the West, either of them—nor either of these, Clay. This idea is worth reflecting upon, and would be a good theme for some eloquent pen.

But I am making a long letter; and as evening is coming on, and as every body is exclaiming about the Bahama Islands being in sight, I must stop, and go to see these pearls in the belt of old Neptune.

Yours,

KATE.

LETTER LIII.

IRVING HOUSE, NEW YORK.

DEAR Mr. ———:

FROM the date of this letter you see that I am at last in the London of the New World. From Havana to this city, we had a delightful run; the genii of the weather being in the best of humors, and Neptune so fast asleep that we only knew that he was alive by the regular, deep pulsations of his broad oceanic heart.

To my surprise, I learned that when the sea is perfectly calm, and its surface glitters with the polished glaciery of a mirror, the *outline* of its surface is never at rest. So far as waves are concerned, there are at such times *none;* but there is a vast, grand heaving of the sea, as if a mighty, living heart were regularly moving and lifting it from beneath. The whole ocean seems to breathe! and its limitless bosom to rise and fall like that of a sleeping man. And this motion of life has been from "the beginning!" Six thousand years it has moved thus in its mighty pulsations, and its heart will continue to move and beat thus after the pulses of the millions that now live will be silent! What an emblem of eternity—a life of six thousand years!

On our voyage, we passed a great number of white-sailed vessels, some going, as we were, northwardly, and others steering towards the warm South; while others

met us transversly, coming out of Baltimore and Philadelphia, bound oceanward, or else from Europe, seeking
those ports. We also saw three ocean steamers, whose
black hulls and trailing clouds of murky smoke, made
them seem, as they moved among the vessels with snowy
sails, like a sort of demons, saucily intruding into the
company of good angels.

It is very pleasant on the sea, nevertheless, in one of
these same "diabolical" looking steamers. Our cabins
were magnificent, and we enjoyed every shore luxury.
They are "Irving Houses" afloat; and we live pretty
much as persons do at "springs" in a rainy day that
keeps everybody *within* doors. There are books in variety for the literary, pens and ink for the epistolarian,
cards for the play-loving, chess for the quiet, back-gam-
mon for the noisy, sandwiches and ale for the hungry, a
smoking-room for the smoky, sofas and lounges for the
idle and lazily disposed, couches for the sleepy, promenades for the restless, and good dinner and plenty of
champagne for everybody.

Our passengers consisted of about forty people, who
represented no less than nine nations: a Chinese, a Pole,
a Mexican, several Englishmen, several Americans, three
Cuban ladies and one Cuban gentleman, four Frenchmen,
a Spaniard, and a German traveler with a red moustache,
who was called by his valet "Baron." There was also
a handsome young man who was a Jew!

Has the Jew a nation?—if so, then we had ten nations
represented in our cabin. How extraordinary that one
can always tell a Jew! or rather, let me call them "Is-
raelites," which is the honorable name conferred upon
them by Jehovah, and by which they like to be distin-

guished—the term "Jew" being quite as repulsive to them as "Yankee" to the New Englander. That this wonderful people bear the impress of their Oriental origin to this day, after seventeen hundred years of exile and dispersion, is a continued miracle. The Jew of Chatham street, in this city, is, in every lineament, the Jew of Jerusalem of to-day, and of the Jews of the days of Jesus. In what this peculiarity consists, it is difficult to determine precisely, though an artist, who studies closely the characteristics of feature, might be able to explain.

It is chiefly in the style and expression of the eyes I think. It is not because the eye is black—for thousands of Americans have black eyes, which are wholly different in expression from the peculiar Jewish eye. The Israelite eye is very slightly almond-shaped, the upper lid droops over about one-seventh of the iris of the eye, and gives an indescribable expression; while the lashes curve backwards, and have the effect of a fringe, more than any other lashes of any other people's eyes. The expression of the whole eye is sad, yet sparkling—dewy, yet brilliant —a sort of April-sky eye. Dear me! how difficult it is to put ideas into words—to find the words that exactly paint that which we are endeavoring to describe. Words are very important dresses for thoughts. But if you have ever observed the eye of the Children of Israel, you will be able to understand the peculiarity I would describe.

How wonderful the presence of this people among us and other nations! A *people*, yet without a country! a religion, yet without altar, priest, or temple! a God, yet punished by Him with a dispersion of one thousand seven hundred years! Their present state is a living testimony to the truth of the Bible, wherein it is predicted, as well also, their future restoration to their own country!

Perhaps, in connection with them, the fact that their number is still, 3,000,000 of souls, will be deemed not the least extraordinary. This number came out of Egypt with Moses—this number conquered the land of Canaan—this number constituted the nation when David and Solomon were its kings—this number was carried captive to Babylon—and the same number restored again to their land at the re-building of the temple,—the same number were taxed by the Roman conquerors when they brought Judea into subjection—and the same number paid tribute to Cæsar—the same number, subtracting the million which perished at the taking of Jerusalem, were cast out among the nations at the destruction of their city by Titus, in the first century, when commenced "the dispersion among the nations of the earth," which still continues in so remarkable a manner; and the late census of their people shows that their number is still 3,000,000. This, then, is a nation in itself, though a broken one, separated by continents and oceans, fragment from fragment—yet one in feature, one in language, one in religion, one in pursuit, one in all things that have ever given them individuality as a nation. Their number is equal to that of the population of the Thirteen Colonies at the Declaration of our Independence—a number large enough, as our history and the testimony of the world shows, to lay the foundation of a mighty empire!

For what is this remarkable and *careful* preservation of the Israelite? Ever dwelling among the Gentiles— yet never commingling with them, they never lose their

nationality. For what reason this preservation of their
original numbers? Without question to be ready to obey
the command that shall one day fall upon their awaiting
ears: "Up, Israel, and go into thine own land, for I
will make of thee a great nation. The glory of Jerusalem
shall fill the whole earth, and the kings of the earth shall
bring their glory and honor into it, and I will make thy
name glorious among the nations."

And what a spectacle will be presented when they arise
as one man to obey the voice of Jehovah! It will be a
second march, like that forth from Egypt. Every land,
every city, every town, almost every hamlet, where men
trade and do commerce with men, will give up this people
among them—and this "nation of merchants," laden
with gold and silver, the spoils of the Gentiles, shall
direct their way towards Jerusalem, the city of their love
and pride. From every sea-port will sail ships laden
with the sons of Israel, steering for Palestina, and from
every inland town go forth wealthy caravans taking the
road towards the City of David. The present exodus to
California and Australia, for gold of the Gentiles, in a
thousand ships, will give a faint idea only of the mighty
movement that shall draw the eyes of the world when
Israel shall arise in her numbers, and elevating the
standard of the "Lion of the Tribe of Judah," gather
her outcasts beneath its shadow for the march.

And when the land of Canaan shall once more shake
with the tread of returning Israel—when the thousand
cities of her green vales shall be rebuilt—when Jerusalem
shall lift up her head from the dust of centuries, and
dazzle the world's eye with her regenerated splendor—
when the ports of Tyre, Jaffa, Sidon, and Cesarea shall

once more extend their marble piers into the sea to embrace the commerce of the world—then will the Israelite take his true place among the nations, and, from his geographical position, command the avenues of the earth's commerce. At her feet, on the east, the Gulf of Persia and the Euphrates will pour the wealth of India into her lap—on the west, the Mediterranean will enrich her with a thousand fleets—on the north, from the Baltic and Caspian, she will receive the tributes of merchandise—and from the south, from Egypt and the Red Sea, she will lay her hand upon the wealth of Ethiopia and Australia. She will sit enthroned in the true commercial centre of the earth, and, from the vast wealth that her people will carry to her from the nations wherein they have been dispersed, they will be able to control the commercial empire of the whole globe; and this same wealth will enable them to make Judea a land of cities that will rival all those of other lands, and render their country the very heart of luxury, and of the splendor and power of the earth.

And this is no visionary speculation. It is to come to pass in the years that are before us, for prophecy hath spoken the word. It is from many hours' conversation with the youthful Israelite, our fellow-passenger, that I have become so interested in his nation—hence my enthusiasm in the foregoing pages.

Very sincerely, your friend,
KATE.

LETTER LIV.

MY DEAR SIR:

YOU will find me, after having been so near you as New York, receding again from you, and my next letter will be from the bosom of my native hills, in the north of dear New England.   My last was written from New York, where we arrived seven days ago, by the Crescent City, as I have already stated.

The fifth day after reaching that Babel of confusion of tongues and of omnibuses, Isidore and Isabel embarked for England in the steamer.   During their brief stay in New York they visited every place of interest, I being in their company, with the addition of Monsieur de Cressy from New Orleans, who had fairly attached himself—not to *me*—no, no,—but to our party.

It was a sad parting that, between Isabel and myself. I accompanied her on board the steamer, and again took leave of her to return to the city.   I shed more tears that day than ever I did before, and my eyes still over-flow when I reflect that I may never see again the sweet lovely girl, who for three years has been my pupil, and who as a married woman is now fairly launched upon the stormy billows of life.   That she will be happy I have no doubt, for M. de Clery is very devoted, and seems every way worthy of her.   My only consolation is now in the prospect of letters from her, as she has promised to write me every two weeks while she is abroad.   The colonel intended to have accompanied his accomplished daughter, but the day before they sailed he received a letter informing him of the death of his over-seer, and of sickness among the slaves upon his estate in Tennessee.   He accordingly delayed only to see them embark, and the next day, after accompanying me to the New Haven and Boston cars, to bid me good bye, started for the West, sad at heart, with parting from so beloved a child as Isabel had ever been.   When he shook me by the hand to speak "good bye," his eyes filled with tears; and he said,

"Be a good girl, Kate!   Next to Bel, you are dear to me.   Write to me often, for in your letters and Bel's remain my only solace now; and look you, dear Kate, don't fall in love and marry somebody or other that can't appreciate you.   Write and tell me all about your-self, and give my love to your dear good mother, and kiss the little folk for me, and don't forget to give them the presents!"

He then whispered in a low tone, "Don't lose your heart, Kate, to De Cressy."

He then—kissed me, Mr. ——, and I hid my face with my thick veil to conceal my tears; and so I saw the dear good colonel no more!   The best of heaven's beni-sons be upon him!

I was not alone in my journey to Boston.   I was placed in charge of our Member of Congress from Ten-nessee, who, with his lady, was taking a trip to see the Yankee Capital, and purchase a few Yankee notions as curiosities for their children at home.   There was, be-sides, in the cars by chance, M. de Cressy, the handsome young New Orleans gentleman, who was on his way to Montreal. He was very civil and kind, and did all he could to make me cheerful, and pointed out the pretty bits of scenery. The ride to Boston was very dull, all that he could do, and I fear I was very poor company for any one. At length we came in sight of the massive dome of the state-house, crowning the city, to which three years before I had bidden adieu on my way south; and before I could believe the fact, I found myself in the heart of the city, opposite the United States Hotel.

We are at the Revere House, a very elegant establishment, kept in the finest way. Boston is an odd-looking city, with inexpressibly tortuous streets, and narrow; while the habitations usually are the plainest structures that brick, mortar, and stone can erect. The door entrances are, half of them, mere square cuts in the brick, wholly destitute of ornament or grace. The public buildings are very grand and massive: but as a city, Boston is surpassed by New York, Philadelphia, and Baltimore. But as to intellect, for great men, for jurists, statesmen, and princely educated merchants, no city is its peer.

I have visited to-day old Fanueil Hall, through which the mighty voice of Webster has reverberated; also the old State-house, associated with the early Colonial history of the Commonwealth; also the place of the British massacre in State street; the site of the famous "Liberty Tree;" the wharf from which the tea was thrown into the harbor; the house where Washington lived; and Bunker's Hill, upon which the monument of enduring granite rises like a gigantic needle, hundreds of feet into the blue ether; "the first object to catch the beams of the rising sun, which tremble last upon its sky-piercing pinnacle!"

These Boston folk are very aristocratic—more so and more English than other Americans. They are very literary, too, and among them are a large number of scholars of both sexes. The Countess d' Ossoli, so unhappily lost at sea, was a noble specimen of these Boston literary women. German is a great deal studied here, and where it is not studied, its knowledge is affected. No person here is considered at all literary without German! and the possession of this, without much brains, is a passport into the "Book Society."

The Boston people dress very primly—the men much more so than the ladies. The latter have a horrid fashion of bundling up themselves in cloaks and muffs in the winter, that is monstrous. They look exactly like Kamschatka merchants waddling about. I had not seen a muff for so many years that they looked perfectly ludicrous to me. I don't wonder the green Mississippi medical student wrote home that "all the girls in Boston carried young bears in their hands when they went out."

The churches here are very tall and numerous, and nice looking; but none very elegant. Trinity is a gray massive pile of architectural *rock*, imposing and fortress-like. St. Paul's is a Grecian temple; Park Street a spire after the old Puritan pagoda fashion, lessening in a succession of white porticoes, one elevated, *ad infinitum*, upon another, till it ended "into nothing," as the Hon. Mr. Slick once graphically described the same structure.

Every body goes to Church here, and it is wicked to be seen in ·the streets in church hours, on Sunday, ex cept for doctors. Tiding men I believe no longer go about at such times with long rods "seeking whom they may devour," that is, such small game as little boys playing truant from their seats in the pews.

I have not yet had the pleasure of seeing dear good old Mistress Partington. Everybody seems to be well acquainted with her, but nobody seems to know where she "puts up." All I can learn is, that her maiden name was Green. As soon as I ascertain, I intend to call upon her and pay my respects; for such an honor to Boston literature should not be lightly passed by. The good dame I understand is very thin, having lost much of her flesh in trying to master the German language, in order to be admitted into the "Blue-Stocking Club of Literary Ladies," the motto of which is "Nulla Comeina sine Germano." The unhappy old lady, it is rumored, dislocated her jaw the third lesson, in trying to pronounce "Ich," which it is said has contributed to her leanness, from inability to take only liquids.

There is a probability of my leaving to-morrow for home, dear Mr. ——, and when I am once more in the quiet seclusion of my native village, I shall have nothing of interest to give occupation to my pen; for the history of one day there is the history of every day in the year. I shall therefore send you but one letter more, informing you of my safe arrival amid the cherished scenes of my childhood.

Your friend, very truly,

KATE.

LETTER LV.

My Dear Sir:

Once more I find myself seated at the humble old fireside, beneath my mother's roof. Once more I see about me old familiar faces and familiar objects, every one of which carries me back by some association to my childhood. There is the tall mantel-piece, with the same bright brass candlesticks, which have been in use since I remember anything, placed symmetrically one on each end; the mahogany clock in the corner, with a full moon rising above its round visage in blue clouds, and with face and eyes exactly like my dear old grandmother, whose smooth countenance was as round and good-natured as any full moon you ever saw. There are the two silhouette profiles in the jettest black of my venerated father and of my mother, facing each other, over the little looking-glass between the windows; my father with a queue, and my mother with a preposterously short waist and high cap—objects that I used to gaze upon with admiration when a child, only wondering why they were *so* black.

There is also in one corner my little red cricket, on which I used to sit at my mother's knee, and learn the old Puritan catechism, and the dreadful story of John Rogers who was represented in a famous wood-cut, tied to a stake, burning, and his wife and nine children, one at the breast, lamentably standing around, with a wicked soldier stirring up the fire. The same little Primer— torn, dirty, with woful-looking dogs' ears—I now see on my mother's triangular little book-shelf in the corner.

There sits my dear good mother, too, in her low rock- ing-chair, where she has sat, when she sat down at all, since my earliest recollection, with the same three-footed little stand by her side, to hold her thread-box and needle- book, and by night a candle. There she sits now in "*her* corner," as the one opposite used to be called "*pa's* cor- ner," and admiring my New York hat, and wondering "how fashions *do* change!" She is still handsome, with the same pure complexion of rose-red and white; the same mild, motherly, kind eye; the same quiet, serene, almost holy, smile! But I cannot deceive my loving gaze by denying that she has changed since I left her. Her soft brown hair is streaked with silvery threads, and crosswise her forehead I discern lines that Time has en- graven there with his relentless burin. She will be fifty years of age next Christmas, and yet so gentle has been her disposition, so quiet the flow of the river of her daily life, that she looks (excepting the cross lines and silver hair) not more than five-and-thirty. She looks happier now than ever; and once in a while I feel that, as I write, her eyes rest lovingly upon me, with a mother's deep love—while gratitude for my return in safety and health fills her soul heavenwardly.

My little brother and sister are seated on the floor, enjoying the numerous presents which I brought them, and which filled a trunk by themselves; for not only the colonel sent them many, but dearest Isabel and Isidore also. My letter to Charlie, which you printed so kindly, was received by him with uproarious joy. It was the village wonder for a week. All the good dames came in to read, or hear my mother read, a *real* printed letter in the "noospapers" to a little boy.

"*Do* tell!" Well, who'd ever?" "Now only *think!*" "A'n't it curious?" were the exclamations of the good souls.

But if my letter in print created such a sensation among our kind, unsophisticated neighbors, what must have been the sensation produced, think you, sir, at my return home? It would be difficult to describe the scenes of welcoming which I passed through. *Everybody* came to see me, old and young, for a mile about; and for three days I have been holding a *levee;* and have had to do talking enough for a three volume-book of travels, in order to gratify their homely curiosity about the South and the "black slaves," and cotton, and sugar, and oranges growing on trees, and how there was no snow, and the mocking-birds, and everything which was different from what they had in New Hampshire.

" So you've seen fig-trees," said old Deacon Starks, looking at me with great respect. " Zaccheus climbed up into one; and you have seen jist sich a tree? And the Master went to one to get figs, and finding none, curst it. Wáll, I'd liked to a seed somethin' with my own eyes as is in the Bible."

" Do you think the leaves is big enuf for aprons, Miss?" respectfully asked an old maid, a stranger and new-comer, who had been introduced as Miss Tape.

" And you say you see pummegranates on trees," observed the deacon, perseveringly; " well, them are Bible fruits, because as they made the seven candlesticks like pummegranates."

"And does every South woman sleep with a gun under her pillow, to keep from bein' killed by the black slaves in the night? I wouldn't trust myself among the kritters. I never sees one here but I feel skeared, they are so black."

"It's a marcy you ever got back safe," said old grandam Ford, who was as deaf as a door, and never waited for or expected replies.

Every dress I have has been borrowed, and my trunks are empty, the contents going the rounds of the neighborhood. The truth is, I am the lioness of the village just now; and I expect that I shall have as many as a dozen offers before New Year's, for it is reported I have "made my fortin teachin' down South," a pedagogical miracle, Mr. ——, which you can vouch for was never yet done on the earth. All the beaux are getting measured for new suits at little Billy Buttonhole's, the tailor, who has promised to make seven complete suits by Saturday night, when the little Shears knows very well, that with his whole force of one woman and a white-headed lad, Tommy, he can't finish one. One thing is very fortunate, that it is not known here that I am an authoress at all, otherwise I have no doubt that Mr. Font, the village editor of the Democratic paper, "A Voice from the Mountains, and White Hills Democratic Investigator," would be annoying me with the honor of soliciting a contribution for his "Poet's Corner."

This letter ends my literary career, Mr. ——. It has been brief and obscure, but nevertheless has been pleasant to me. Monsieur de Cressy (who chanced to occupy the same car with me as far as the depot near this village, and then continued on to Montreal,) insists that my letters be collected and published in a volume. Dear me! *I* write a bound book? The idea is alarming. I fear my letters, which may do well enough for a newspaper, would make a sorry figure between covers. But they are yours, Mr.——, and if any of your readers (those dear friends whom, having not seen, I esteem and love) express a desire to have them put into a volume, I yield my own views to yours and theirs. If they should merit the honor of appearing in a book-form, I would like, if it were not too presumptuous, to call the book:—

ISABEL;

OR,

THE GOVERNESS AND PUPIL:

A TALE OF THE WEST AND SOUTH.

IN A SERIES OF LETTERS,

BY KATE CONYNGHAM.

I suggest this title because the letters embrace a little *romancero*, as you have perceived from the beginning to the end, of which Isabel (not Kate) is the true heroine.

Good-bye, Mr. ——, I thank you for your condescension in admitting my poor writings into your columns, and I feel grateful to those dear friends who have spoken kindly of them.

With blessings on you all, I remain,

Your sincere friend,

KATE CONYNGHAM.

LETTER LVI.

My dear Mr. ———:

I know not how, patiently, to reply to your saucy letter to me! Indeed, you write as if you fancied that "a correspondent once" is a correspondent forever of your Journal. And then to intimate that my *little* Needle possibly *may* stand in the way of your getting large Needles for your paper! How *did* you find out that I was married? and *how* did you learn where the quiet corner of the South is where I have been for nearly two years a happy wife?

Your letter took me quite by surprise, and my sharp-eyed little Needle, Harry, as I was reading it, snatched it with his fat fist, and nearly tore it into fifty atoms, before I could rescue it from his fierce gripe. It was well for your sake it was not your head, Mr. ———. And you have the coolness to say (I read after I had smoothed and put the pieces together as well as I could)—the cool effrontery to all married dames to say, that you do not think "that my having got married will lessen aught the interest of my 'Needles' if I will kindly contribute another series!" For *that* speech, in pen and ink, you deserve that every married lady should stop your paper. Indeed! My being married has not upset my wits, nor quite made a fool of me, Mr. ———, though if you should sometimes chance to overhear me talk to Harry in a language which has neither dictionary, grammar, nor meaning, you would asseverate that I was for the time a *little* out!

But baby-talk is a young mother's privilege. You men may growl at the cherubs in monosyllables, but you can't talk baby! Harry opens wide and wider his great black eyes at all the pretty things I tell him about "horsey eaty corney; cowey moo-moo-mooey; doggy barkey boo-woo-woo; chickey crowey doo-dle-doo-oo; turkey (which baby calls 'daggins') gobble, gobble, gobble;" and so on, giving extraordinary, and, in my own estimation, very respectable and praiseworthy imitations of the noises of animals, especially the barking of Bruno, our huge mastiff; at which I feel assured I am very successful, for the deep notes always set my little Needle to puckering his woful lips, and ending the imitation by a genuine bellowing of his own; and the cry of a child thirteen months old is no trifling affair, especially if mamma is out of sugar-candy.

In such cases nothing stops the dear little angel of a boy but my blowing tremendous blasts upon a tin trumpet, on the homœopathic principle of like curing like; and his astonishment at the superiority of my tin trumpet performance to that of his own lungs is so great, that he pauses, and gives in—fairly beaten.

These "little Needles knows a heap," as Aunt Chloe, his old black nurse, said to me this morning, as Harry knocked over a little wooley-crowned black baby, Chloe's grandson, which had crawled near him, and began to amuse himself by sucking an India rubber tooth-biter. "Mass Harry make little nigga know hi' place!"

I could not help laughing at the old woman's remark;

at the same time could not but feel its truth.   The white infant on a plantation very early understands, as if by instinct, its superiority; while the African child tacitly recognizes it.   This African element infused into our humanity is a great mystery.

Excuse this blot, Mr. ———; Harry has pulled at my sleeve in trying to walk round my table, and upset my inkstand shockingly.   And while I shake my finger at him, he shakes his wise head from side to side in a cunning way, as much as to say, "No—no, you won't whip baby!" and then he smiles with enchanting confidence, looks up into my face with eyes full of love and fun, and ends by putting up his little mouth for a kiss; for the rogue is conscious that he has done a great mischief, which he so often perpetrates in some shape or other through the day, as to be quite familiar with my reproving exclamation of "Ah! naughty Harry!"

Dear little fellow! I would not lay the tip of my finger upon his beautiful body, in retribution for all the blots, work-baskets turned topsy-turvy, books torn, and all his miscellaneous misdoings generally.   I would not for India's wealth arouse in that dear little heart of his, fear of his mother! There is so little pure affection on this earth, let it be found sacred and unmarred between the young mother and her heaven-given babe !

You should have seen poor little Harry when he was christened, Mr. ———.   He was then ten months old, and a stout, strong, rosy rogue, with a laughing face that seemed to over-run at the bright eyes with the light of joy.

But when the minister took him into his arms, Harry looked up into the stranger's grave face with a stare of

wonder and a slight inkling of fear; the first shadow of
which I ever saw pass across his sunny brow. The deep
voice of the clergyman in its solemn tones seemed to
make a strange impression upon the child's sensitive
nature. All at once he put up his rosy mouth, sweetly
open like a young robin's, and with a half-timid, half-
coaxing look, pulled the minister by his bands, and drew
his face down close to his that he might kiss him! It
was beautiful and touching! The dear, half-frightened
child evidently wanted to conciliate and win his enemy
over by love!

The good man paused in the service, and with a fine
smile bent down to the little open mouth, and kissed him
so affectionately, and then patted his cheek so kindly,
that Harry at once took courage and confidence, clasped
his little fists together, a smile like heaven lighted up
his face, and he nestled in the arms of the clergyman
with a confidence and trustfulness, in singular contrast
with his doubt and timidity a moment before.

Oh! how powerful is love! It is thus that God would
have us lift up our lips to Him in prayer, and thus He
will bend down and bless us, making us happy and at
peace with the assurance of His tender affection. Harry
received the cold baptismal rain upon his curly head
without a change in his smiling face. With "the cross
upon his brow," I received my child back from God's
altar, where I had thus dedicated him; and like a Crusader
bearing the cross, I trust he will be to his life's end a
faithful soldier in the host of the Captain of his salva-
tion!

How can a mother clasp to her heart from week to
week an unconsecrated child, remaining as it was born,

unsanctified by the living waters of the church's fountains? It was the *little* children Jesus took up in His arms; it was the *little* children He commanded mothers to bring to Him! Since the christening of my dear Harry I love him far more, and I lie down with him in peace, knowing that, should he be called from my arms, he was first placed by me in the arms of Jesus, in the bosom of His church.

But to your letter, Mr. ——, desiring me to do you the favor to renew my letters, or "Needles," which you kindly say "were not only well received, but are yet much inquired after!" I am not ungrateful for the kind interest my poor epistles have awakened in the hearts of many, whom I shall never know in this world. For their pleasure, I am ready to begin a new "paper of Needles;" but now, that I am married, these dear readers must expect that my little Needle, "Harry," will figure a good deal in them.

I am living very retired, with but few subjects of interest, other than domestic ones. My house is a paradise of love and peace. My husband seems to think only of me and Harry—to forget *himself for us!* In my next letter I will describe my home in the Sunny South, and, perhaps, I may find subjects enough around me to give some interest to my Needles. But I have first a word to say, Mr. ——, before I fairly consent to be your correspondent. I do not wish you to alter my letters, or, in your masculine dignity, cut out any "baby-talk," or baby affairs, that may be in them; for my nursery is my world just now, and Harry the most important personage in this little world of cradle and

painted toys! Perhaps in that greater nursery, the
WORLD itself, bearded men are quite as much,

"Pleased with a rattle, and tickled with a straw,"

as Harry in the lesser one.

Farewell, Mr. ——,

Your friend,

KATE DE C.

LETTER LVII.

My Dear Mr. ———:

How provoking it is to be mistaken for somebody else besides one's self! Until a few days ago I was not aware that the celebrated Miss Conyngham of England, who traveled through Italy and Austria distributing tracts, for which she was imprisoned, was thought to be *me!* I really hoped that my thousand dear friends who knew me through my pen, had a better opinion of Kate than to suppose she could give herself up to such a fanaticism as marked the wild career of the Miss Conyngham who frightened Austria, and like to have set England and its Emperor by the ears!

It is true, our party went to Europe after Isabel's marriage, where my husband and I joined her, and we were traveling at that time; but while Miss K. Conyngham was in prison in Austria, Miss *Kate* Conyngham as a bride, was climbing Ben Nevis in bonnie Scotland, leaving none but her own *tracks* (French No. 2's) in the heather. This I wish to be distinctly made known; for though I have no objection to be a tract distributor, yet I hope I have common sense enough not to court martyrdom as my namesake seems to have had a fancy to do.

I do not know but that I shall be compelled, Mr. ———, to send you a full account of my travels, to show

you I never was arrested by Austrian police, but in all
my journeyings behaved myself like a nice young wife,
who has no taste for dungeons, except in Mrs. Radcliffes
novels, and who has a perfect horror of a diet of dry
bread and water. If I should send you my travels, I
should write about the wonders of our voyage: the things
I saw in England, what I saw in France, the adventures
we met with in Spain; of our sojourn in Florence and
Naples; our yachting cruise over to Malta, and the
various escapes and marvelous incidents which gave zest
and romance to our tour; and I should be sure and not
forget to tell all about my marriage, and how I saw and
spoke with the Queen by an odd accident, with all sorts
of things besides.

But as I have promised to give you in this letter a
description of my dear home in the South, whence I
write these letters, I will here fulfill my promise, and
leave my "Tour to Europe" for subsequent "Needles."

If you will take the map and find New Orleans, you
will soon learn where I am by following the noble Father
of Waters up as far as Donaldsonville, twenty-five leagues
north from the city. At this pretty French village,
which sleeps half buried in the foliage of China shade
trees and Acacias, is the mouth of the lovely stream
called Bayou La Fourche. A bayou is not, however,
exactly a stream, but a sort of *natural* canal going
laterally from one piece of water to another, uniting
both; as for instance, a stream flowing from the Delaware
straight across to the Schuylkill, would be a bayou. In this
part of the world, where the green land is as level as the
blue sea, these intersecting branches form a net-work of
internal navigation, as if the whole land were cut up into

winding canals. This feature of the country makes it very beautiful, as oaks, and elms, and laurels, fringe their banks; and in their graceful curves they embrace now on one side, and now on the other side, crescent-shaped meadows waving with sugar cane, and dotted with majestic groves like islands of foliage resting on the bosom of the pleasant land.

For thirty miles in the interior this lovely region is level as the sea, and islanded by dark green groves of oak, at intervals of a half mile or mile apart. The boat passes villas inunmerable, whose gardens touch the water, and old French villages half hid in shade, while in the distance, for every half league, tower the turreted sugar-houses, like so many castles.

It would require a highly poetical pen to picture justly the beauty of such a thirty miles trip into the luxurious heart of Louisiana. At length four hours after leaving the Mississippi, appear, over the woodlands of a fine estate belonging to an eminent judge, the spires of Thibodeaux, an old French town, extremely quaint and picturesque. Here the steamer stops to land its passengers, who are mostly French, and will also land you, Mr. ——, if you are on a visit to see me.

Standing on the Levee, you will see the steamer move on again further up the pretty bayou, and still for an hour, when ten miles off, its black pillar of smoking cloud can be discerned, ascending along the horizon like the jet from a far-off volcano. If the steamer you have left continues on her winding course west and south for five hours, she will reach the Gulf of Mexico, and so passing round the Gulf coast re-enter the Mississippi, at its mouth, and so get back to New Orleans, thus compassing, by the aid of river, bayou, and gulf, a complete circle around the city with a radius of a hundred miles. Planters often make use of this mode of communication to ship their sugar to schooners anchored at the Gulf mouth of the bayou. If the English had been acquainted with this inland water route they would have reached New Orleans, surprising it by a descent from *up* river upon it.

It was to Lafitte they made such magnificent offers to pilot them through such a bayou, that of Barataria; which, outlaw as he was, he nobly refused. Parties on excursions from plantations frequently, in their pleasure boats, go down to the Gulf and spend a week or two; living a sort of wild and romantic gipsey life on the green islands that gem the shore of the Gulf. One of these parties I recently joined, and may some time give you a description of its pleasures and famous adventures.

But I will not leave you standing any longer with carpet-bag in hand on the Levee of Thibodeauville, Mr. ——, but direct you up the tree-bordered bayou bank to another bayou, which comes into the larger one close by the chief village street. It is a pleasant walk. You will find little French negroes rather troublesome, asking "mass, for tote he saddle-bag;" but you are an old traveler, sir, and have escaped alive from the landing place at Calais—a dreadful place, and which I shall never forget.

The pretty walk along the water bank will, in five minutes, bring you to the bayou, TERRE BONNE. Its course is at right angles with the bayou LA FOURCHE. THIBODEAUX village stands right in the angle between the two, one being in front, the other on the west side. When you come to this bayou you will see that it looks like a canal, rather than a natural stream. A small bridge crosses it, and leaning over its railing you will see gray-headed old Frenchmen fishing, and boys catching shrimps in nets. Trees bend over them, the water sparkles below, brown creole laundresses are singing as they wash their clothes in the water, and altogether it is a pretty scene. Near the bridge you will see four or five barges or market-boats, with brown lateen sails, and laden with vegetables and fruit. They are manned by two or three sable-skinned slaves, usually by an aged, gray-headed African and an ivory-toothed urchin. They have come that morning some five miles, some fifteen, from their master's plantations, to sell marketing, and make purchases for home. These boats are constantly going up and down this narrow bayou, TERRE BONNE, for it flows through a rich and populous sugar region of the finest sugar estates in the South, and forms their only water communication with the villages and towns.

But you will be likely to see, moored about in the shadows of the bridge, one or more pleasure yachts, in which some members of the family have come up from their plantations, situated where the sky and level horizon meet. Perhaps one of them brought down a freight of lovely girls and their noble dark-eyed mamma, and good-looking aunts, to shop among the treasures of dry-goods, jewelry, and millinery, of the fashionable stores in Thibodeaux; or, perhaps, a plantation household of merry children are come up to the village to see the circus, and especially that wicked, good-for-nothing Dandy Jack ride the pony; the boys of the party going home

again, to turn the lawn into an arena, and all the shaggy
ponies into circus steeds, compelling some plantation
native Dan Rice, jr., to be clown."

Or, perhaps, you will see there the elegant yacht of
the two rich brothers, M. Louis and M. Adolphe ——,
who have come up from their estate, two hours' sail
down the bayou, to pass an afternoon, playing billiards,
and to meet the young girls that happen to be in town
shopping, from the neighboring estates, for on certain
days (usually Saturday, by general consent), everybody
goes to town, and anybody that wants to see anybody is
likely to find everybody on the street. Indeed, for the
surrounding planters, the village is an "Exchange" on
that day, not only for young fellows and maidens to exchange glances, and, perhaps, hearts, but for their papas
to get money for their sugar, or see to its shipment, and
lay in their stores.

If it should be on Saturday that you arrive, Mr. ——,
you would see many a cushioned barge lying in the bayou
waiting for its fair occupants to return to their homes.
Also, you would find no lack of handsome carriages and
caparisoned saddle-horses under the care of servants;
for along the bayou winds, *at one with it* in all its mean-
derings, a summer road, level as a bowling-alley, bordered
by woodland oaks, orange groves, country-seats, flowering gardens, fields of waving cane, bending with a billowy motion to the overpassing wind, like the surface
of an emerald sea. If you wish to reach my home early
in the day, you had best take the road, for the land
route will bring you much sooner. But if you are at
leisure, and enjoy a moonlight sail, you will take one of
the boats. But as they are all private barges, you will be

so kind as to step on board that one which you see is
painted green, with plum-colored cushions and a little
flag pendant over the stern, on which, when the wind
blows out its azure folds, you will read "The Isabel."

That is my yacht, and I know your good taste will
admire it very much, and thank me very kindly, as you
suppose, for sending it for you. But I did not send it,
being ignorant wholly of your visit, Mr. ——; nevertheless, step into it, and tell "Zephyr," which is the
name of the respectable-looking negro pilot you will see
in care of it, that you are Mr. ——! That name will
be a talisman! You will see his eyes shine, and his lips
open wide, with a quiet laugh of internal satisfaction.
"Ah, bress my soul! Missy Kate mity proud to see
Mass' Editum. I berry grad to hab dat honor miself!"
and Zephyr will take off his straw hat and make you as
superb a bow as a king's, nothing less dignified, and he
will then look around upon the other boatmen with an
air of triumph, as much as to say, "Go 'way! Here's
Mass' in dis boat here! De greatest gemman in Philla-
mydellfum! Back you oars, niggas! you got notin' to
do in dis bayou!"

Such would be Zephyr's probable salutation. But he
will not at once set off with you. He will tell you he
expects Massa and the ladies, and in a few minutes you
will see a gentleman and two lovely girls approaching, followed by two servants laden with their purchases. The
gentleman has a very dark, handsome countenance, lighted
up by fine hazel eyes. His complexion is a rich, warm
brown. He wears whiskers, no mustache, but his coal-
black hair flows long and in very slight curl to his shoulders. He wears a huge broad-brimmed sombrero, and a

complete suit of white linen. He has the quiet, self-possessed air and gentle bearing of a man of education and taste. You will see that he is a "gentleman," and you will take a liking to him at sight; he has such a frank smile and so handsomely shows his splendid teeth. Guess who he is, Mr. —? You would not suppose that he was more than seven and twenty, but his intellectual and thoughtful brow gives the appearance of three or four years more. Not to keep you in suspense, as he and his beautiful companions are close upon you, I will introduce you.

"My husband, Mr. —!"

I see you look surprised, and bow imperially, with a little snip of jealousy, for I know you were never reconciled to my getting married! Somehow you editors fancy that your lady contributors are betrothed to you, (editorially,) and that the Journal is their husbands! Dear me! what an idea!

When Zephyr shouts out your name, my husband, who has already known you by reputation, will give you a right down hearty and hospitable welcome; and introduce you to his sweet cousins, who will express their delight at seeing you; and so they will take you prisoner into the boat, and you will have one of the most charming boat rides you ever enjoyed, for five hours at four miles an hour. You will be rowed when the wind lulls, and go under sail when there is any stirring. You will wind round sugar fields, you will pass between gardens, you can talk with the people as they sit on their piazzas, and perhaps pacing along the bank road, will be two or three cavaliers who ride by the side of the boat as it moves on, as they would by a carriage, and chat with you. Night with its stars and silvery moon finds you still moving along amid the bosom of the beautiful level land, which, in the obscurity, with its groups of great trees, seems like a dark sea studded with rounded isles.

Twenty miles from town you reach another bayou, flowing westward. A league farther, mostly among the gigantic trees of a Louisiana forest, and your boat comes suddenly into an open lake, a mile wide and three miles long, a gem of lakes buried in the green heart of this lovely land. A few minutes afterwards you land at a pier near a garden gate; and the next moment I grasp your hand and welcome you to my home.

Yours,
KATE.

LETTER LVIII.

My Dear Mr. ———:

In my last letter I took you, will you nill you, on a journey to my forest-emburied home. Landing you safely upon the pier, at the gate which enters the lawn of live-oaks, that stretches between the house and the beautiful expanse of water in front, I gave you a warm and hospitable welcome. The same welcome I will joyfully extend to any of your friends, who think enough of me to turn out of the way of the great Father of Waters, to seek me out amid the heart of this lovely region of the South.

I will describe to you my home, or rather, as you have been here, (haven't you?) I will imagine you writing a description of what you saw home to your wife in some such sort as follows:

"Dear Wife:—This epistle is written at 'Illewalla,' or 'Lover's Lake,' which is the translation of the soft Indian name. It is the romantic and charming home of my old correspondent, 'Kate, of the Needles.' I cannot, with my prosaic pen, begin to present to your mind's eye the peculiar beauty of this retreat. On my way up from New Orleans to Louisville, I determined to stop and see my fair friend, in her own home; and having obtained the direction, I embarked at New Orleans on board the steamer 'Dr. Beattie,' for Thibodeaux.

"We steamed up the Mississippi to Donaldsonville, eighty miles, and thence diverged into a narrow stream, called Bayou Lafourche. Along this winding water we sailed thirty miles more, through a lovely land of groves, sugar-fields, meadows, villas, and villages. At Thibodeaux, I embarked upon another bayou, crossing the level country, and two hours after the rising moon, reached the abode of Kate, situated picturesquely on the green shore of a small Indian lake, that one can row around in an hour. The shores are fringed by noble trees, and bordered by a belt of the purest sand. Silence and beauty reign there. One fine feature of this land is, that the forests have natural lawns, beneath like the leveled sward of an English park. Hence it is pleasant to roam on foot or ride through them, and one can gallop all around the lake amid the forest trees without checking bridle. This lake is fed by a living fountain in its pellucid depths, and so clear are its waters, that the trout, pickerel, and other angler's finning game, can be seen darting far beneath the surface in glittering lines; while, in the stillness of the night, their splashing leaps at intervals break the starry silence.

"At length, I approached the house. Vases of large size, containing rare West Indian plants, stood on each side of the spacious steps, filling the air with delicious odors. Crossing the noble piazza, which was broad enough for a company of soldiers, fourteen abreast, to march round upon it, I, as the chief guest, was ushered by 'Kate' into a wide and high hall adorned with exquisite statuary and noble pictures. The drawing-room opened into it. This was furnished with light and elegant furniture, chiefly of Indian-cane and rosewood. Everything had that undeniable air of taste and comfort, without garish show, which a poetic mind loves to dwell in.

"I passed a delightful evening. I felt perfectly at home. Col. C., the husband of Kate, seemed to vie with her in making me feel so. The library opened from the drawing-room, and when I say its walls were wholly concealed by carved oaken cases, filled from floor to ceiling with all the wealth of a real scholar's book-treasures in all tongues, you will understand how elegant and tempting a place it is.

"My sleeping apartment opened from this pleasant library, and also looked out upon the lawn. So delightfully situated, I could not resist the temptations which environed me. Instead of retiring, I lingered till midnight in the library, gazing over the rare volumes which then, for the first time, met my eye; and when I resolved to go to bed, a glimpse of the lake through my window, shimmering in starry brightness, chained me to it for half an hour, listening to the leaping fish, the distant notes of a mocking bird, or contemplating the calm beauty of the scene. It was past midnight when I sought my pillow, thankful to the Creator of the world that there lingered yet on earth many such fragments of our Lost Paradise in Eden; and inwardly determining to find soon for myself such a piece of paradise as this one, and under my own oaks, dwell at peace, far from the roar of the drays of commerce, and the din of town.

"Your affectionate husband, (and *all that*.)"

There, Mr. ——, there is your letter!—You certainly describe pretty well, but permit me to say, that I have no objections to your letter, except that you did not say *one word* about my *babe!* Now if you were a bachelor, I could easily account for this silence; for it is, to be sure, beneath the dignity of old bachelors to allude to such subjects. But as you are a married man, and have, I don't know how many, roguish mouths to kiss and feed, your silence is quite shocking. The truth is, Mr. ——, you have never forgiven me for taking a husband; now I can assure you I can write just as well, as when I was a spinster, and perhaps a great deal better; for I shall be able to draw on my husband's fine mind for ideas when my poor brain runs shallow.

Now that you and my dear thousand friends know where I am, and all about my home, I will, for the rest of my "Needles," say little more about it. I only wish you all to know that I am charmingly situated, happy as I deserve to be, and only wish that all for whom I take such pleasure in writing these letters, were *as* happy. HOME is heaven's type. What place this side heaven, besides "home," a home of love and confidence, resembles the Paradise above? Jesus, to express his desolateness, said touchingly, "I have not where to lay my head!"

Among the myriads of elegant and happy homes of earth, not one was His! There can be no more eloquent expression of human desolation than His sad words convey. And to throw a sanctity about earth's homes, (which were not for Him,) He calls heaven a place of "homes." "In my Father's house are many mansions." There we shall not be wanderers through the infinite spaces of the heavens, but shall have *homes*, where we can gather around us all the loved and lost of earth! Let us, therefore, love our earthly homes, and make them as much like heaven, *in love*, as we can, that we may be better fitted for the heavenly habitations that adorn the golden streets of "the city of God." Without love there can be no true *home*, without home no heaven.

A *home* in the country is the loveliest of all earthly ones. One is more with nature? One communes with the stars, the clouds, the trees, the water, the birds! Man was not made for towns! Adam and Eve were created and placed in a garden. Cities are the results of the fall. The first thought of the sinful men after the flood was, " Go to ! Let us build us a city !" If men had remained in a nomadic state, the race would have been far better and happier, that is, if cultivated by arts, letters, and religion. Cities are the effects of sin. There is no greater truism on record than this, that " God made the country, and man made the town."

When I ride out of a morning, instead of threading my way through crowded and noisy streets, I canter with joy and freedom along a beautiful lane two miles long, with waving fields of sugar-cane on either side, and hedges of Cherokee rose bordering the way, and shade trees meeting almost over my head, their low and far-reaching branches sometimes compelling me to stoop to the pummel, as I dart like a deer beneath. Sometimes, indeed, I have a race with a deer or stag, which, caught browsing in the green lane, and seeing me coming, darts off like an arrow, a challenge which "Buccleugh," the name of my handsome brown horse, (though called "Buck" for short,) never refuses to accept, nor his mistress either; but we are always beaten, of course, for the stag seems fairly to fly, and soon loses himself to sight in the shady recesses of his native woodland! Some mornings I rise with the crows, (for they are the earliest risers of all the winged fowls,) and take a canter around my Lake, upon the white, hard sand-belt that enriches it. It is a three miles' complete ride round, and the only sound heard in the stillness is the patter of the hoofs of Buck upon the beach. On the bosom of the Lake float flotillas of wild swans, fleets of black ducks, and the long-legged heron wades far out from the shore to catch his morning's breakfast. As I advance, I awake all the birds, startle the squirrels, and put life into the groves that border the Lake.

Now is not all this far better than any thing a city can give? And then I can ride in what costume I please. I can hang my bonnet on the pommel of the saddle by the strings and gallop bare-headed; and, if I want to sing and shout, I can do so, as loud as I please, and nobody to say a word about "propriety" and "becomingness," and all that primness; nobody but Mr. Echo, who always joins in with me, and shouts as loud as I! A merry and social solitary gentleman of the forest he is, who never ventures into cities, but keeps all his accomplishments for the country; but then he will always have *the last word!*

A favorite termination of my ride is a little mound, green and flower-besprent, about half round the Lake and close to the water. It is called the grave of Norkamah and Anama, two Indian lovers of hostile tribes, who, rather than be separated, walked one moonlight night, their arms folded about one another, slowly out into the Lake, singing as they went, their death-song. This was their doom, to which the chiefs con-

demned them, unless they would cease to love! Cease
to love! How little those stern warriors knew of the
hearts of the young! how little knew what youthful love
is! Cease to love! True love never ceases, Mr. ——!
It is immortal! As well might these chiefs say to the
rose-tree, Cease to blossom! to the full fountain, Cease
to flow! to the stars, Cease to shine! as to the young
heart, " Cease to love!"

So they could not cease to love, Norkamah and Anama, and with hand clasped in hand, and singing, they
walked down in the water. Their song ceased only when
their lips were kissed by the limpid waves that opened
to make within their deep bosom a grave for love!

Hence the Lake is called Illewalla, or Lover's Lake.
Their spirit-forms are said to hover about the place
where, on the banks, their bodies are buried in one
grave, above which the Indian youths and maidens
erected the green mound that now marks the spot. It
is said that on the anniversary of the night of their
death, they are seen coming up out of the water, together, as they went down into it, arrayed in pure white,
with a star upon each brow, and that they are heard to
sing not their mournful death-song, but a song that tells
of never-dying love! and that all the singing birds take
up the sweet refrain from every tree, and that the whole
shore of the Lake is vocal with

" Love, love, never ceases! Oh, love never dies!"

A pretty idea, Mr. ——, and I wish some one of your
talented poetic correspondents would put the words into
a song.   Very truly yours,

KATE.

LETTER LIX.

DEAR MR.———:

THIS evening, about an hour before sundown, I was seated in the library, looking over a port-folio of superb engravings, which my ever attentive husband had brought with him from New Orleans, as a birth-day gift to me; for he is very good to remember every anniversary in any way associated with me, or my happiness. One of these engravings was a large representation of "The Descent from the Cross." While I was sadly contemplating it, and trying to realize that such a scene had actually passed on earth, I heard behind me an exclamation from my old black nurse, "Aunt Winny," "Bress de Lor'! dat am zact image ob de Lor'!"

I looked round and beheld the eyes of the good old African woman fixed steadily and in a sort of adoring wonder upon the pale, majestic face of the pictured Saviour. In her arms struggled little Harry, with hands and feet outstretched to get at the picture, for he has a great fancy for engravings.

"Sure, de young Mass' Harry shall see it! Look, Missis, how he lobe de Saviour 'ready!" and she held the child so near that it put out its little rose-bud mouth and kissed the face of Christ; for the little fellow is full and running over with love, and kisses everything that pleases him, sometimes his toys and bouquets; and once, I caught him kissing with great delight his own little, chubby, dimpled arm.

"De marcy! Did you see dat, Missy Kate!" exclaimed Aunt Winny, with amazement and joy. "Dis chil' good nuff to go rite up to Heaben! who ebber see de like?"

Aunt Winny, with her Nubian-eyed daughter Eda, was a present to me from the colonel, Isabel's father, whom I trust you have not forgotten. Isabel is living near Mobile, on the Lake Ponchartrain, in an elegant villa, in sight of the sea; and as I shall soon pay her a visit, you will hear from her through my gossiping pen. She is a dear, good, old, pious soul, (I mean Aunt Winny,) and looked up to by the rest of the servants as a sort of saint, *en silhouette.*

"Aunt Winny, how came you to say this face in the picture is that of the blessed Lord?" I asked; for I knew that there was a devoutly believed tradition in the colored part of the family that "she had seen Jesus in a vision;" and I presumed her remark had in some way reference to this.

"Coz, Missy Kate, I hab de fabor of habbin see de Lor'," answered Winny, with a solemn air.

"How was it, Aunt Winny, and when?" I asked.

"Ah, bress de baby! If he wos on'y quiet one minute, and not kick so like a young bear, I'd gib you my 'xperience."

"I would like to hear it of all things," I answered. "Florette shall take Harry down to the Lake to see Neptune swim."

So the noisy little fellow was transferred to a pretty, little, dark-eyed, Creole maid of fifteen, who speaks only

French, and which my husband's mother presented to me; and who acts as a sort of sub-nurse to Aunt Winny, Eda being as formerly my tasteful dressing maid.

"Well, Missy Kate, de Lor' is good! I hope to lib to see dat Mass' Harry a grand Bishop. He know'd de Lor' soon as he seed him on de pictur'! Sartain de chil' did. But den babies is so little while ago come from the Lor' up in Heaben, dat dey a'n't had time to forgot him. Dat de reason Mass' Harry 'member him and kiss him!"

"This was a good reason, no doubt, Aunt Winny,", I said; "but now to your experience. While I am finishing this piece of crochet-work, you tell me your whole story."

The dear, good, old woman, whose face is the very picture of human kindness, (done on a black ground,) then clasped her hands in a pious way and rolled her white-orbed eyes solemnly to the ceiling—a queer expression, which little Harry, who imitates everything, has caught to perfection, giving it with the drollest precision. She then heaved a long sigh and began:—

"You sees, Missy Kate, I wos com' from ol' Wirginny to Tennessee, an' I had a heap o' troubles leavin' my folks, an' two childer, an' everybody I know'd way 'hind me. So I felt drefful bad-like, and took on miserable about it; an' after we'd got into Tennessee, and moves to Big Barren Creek, I cried many a night about it; and went 'bout mazin' sorry-like all day, a wishin I was dead and buried!"

"Why, Aunt Winny!"

"Yiss, I did, Missis! I wasn't 'ligious then, and didn't know how to take troubles. Well, one day as I was gwine down to de spring in de hollor, I hearn a voice right ober my head. It say,

"'What you do now? You got nobody care for you in dis wil' country! Whar you get friend but Jesus Christ?'

"Bress de Lor', Missis, it made me look up skeared eenamost to nothin', coz there wasn't no tree nor nothin' it could come from ober head, on'y de open blue sky."

"But *did* you hear a voice?" I asked with a tone expressive of my full scepticism.

"Hear? bress de heart! to be sure, Missy Kate, I did hear de voice plain as I heard you speak dis blessed minute. It sounded like a silver trumpet speakin' to me!"

"Where did you ever hear a silver trumpet speak?" I asked wickedly of the good woman.

"Nebber, Miss, but den I hear read bout 'em in der Bible, and *knows* how I *tink* dey sound."

This was emphatically said, and silenced me.

"This voice I know'd was Master Jesus Christ himself talkin'," resumed the old nurse with dignity. "It made me feel mighty bad, and I determined from dat minnet I'd get deligion! Well, Missy Kate," continued Aunt Winny with a sigh, "I was four long months fightin' hard wid de Debbil."

"What, have you seen that gentleman in black?" I asked of my nurse, with a grave face.

"He any ting but gemman, Missy," answered the African lady with a look of indignation; "and he an't black, but red as a coal ob fire—gist a *fireman* all ober. Seen him, Missis? I seen him fifty times, and onct I had 'mazin' hard fight wid him! He wos use to gib me mortal trouble when I wos tryin' to git deligion, but whensomebber I seen him comin', I sot to prayin' desput, an' he put off wid hesef, for de Debbil can't stan' a prayer, *no how!* He get out ob de way rite off."

"How did he look, Aunt Winny?" I asked.

"Oh, dear sus! I couldn't tell ye, Missy Kate, but he was drefful ugly beas', an' hab cloven hoof and sebben horns, and a switchin' tail. But, bress de goodness! he don't come near me now! He han't troubled me for good many year since I *got* deligion. He *lost* one, when he los' *me!*"

This last sentence was enunciated with great unction and emphasis; and accompanied by a look of pious satisfaction.

"Well, Missy Kate," resumed the old nurse, "I wor four months tryin' hard to git deligion an' I couldn't."

"And why, Aunt Winny?" I asked gravely.

"Because you sees, I wosn't born agen. Nobody can git deligion," she added with reverent looks, "till dey is born ob de Sperit! Don't you 'member, Missis, how ol' Nicodemus was stumped on dat kwestion? But I didn't know bout de Bible den as I does now. Now I can read ebbery word ob it."

"*Read* the Bible, Aunt Winny?" I exclaimed with surprise, knowing she could not read at all.

"To be sures I ken, Missis," answered Winny with dignity. "I reads it by de eye ob faith. Bress your dear heart, Miss Kate, when we is born'd agen, we can read Scriptur' doctrine jis de same wid de eye ob faith as white folk can wid de eye ob de flesh if dey isn't born'd agen. Didn't de 'postles speak languages dey nebber larnt when de Holy Sperit descended 'pon dere heads? Sure dey did, sure. It teach me all de Scriptur' doctrin' since I was born de last time! Well, Missis, I didn't know nothin' bout Scriptur' doctrin' in dem days, poor ignorum black woman, an' so I prayed and kept on prayin', and it didn't do no good, and jiss coz I wosn't baptized."

"And how did you find out you ought to be baptized?" I inquired of the good old lady; and here let me insert that I have taken down this conversation actually as it occurred; and that I record it, not with any irreverence for such a sacred subject, but to show how religion affects the mind of the thoughtful slave. Doubtless thousands of the poor pious negroes can relate experiences and spiritual operations almost precisely similar; hence the deep interest which attaches to a fair recital of one of them, as in the case of Aunt Winny. Nearly all negroes, according to themselves, are converted by some great miracle. This is the test of their being religious with each other. A conversion without a "marvel" in it goes for nothing among them.

"I foun' out in dis way, Missis," answered Aunt Winny. "You see I prayed all de time I could git. I wos in a wild country, and had no 'lations nor kin of no kind dere, and I felt lonely like, and I knew if I could get Jesus Christ to love me, he'd be 'lations, an' friends, and childer, an' ebbery ting to me. So, one day, as I was a-prayin' 'hind a bush, I felt a hand laid rite on de top of my head, dis a-way! (here Aunt Winny suited the action to the word,) and a voice sed, 'Sinner, when are you gwine to be baptize?' Dis was nuff! I seed den wot I wanted! So I went rite off and told the preacher (his name was Petitt, Miss) now as I wanted to be baptize. Well, de branch was up wid a oberflow, and he couldn't do it den; an' when de branch got low he was took sick, and so it was three week afore I could get baptize. But oh, I saw Jesus an' de angels in dem free weeks!" she added clasping her hands in a sort of devotional ecstasy.

"How was that, Aunt Winny?" I asked, laying down the crochet-work I was upon, and looking her with some surprise, full in the face.

"I was comin' home from a neighbor's whar I'd been on a narran'. All at onct I seed de hebben open—"

"Over your head?"

"No, Missis, not 'zactly ober my head, but in de east like—right ober in de east quarter; an' dere I see Jesus Christ standin' up in hebben, wid he arms stretched out, dis a-way," (here she suited the action to the word,) "and smiling on millions ob thousand ob angels, dat were lookin' so happy, an' smilin', and praisin' God; you nebber see any ting so b'u'ful, Missis! an' I see de line *ob mark*, straight as a clo'se line, drawn across ober de hebben to separate de bad folk from de good people ob de Lord."

"Then you saw *bad* folks in heaven, Aunt Winny?"

"No, Missis, not *in* hebben, but kind o' one side like —on de lef' han', an' de line keep 'em back! Oh, no, I seed no *bad* folks dar, dey couldn't come dar at all! dey couldn't get ober *dat* line! De Lor' an' de angels wos all clothe in clouds."

"In clouds, Aunt Winny?"

"Yes, Missis; in de brightest clouds ebber was! Ebbery one ob dem hab a star shining on he forehead, and a splendimos' cloud, like de rainbow, floatin' 'bout der bodies like de robe ob righteousness. Ah, Missis, it wos de handsomest site ebber any body see!"

"Did you see any black folks in heaven among the angels?"

"Plenty, Missis," answered Winny, with emphasis. "But dey wasn't black *dere*,—not one ob 'em, but white as de angels, an' der faces shine like Moses' face, an' *dey* hab shinin' clouds 'bout 'em too! *I* expec' to be dere one ob dese days, bless God! Black? no, no! No *black* skin dere—all white as de light!"

"And have you seen heaven since then, Aunt Winny?"

"Oh, dear sus! Whenebber I feels happy, I can see hebben any time. Eye ob faith see any ting! Don't I know my Saviour? I seen Him too often not to know Him as quick as I knows you, Missy Kate. An' now I tell you 'bout my baptism! Soon as I was put under water I seed hebben agen, an' hear de angels shoutin' ober head, 'Glory!' an' soon as I wos lifted out again, de Sperit lit rite on my shoulder, like a little bird, an' whispered in my ear dese words, and I hearn 'em as plain as I hearn you speak jus now; he say—

"'De whom I am well pleasen!'"

"Said what?" I asked, with amazement, and not fully comprehending the first word.

"'De whom I am well pleasen,' he said to me," answered Winny, with marked decision. "Well, I know'd den I was born agen! I felt happy as I could live! I went home a-shoutin' 'Glory an' amen!' an' I seemed to hear all de birds in de woods singing 'glory' too! De next mornin', when I got up afore day, to go into de field, I saw a light fill de cabin, an' when I look, I see

it shinin' out of my hand. When I look, I see writ inside ob it on de palm de name dat no one can read but
dem as is born agen, an' dey has it writ on dere palms
an' on dere hearts."

"You must be mistaken, Aunt Winny, about seeing
this writing," I said, with manifest incredulity.

"No, I wosn't, Missis! I seed it plain as eber I seed
de writin' you make wid you pen at dat writin' desk,
ony dis wos gold writin'. When I shet my hand it was
dark in de room; when I open de palm, it was bright as
moonlight."

"Could you read the writing, Aunt Winny?"

"Yes, sure and plain enough, by de eye ob faith, an'
soon as I'd read, it just faded out, and went up my arm
an' into my heart, and dere it was 'graven on my heart,
and *dere* it is now, an' Jesus Christ will read it dere at
de last day, and know who am his!"

"But *what* was the writing, Winny?"

"Dat can't be read nor know'd but by *faith*. It's
writ on my heart—dat's all *I* want, Missis," answered
the old black lady, (for a *lady* Winny is, as well as a
pious good soul,) with a solemn air, and an expression
of inward hope and faith.

Some further questions and answers of no particular
moment terminated our conversation, and Aunt Winny,
making me a low courtesy for my kindness in listening
to her, left to look after Harry.

This whole "confession" was so extraordinary—it
came so unexpectedly, from such a staid, quiet old body
as Aunt Winny—it was such a complete and continuous
history of religious experience in an uncultivated mind—
it gives such an insight into the alleged *modus operandi*

of conversion among our African population—it presents, altogether, such a history of mingled truth and error, faith and superstition, that I could not resist penning it down at once for your perusal and reflection.

It was told, too, in the most serious and earnest manner, with such sincerity of look and tone of voice, and such absence of fanaticism or excitement in telling it, that I could not but respect her "faith;" and I have more than once asked myself, "May it not be possible that God has "hid these things from the wise," and "revealed them unto babes?"

The whole "experience" furnishes subject for profound and serious meditation. There can be no doubt of Aunt Winny's *piety.* She is a good Christian woman in all her daily walk and conversation. She would not wilfully speak an untruth. She is not given to "high-flights;" but, on the contrary, is usually staid and sober-minded. How do we know that God does *not* vouchsafe special and peculiar revelations to the ignorant, who cannot *read* His word? May He not, to the poor African, who otherwise cannot know Him, reveal *what to the wiser is concealed?* for the wiser may have access directly to God's word.

These ideas shape themselves into questions under my pen, and questions they must ever here remain; for, in this world, they will find no answers. Not knowing all the "secrets of God," we ought not to despise one of these "little ones," who believe in Him, and "whose angels always behold the face of the Father."

The assertion that negroes are highly imaginative, and that all negroes have similar notions, does not lessen the impression which such an "experience" as the above makes upon the mind ; but, on the contrary, serves to render it more striking. The universal experience, from their *own* confession, that they have such revelations, would lead irresistibly to the conclusion that they *do* have them.

I now hear you, Mr. ——, putting the question point-direct—

"Do *you*, Lady of the Needles, *believe* Aunt Winny saw all and heard all she says that she did?"

Now, my answer to this very inquisitive interrogatory from you, whereby you desire to commit me, you will please find in Proverbs, xxix. 11.

Yours respectfully,
KATE.

LETTER LX.

Dear Mr. ———:

I HAVE been down to the great city since I last wrote you. Leaving my quiet Lake home early in the morning, on Monday last, we reached Thibodeaux village in time to take the steamer down the La Fourche, which brought us in sight of the city just at twilight. It was a superb and bewildering spectacle, as we steamed in the gathering darkness past a thousand lights from ships, and streets, and buildings, and the roar of the city came off to my ears across the water, like the sound of the surge of old Ocean.

For a country lady, like myself, the bustle of the city completely confounded my poor head when, the next day, I walked about shopping, for I had not been beyond the noise of the woodpecker for twenty months. What surprised my rustic head was first the new fashions. I saw the ladies not only did not wear their bonnets still *on* their heads, but on their shoulders, and that the style of walking was to lift the skirts and display an extraordinary surface to the eyes of passers-by of intensely white petticoat! At first, I thought it was accidental in the fair promenader to escape a pond of tobacco saliva on the walk, and I was only assured of its being "the fashion" by a remark from Chloe, my waiting woman, who was walking behind me, dressed in a neat black silk, and a crimson handkerchief tied turban-wise upon her head, the usual head-dress of the colored aristocracy.

"Do see, Missus! Did ebber know de like?"

"What is it, Chloe?"

"All de ladieses holds up de dress mighty high, I tink it fashum, Missy Kate!"

Its prevalence convinced me that Chloe was right. In half an hour more, what should I see but old Chloe stepping along with *her* skirt in her hand, looking as fashionable as any of them? Imitation is one of the most remarkable features of the negro race. They originate nothing, imitation is nature in them and irresistible. How absurd are fashions! How they can destroy delicacy, and even modesty! At the house of M. de S——, where I passed the evening of the day, I saw two young ladies, who wore their dresses so low in front as to make me blush for them, who, a year ago, would have blushed and felt deeply mortified and ashamed to have been caught by a gentleman in this nude dishabille; yet now they were smiling, and talking, and *seemingly* as unconscious of immodesty, as if they were not compelling the venerable Roman Catholic Bishop, whom they were talking with, to drop his eyes to the floor.*

American girls are, I believe, purer and more maidenly delicate than those of any other nation. I pray that

* [Having seen, perhaps, considerably more of the world than our much esteemed correspondent, "Dear Kate" must excuse us if we differ from her in the assumed and sweeping conclusions at which she arrives, and also as to the *utility* of printing all her conclusions in reference to the doubtless innocent votaries of that very changeable, and, to say the least, oftimes most imprudent goddess, Fashion.—*Ed. A. C.*]

they may continue to merit this distinction. But so long as they slavishly copy the fashions set by corrupt courts —by ladies in France and England—and outwardly wear the livery of vice, they will forfeit a pre-eminence that they have hitherto enjoyed. These fashions are usually started by women who have no character; indeed, the *style of the fashion shows how impure the mind was that originated it.* If gentlemen see ladies following such fashions, they have a right to suppose that they are no better in heart than in dress; and have characters of the same value with the inventors of these immodest and un-lady-like fashions. Upon my word, I have no patience with my fair countrywomen, when they let milliners and mantua-makers lead them by the chin at their pleasure. If the Amazonian custom of dropping the dress from the left shoulder entirely to the waist were introduced, I fear that there would be found foolish girls enough to adopt it, throwing delicacy overboard, for the sake of fashion, as they now do in their immodestly low dresses.

And then the way the bonnets have been, and are still worn! hanging almost down the back! What should we think of a gentleman wearing his hat in such a style? But the girls say: " There are no other sorts of bonnets made, or to be had at the milliners' !"

Without doubt they speak the truth. But what right have milliners to compel the wearing of such bonnets that *won't* stay on the head? American ladies put themselves too submissively into the hands of these Mesdames de la Mode! The only way to destroy their bondage, and have liberty and independence, is for the real *haut ton* ladies to form a " Club of Fashions,"—an Academie des Modes—choose a President and twenty-four directors, and appoint committees on the fashions as they come out, and alter, and add, or take away, as their taste dictates, before it receives their seal and signature! They also should have the privilege of originating fashions. As we are politically independent of Europe, let us be so in fashions. Let this "Club of Fashions" be established in the principal cities, with inter-communication continually kept up by interchanging "reports;" let it meet four times a year to decide upon the fashions for each season, both of hats and of dresses, for Winter, Spring, Summer, and Autumn. Let them issue a Gazette of fashions, to be published quarterly; and let the American ladies yield graceful submission to this American Congress of Modes, and so emancipate themselves from the corrupt fashions which great ladies, of doubtful position, in Europe, and milliners of uncultivated taste, force upon the good sense and pure taste of American women. Such a club would give a tone to fashion that it is sadly in want of; and if fashions must rule, let them rule with authority, dignity, and grace, in the hands of our lovely, and modest, and tasteful American dames.

I wish you, my dear Mr. ——, to advocate this measure with all your talent and skill. I fear you will think this *Needle* is rather more keenly pointed than usual; but go into a ball-room and see if it is not merited—that is, if you are not too modest to see.

There is something very amusing in the universality which an absurd fashion speedily attains. On the first day of May, 1854, ladies appeared on Broadway with their bonnets resting on their necks. Three weeks afterwards girls rejoiced in hanging bonnets by their combs in Portland, Maine, and in New Orleans, and in

St. Louis; and in two months more the girls of San Francisco bared the tops of their heads to the sun and rain; and by this time this ridiculous fashion is in vogue at the Sandwich Islands! Twenty years ago there were, in New Orleans, (so an elderly gentleman tells me,) more veils seen in the streets than bonnets; and even now one sees this graceful ornament of the head without the bonnet. Why not drop the bonnet altogether, since it it is of so *little* use, and wear the veil a la Espanola? Ladies would lose nothing and gain every thing in grace and elegance.

Our object in going to the city was to lay in stores and clothing for the plantation, and for my husband to dispose of his sugar, and also to purchase a few luxuries, among which was a rocking horse for Harry, and other playthings. We did not forget all the late publications, some of which I will give you my unasked opinion of, when I have read them.

We are preparing for our pic-nic to the Gulf, to be gone ten days. The party will consist of eleven of us, not including servants. We start the day after to-morrow. The young gentlemen who are to join us are busy in preparing their guns and fishing apparatus. Champagne, and fruits, and delicacies of all sorts, have been ordered for the occasion; and we anticipate a merry and adventurous time. In my next, I will give you an account of our expedition in full. It will be a sort of campaign; as we go provided with tents and every convenience for campaigning out upon the island which we intend to visit.

Your friend,

KATE.

LETTER LXI.

My Dear Mr. ———:

I HAVE opened my writing-desk and taken a nice new pen to give a full description of our excursion to the Gulf. As Harry is in bed fast asleep, and "dreaming about the angels," as Aunt Winny says all babies do, I shall be able to write you an hour without interruption.

It was a busy time with us all, for a day or two before we were ready to start. The gentlemen had to get their fishing lines, dip nets, guns, and rough-weather coats, and hats ready, and we ladies to fit ourselves with plain substantial dresses, chip hats, stout shoes, and all things needful for a campaign so formidable; but the gentlemen were most concerned that we should have plenty of good things to eat, of which department I was unanimously appointed commissary.

Early on Monday morning, two weeks ago, we were roused at day-dawn by the pre-concerted signal—a gun fired off by Scipio Africanus, my husband's chief boatman. We were soon alert, and the whole house was activity and bustle.

"Kate, don't forget the marmalade; and are you sure you put up the guava jelly? and did Dick pack the basket of wines?"

These inquiries were made by my lord and husband,

who, as you may judge, is something of an epicure, in his way.

"Aunt Winny—don't forget the baby!" I screamed, seeing her leaving the house without Harry.

"Lor, bless us, Missus, Mass' Harry done gone down to de boat on de Doctor back!"

"All well aboard," cried my husband as he handed me in last; for I had delayed to give my orders to old Chloe, my housekeeper and factotum, and to tell her that if any of our friends came while we were absent, to entertain them with the best the house held, and try and keep them till we returned; and in order that she might carry out this hospitality, I left her in possession of all my keys.

It was fairly sunrise when we were safely on board the yacht and away from the shore. And a lovely morning it was. The eastern sky looked like a broad lake of gold and green, stretching away into heaven and decked with purple islets of clouds. Not a breath moved the serene air or disturbed the placid surface of the water, over which we glided to the music of the rippling keel and dripping oars of two of our slaves, whose red Saracenic turbans, blue shirts, and white full trowsers, gave them, with their dark faces, a picturesque appearance. And for that matter, we were all picturesque-looking enough, to please the fancy of any romantic school-girl. Our barge itself was a long, graceful, xebec-modeled craft of three tons burthen, a tall tapering mast of the light brown tint of amber, terminating, twenty feet from the deck, in a white top-mast, crowned with a gilt arrow. To a very long pliant yard slung across it, was suspended a broad latteen sail, the shape of a swallow's wing.

Never was a more bird-like looking boat, and when it was racing before a wave-capping wind across the lake, it looked like a swift albatross winging his way to his covert, amid the dark shades of the forest beyond the lake.

In the after part of the boat is a deck that covers an apartment which sailors call a cabin, or cuddy, large enough to hold six persons; if they are very fleshy they will be somewhat pinched for space, and if very tall, they will have to stoop as they sit down. On each side are two berths, and a table in the centre. The whole place is beautifully finished off with rosewood and gilding, rich blue drapery conceals the sleeping places, and a Turkish carpet and lounges add to its comfort. It is a lady's boudoir afloat. Last, not least, it contains a little cupboard, which holds a complete dining set for six, and tea sets to match. The forward part of the xebec has a covered forecastle for the steersman, two oarsmen, and steward. The length of the whole vessel is thirty-two feet. In the space between the forecastle and cabin, are seats cushioned, where we sit by day, as we sail along; and if the sun is hot, an awning is drawn over our heads, but not so low as to prevent us from seeing the scenery on both sides of the boat.

As for our party, it consisted of my husband; two fair Louisiana belles, his cousins, of whom I have before spoken, who are on a visit to us from their father's sugar estate, near New Orleans; and young Dr. Louis de F——, who has just returned from Europe, and lives on the next plantation to ours, and who is very much in love with Mathilde, the eldest cousin, a splendid dark-eyed queen of a girl, who loves him back again with all her warm and generous heart, and what can a lover ask more, Mr. ——? I make the fifth member of our party, and lastly, and the most important personage of all, is Master Harry, my baby. Then there is good old Aunt Winny, whose "experience" I sent you, for I cannot stir without her, as she is Harry's ambulance, and there is Petit Pierre, a slight, golden-skinned, girlish looking lad, who is my page in general, and also waits on table, draws corks for the gentlemen, baits our hooks, and amuses Harry; a miscellaneous useful little fellow, with a smile full of sweetness, and eyes superbly large and expressive, like the eyes of a gazelle. His proper appellation is Pierre, but he is so slight and under sized, that every one calls him "Petit" also, to which name he usually answers.

Now let me sketch you our party, as we move along in the morning sunshine across the blue lake, towards the narrow, tree-shadowed outlet of the bayou, into which we are soon to enter.

At the helm stands the steersman, Uncle Ned, a tall, grave, pious black man, whose true name is Sambo. His visage is jet black, honest and sensible in its expression, and withal humble and deferential. He would lay down his life for his master, who I believe would as readily lay down his life for him. When my husband was a child, Sambo, then a half-broke plantation urchin, carried him in his arms, and became his out-door nurse. They grew up together, and when the child became a man, and the boy-nurse a servant in his family, the attachment, which they naturally manifested, was beautiful. At present Uncle Ned has the responsibility of the whole party, and his grave face shows that he feels it. His whole heart is upon his duty. His head is surmounted by a broad-brimmed white hat, with a streamer of black crape far pendant behind; for Uncle Ned has recently lost his help-meet, Dinah, and shows the depth of his grief by the length of his mourning weed; for your true African re-joices in a craped beaver; and I verily believe the grief at the loss of their kindred is compensated, in a measure, by the idea of "the black craped hat." Uncle Ned has gray, military cut whiskers, and a white cravat closely tied about his neck.

Genteel negroes like Uncle Ned affect "white ties." He wore a black coat and white vest, and snuff-brown linsey-wolsey trowsers, and looked the character he was on the plantation of a Sunday, "a colored clergyman." Yet he was a good coachman, a better boatman, as well as a true gentleman, at heart and in sentiment. Old Ned's only dissipation was his pipe. This he never was without, out of doors, if "de ladies would let him smoke de pipe in dere presence."

The two girls, Mathilde and Marie, were dressed in closely-fitting spencers, which set off their superb figures splendidly, and made the elder, who is just nineteen, look like a Southern Di Vernon; and her dark tresses, stealing out beneath her wide straw hat, laughed in the winds. Marie was a fair blonde, with an eye of blue, like rich turquoise set in pearl, or to use a soft and ten-der simile, "like a violet cupped in a lily." The elder was Juno, the younger Euphrosyne. One captured hearts by the lightning of her glorious sunrise-looking eyes; the latter won them with gentle influences, as the moon attracts towards itself the beauteous lake, that re-flects its image. The two lovely sisters, in their flapping

Panama hats, and gray pic-nic habits, and jaunty, half-gipsy air, looked romantic enough for Mr. Alexander Smith; who is the moon's own bard, and who, had there been no moon, no poet had been.

The handsome Louis, who stands amidships, pointing out to Marie a flight of birds, is dressed like a buccaneer, and I believe intended to be Mr. Lafitte for the present expedition only, inasmuch as we were bound to the neighborhood of this celebrated sea-king's island of Barataria; nay, we expected to pay it a visit in our absence. Louis has a fine face, but its beauty all comes from his heart, which is one of the noblest, and kindest, and manliest that ever beat. His features are not regularly formed, and his forehead is too low, but when one knows him well, and knows what a pure soul he possesses, what superior intellect, and commanding talent, one loves and honors him without any reservations.

Then, there stands my husband! Of course he is not to be paralleled or compared. He may be ugly; but if he is, I don't know it, for my love throws a golden veil over every defect, and illumines every feature with the light of beauty, not beauty such as woman has, but the beauty of a man—who stands out commandingly the image of his Maker.

I say that my husband, Mr. ——, *may* be ugly, but to me he is perfect. His hazel eyes beam on me only with love and pride, and husbandly tenderness; his mouth speaks to me only the kindest and most pleasurable things, his voice, when he turns to address me, changes its tone from that he gives to others, and falls upon my ear like some mysterious music, that thrills and moves the heart, the dear listener knows not how or why. The voice *may* be harsh, the mouth unhandsome, the lips without regularity, the eyes without beauty, but to *me* they challenge comparison with the eyes, lips, and voice of Apollo, or any admirable Crichton of them all.

There! my heart's confession is made, Mr. ——! You see I am not ashamed of my good husband, and I don't intend to be; on the contrary, I mean all my readers shall think of (I was going to say *love*) him as well as I do. As to loving him (I mean the fair girls who read this), I would simply hint that I have a monopoly in him, and don't intend any body shall love him, or look at him even sidewise, but me. Even the superb Mathilde, cousin as she is, sometimes makes me feel like pulling her ears, when I have seen her *look* as if she loved him *more* than a cousin ought to love a cousin! Harry I will not describe—he couldn't *be* described! Imagine a perfect Cupid, (I mean, of course, sir, with a pretty plaid frock on, tiny gaiter boots on his charming feet, a Scotch cap and feather set aside on his curly head, black eyes full of fun, rosy cheeks, chubby arms, chubby hands, chubby bare legs, and lips like the rosy lining of twin sea-shells,) and you have " Mass' Harry," and with him the whole " ship's company."

We moved delightfully along the shores of the tree-fringed lake for a half mile, when visible right ahead, was the opening of the bayou, for which we were steering. We soon entered, all at once, losing sight of the sun-bright lake of my villa-home. The bayou was about as wide as Chestnut street, with just room for meeting boats to pass. For the first mile we moved on beneath mammoth trunks of old live-oak trees, that threw their gnarled arms far across from side to side. Wild vines, gay with strange and beautiful flowers, grew close to the water, and winding their serpent-like folds about the trees, climbed up and along the branches, and formed a thousand festoons from bank to bank, beneath which we glided, and using them to propel us onward, instead of the oars, we darted swiftly beneath, leaving far astern a wake of gurgling waves, agitated by our keel. A deer, startled by our shouts of laughter, (for people in the woods somehow are always more noisy than when at home,) plunged into the stream, and after a dozen of vigorous strokes with his hoofs, dashing the water high above his antlers as he swam, landed on the wild-wood side of the bayou. Louis raised his rifle with a true hunter's instinct. Mathilde, with a "No, Louis, don't! Let the poor fellow live and enjoy the freedom of his forest home, gently laid her hand upon the gun and disarmed him.

"It is your deer, Mademoiselle Mathilde," he said, gallantly," "and when I return I will ensnare him and present him to you alive."

At this moment, we emerged from the entangled forest, and on each side extended the level sugar fields a mile broad, waving like the "green and laughing corn," or rather looking like an undulating emeraldine sea. In the distance ahead, rose the lofty towers of the sugar-house, or "sucrérie," and amid a grove of tropical shade trees, half a mile to the right, were visible the roof and cupola of the mansion, where we were to receive an accession of two more boats to our party.

In an hour after leaving the lake, we reached this luxurious abode of refinement and wealth, were welcomed by a happy group upon the green bank, and escorted with great triumph and rejoicing to the house where breakfast was waiting for us; for it was in *carte* of the day that we were to *dejeuner* here. By nine o'clock we were once more on board, and with the addition of two more ladies and three gentlemen, we voyaged a-down the bayou, a merry fleet, steering the whole forenoon amid sugar fields that kissed the wave, or past villas where we were cheered by groups of friends, who followed us as far as they could be heard, with "Bon voyage, bon voyage, au revoir!" while little Harry, held high in air, by proud Aunt Winny, would prettily smack his fat hands and toss an imaginary kiss, (an accomplishment which his father had taught the little rogue,) back to the joyous throng. The remainder of my narrative, I will defer, Mr. ——, for another letter. Until then, adieu.

Yours respectfully,
KATE.

LETTER LXII.

My Dear Mr. ———— :

You know when one sits down, pen in hand, and with kindly feelings, to write about what one has seen, and wishes one's readers to see with the same eyes, that the subject grows, enlarges, expands under the ready pen, until what was meant for a letter only, becomes a book. So, under my pen, enlarges my narrative of our excursion, which I expected to stitch up for you with one needle full of thread, but which I see will take two, and perhaps three of them. A lady with a talkative pen is quite as much a horror, I confess, as one with a talkative tongue.

My last Needle left our little fleet of pleasure-barges winding our pleasant way down the bayou Terre Bonne, southwardly, towards the pretty village of Thibodeaux, which please turn to your map and find in the bosom of the delightful sugar region of Louisiana. It was a bright autumnal day, and we all gave full rein to our wild spirits, awaking the echoes of the groves, past which we sailed, and causing the groups of slaves in the fields to pause, leaning on their long-handled hoes, and gaze upon us with shining eyes and glittering teeth; while Uncle Ned at the helm drew himself up in the presence of these "colored folk," with all the dignity which his responsibility as helmsman of our yacht entitled him to assume before barbarian "field niggers," as the aristocratic house-servant terms the cultivators of the soil.

At noon, we reached the estate of a friend; where we landed and dined beneath the trees on the bank; the hospitable family, seeing we would not go in, added all sorts of luxuries, which half-a-dozen slaves brought out to us upon waiters. It was sunset when we reached the outlet of the bayou at the village of Thibodeaux; but as the moon rose full and glorious before darkness could begin to draw its starry veil over the sky, we resolved to continue on our way and bivouac for the night at the plantation of M. M——, a relative of my husband's, who had been notified of our coming down upon him "in force." So we left the narrow bayou, passing beneath the old French bridge that crossed it at its mouth, near the end of the village street, and pulled out into the broader and deeper current of the Bayou Lafourche, on which the village stands. There was a soft haze settled over the town, above which the spires caught the moon-beams like minarets of silver.

When our whole fleet had got out into the broader waters of Lafourche, there was a council of war held by the gentlemen of the several boats, and it resulted in my husband being chosen Admiral of the Fleet; and our boat was therefore made the flag-ship, out of compliment to me, a grace at their hands, which I here publicly acknowledge. We, therefore took the lead, and the other four boats followed joyously astern; for besides the two yachts which joined us *en voyage*, we had two "transports," boats containing our tents, nets, fishing-poles, guns, provisions, and dogs, and every possible extra, that a campaign of ten days might require.

As the town, with its sparkling window-lights, and with here and there the distant music of a skillfully thrummed guitar, receded, we drew near the Cathedral church, about half-a-mile below the village. Its bell was heavily tolling across the water, and we saw a procession coming forth with torchlights; and winding its way beneath the trees towards the cemetery. The solemn chanting of the service of the dead reached our ears when we had gone far down the bayou, and, what with the hour and associations, it all deeply impressed us. We learned, on our return, that it was the funeral of a young nun who had died the week previous, at the Convent du Sacré Cœur, and her body having arrived late at her former home, had been the same night conveyed beneath the pure moonbeams to its last resting place by the church in which she had, as an infant, received holy baptism.

There is something, to my imagination, extremely attractive in the æsthetics of the Roman Catholic religion; but not to my reason nor to my heart. I could never bend my knee to the "Virgin Mother," nor use words of prayer to the "holy saints" asking their intercession, while there stands in my Protestant Bible these words: "There is one intercessor between God and man—the man Christ Jesus." Theirs is a romantic, imaginative, and touchingly superstitious faith, and is only received fully by an imaginative people.

Americans can never be Romanized. They are too practical—too *un*imaginative, too little disposed to devotion at all, to commit themselves voluntarily to a faith that is ever genuflecting, ever going through the externals of worship. A people who find it hard to ac-

knowledge and pray to one God will hardly pray to a
thousand.

So the Pope and his council have decreed that the
mother of Jesus was a Divine Person, and therefore deny
that she is a woman! What a monstrous doctrine! and
it is decreed, too, by the papal "bull," that it is heresy
to deny it. Do you not remember a verse in the First
Epistle of John, chapter fourth, second and third verses;
also the Second Epistle of John, seventh verse, which
says, "For many deceivers are entered into the world,
who confess *not* that Jesus Christ is come in the *flesh*.
This is a deceiver and Antichrist?" Now, if Jesus'
mother was a *divine* and sinless being, she was not a
"woman." But the prophecy was that Christ should be
the seed of the woman—born of a woman. If Mary was
not a woman, (but a sort of divine goddess as the Papal
decree makes her,) then Jesus was not born of woman;
and hence he is *not* the Christ; as he was not that "*man*
Christ Jesus" foretold; for he could only be *man* by
being born of a woman. The establishing, therefore, the
divinity of Mary, destroys the manhood of Jesus, and
ignores his having "come in the flesh." But this is a
question for theologians, yet it is one that every Christian may freely discuss.

Our voyage down the bayou under the splendor of the
gorgeous southern moon was delightful. Every half
mile we glided past a villa either on one hand or
the other. At one place we were serenaded, in passing,
by a party in a garden, who sang superbly and with fine
effect :—

> "The bonny boat with yielding sway
>   Rocks lightly on the tide," &c.

The gentlemen and ladies of our party responded by singing in full chorus the Canadian boat song :—

> " Row, brothers, row, the stream runs fast,
> The rapids are near, the daylight's past."

About nine o'clock we came in sight of the plantation of M. M——, my husband's relative. We saw lights moving upon the landing-place, for we had signalled our near approach by a gun fired by Louis de F——.

Here we were welcomed with great enthusiasm, and when Monsieur M. saw our large force and formidable armament (for we had not less than seventeen guns of all sorts and sizes), he playfully made grave objections to our landing, asseverating that we had, no doubt, come to invade and, peradventure, conquer his domain; but being assured that we were bound only against piscatorial foes, he suffered us to debark, at the same time hinting that we were evidently on a secret Cuban expedition; and your admiral (my husband) will be emperor, and "your fair lady Kate," he added, as he assisted me to the pier, "will be empress. I much fear I shall be called to account by my governor for aiding and abetting a foreign invasion if I harbor you to-night."

We passed the night at this princely home of one of the best hearted southern gentlemen it was ever my lot to meet; and resisting his pressing appeals to us to remain another day and night, we took our departure, taking Monsieur M. with us; "for," he said, "if he could not detain such good company, the good company should retain him."

We arrived, at nine o'clock at the estate of a New Orleans gentleman, who was a non-resident. In his beautiful garden, which the waters of La Fourche have, we spread our morning meal, and never a pic-nic gathering had so mirthful a repast. After breakfast we re-embarked, and, under the cheering command to the rowers, "Give way heartily, boys!" we moved rapidly down the bayou, the wide savannahs of the level sugar fields stretching away on either hand to the horizon; the uniformity of the immense surface of waving cane, relieved here and there by clumps, or by single live oaks, by groves concealing residences, and by the tall "Begasse chimneys," of the sugar houses, which made these huge brick buildings look like convents.

About eleven o'clock a pleasant wind arose. I could see its effects, as I stood upon the deck of the yacht, a mile before we felt it, in the sea-like motion which it communicated to the tall tops of the sugar cane, which heaved and swelled beneath its invisible power like a green, billowy sea.

To a northern eye, the best idea of a field of sugar-cane here, will be conveyed by imagining a perfectly level country, leagues in extent, without a fence, covered with corn, just as it is ready "to tassel," and if he imagines through this vast domain of level savannah a river, half the breadth of the Schuylkill, flowing almost level with the land, with here and there a group of trees dispersed over the green extent, and every mile or two a villa and a tall, tower-like chimney and sugar-house rising near it, a good idea of the country, through which the "La Fourche" winds will be obtained.

When the breeze came to us we hoisted sail, and our black oarsmen rested. Under the wing-like canvas our little fleet flew cheerily onward; and as we drew nearer the Gulf the country became less picturesque, the sugar fields less numerous, and the abodes of planters farther and farther apart.   At length we came, about two in the afternoon, to the *last tree* that stands on the coast between it and the Gulf, twelve miles distant.   This tree was a venerable live oak, and seemed to have stood there, the monarch of the savannah, for centuries.   Its huge arms were broad enough to shelter five hundred men. Its situation was "sublimely lonely and solitarily grand," as one of the young gentlemen of our party, who writes poetry, said.

As we came near the oak, we startled two deer from beneath it, which, after surveying us for an instant, took to flight, and were lost to the eye in a moment in the high gulf grass that grew close up to the tree, which stood on a little island of its own, for around it was the saline marsh that now took the place of the cultivated sugar fields, which we had left behind.

It was decided by the "Admiral" that we should moor our fleet beneath the tree and here dine.

You should have seen the bustle of preparation, Mr. ———.   Our party consisted, all together, of descendants of Japhet, fourteen, and of descendants of Ham, nine, in all twenty-three persons; for to such a size had we increased by volunteers from the estates we took in our way.   We were all friends, and knew one another well, so that, I verily believe, everybody called everybody (married or not) by their first name.   Dignified married lady as I am, they every soul called me "Kate," as if I had been everybody's sister, or at least "cousin."

While we were dining at tables beneath the tree, with servants in waiting, and every thing as nice and recherché

as if we were in a dining-room, Petit Pierre, who was
drawing a cork from a bottle of Chateau Margaux, suddenly uttered a formidable screech, dropped the bottle,
and fled yelling for the tree! We ladies, of course, were
all alarmed, and the brave gentlemen sprung to their
feet; when Uncle Ned, from the boat, called out,

"Big alligator, master!"

True enough, not fifty feet distant, a monstrous alligator was seen swimming across the bayou, just above
us, to our side of it. Guns were in requisition! Dogs
were alert—and for a minute or more all was intense
excitement. Bang, bang, crack, bung, ping! went off
all sorts of fire-arms; but the king of the marshes did not
wait to contend matters, for he no sooner discovered into
what a snare he had inadvertently put his royalty, than
he made a queer noise like an elephant when teased,
and dived down out of sight. Close watch, with guns at
aim, was kept for his reappearance, but we saw him no
more. Petit returned from the tree to terra firma and
finished drawing the cork, and we resumed our meal,
which was interpolated by alligator stories, told by the
gentlemen.

After we had well dined, about four o'clock, we re-embarked. The wind was fair and free, and our five boats, all
under snowy canvas, went careering onward towards the
Gulf.

In about half-an-hour one of the young gentlemen in
another yacht, who had climbed the mast, called out,

"Gulf, ho!"

At this sound we were all upon our feet, for some of us
had been taking siestas in our berths; but on going out
all I could see was the tall sea-grass spreading for miles

around us; and even the old oak being no longer visible; nothing but an ocean of brownish green grass eight feet high, that tossed in the wind like a wave-moving sea. But in a little while a bend in the bayou opened the Gulf full before us, and with clapping hands and exclamations of delight at its broad blue expanse and green islands, we hailed the welcome sight.

But another letter must take up my narrative. Till then, farewell.

Truly your friend,

KATE.

LETTER LXIII.

My Dear Mr. ———:

The kind compliments which the newspapers and some
of your correspondents have paid my poor "Needles,"
not only encourage me and inspire me to try and deserve
their commendations, but make me grateful. Nothing
makes me so happy as to make happiness for others; and
if the perusal of one of my letters has beguiled a half
hour of any one, I am well repaid. The greatest reward
of a writer is the happiness to which his pen has contributed.

To be sure, he must be paid in money to buy ink, and
pens, and paper, but those are to enable him to write;
and money, also, is a very nice thing when one wants a
new pair of shoes, or a shawl in cold weather, or bread
and butter, and tea. True, authors are not so much
paid for what they write, as that they receive *means* to
enable them to write! The writing is given, but the
bodily strength, the ink and paper, the table to write on,
the floor on which the table stands, the roof over head,
the window or lamp for light, the fire to keep him warm,
his breakfasts, dinners, suppers,—the editor and publisher gives him money only to pay for these; supplies
the fuel " to keep up the steam," to use a plain American
phrase.

But I will not stray away from the proper subject of

this letter, which is a continuation of the journal of our romantic expedition to the Gulf and its green islands.

My last closed just as our fleet of pleasure yachts came in sight of the broad horizon of the Mexican Gulf, on the afternoon of the second day after leaving Lake Illiwalla in the interior, our course by the bayous having been nearly one hundred miles altogether.

The sight of the gulf was hailed by us with shouts. We had to go yet six miles before debouching into it from the bayou, which glided like a tortuously moving and shining serpent between the borders of tall reddish grass. This grass was the size of a quill and seven feet tall, and grew not of visible soil, but out of mud under the water.

As far as the eye could extend there was one vast plain of grass, level as the sea; but there was not anywhere visible a foot of land, not a place where Noah's dove could rest its poor little weary feet.

The sable oarsmen now pulled cheerily to their oars, as we intended to gain an island a league off the coast, which was visible like a pale green streak of cloud, asleep on the horizon. Near this island, as we approached the mouth of the bayou, we discovered at anchor a small sloop, which the gentlemen said was waiting for a wind to run up the bayou we were in, to load with sugar from the plantations, and take it down and round to New Orleans, for many of the planters send their staple to market in this way rather than up the bayou, past Thibodeaux, and so across into the Mississippi and to New Orleans. This present mode had the advantage both of economy and security.

When within a mile of the mouth, a breeze caught our

little flags, and we hoisted sail and gave our rowers rest, though they showed no fatigue. Indeed, the endurance of the African slaves is marvelous. They will row hour after hour, and at the last are as brisk and lively, and sing their songs as cheerily as in the outset. There seems *no* tire to a negro; no end to his good humor when he is on a party of this kind, for they enjoy it quite as much as "massa and missus." Such delightful, willing, apprehending, anticipating-your-want servants, never were as this race of bondsmen. They seem in servitude to be where they wish to be, for they are by nature dependent, and they love to look up to some one who "takes the responsibility;" and for this responsibility they are ready to give in return their labor and life-service. Certainly *free* negroes are the worst possible servants, and for want of healthy authority, and some stronger head to think and do for them, they become very degraded. I have just seen a book called "A South side View of slavery," by Rev. Dr. Adams, of Boston, which every man and woman north ought to read. It is the only reply that has been made to "Uncle Tom's Cabin," lately published without intending to be a reply to it. If our northern friends would read this book, they would leave slavery to the south and to the Providence of God for the final adjustment, of all vexed questions it has given rise to. The south feels the responsibility as profoundly as the north. The Christians, and wise, and thinking men in the south have this subject at heart, and will be the instruments (not the northern abolitionists) chosen of God for the amelioration and final emancipation of the race, if God ordain that they shall ever be free. But every step made by the north to

coerce, is naturally met by southerners (who are quite as
humane as gentlemen, and gentle as ladies, as the northerners,) with barriers and defences, and more formidable
entrenchments thrown up about their institutions. These,
Mr. ——, are the views of a northern woman, who has
dwelt long enough in the south to see things as they are.
Abide God's time! Wait for the Moses of the Lord God
of Hosts! All the efforts of supposable philanthropists
in Egypt could not have hastened one day sooner the
deliverance from bondage of Israel; nay, the first movement towards it of Moses himself, only caused Pharaoh
to heap additional burdens upon them. Such has been
the result of the mere *human* movement of the northern
fanatics; they have taken away the straw from the laborers, and made firmer their bonds. In God's time His
Moses will be found borne upon the waters of time, and
God, and not man, if the slave is to be free, will lead
Africa, as once he did Israel, out of the House of
Bondage.

How shall I describe the beautiful spectacle our little
fleet presented, with sails all a-spread, as we darted like
a flock of gulls out from the *bouche* of the narrow bayou
into the open expanse of the gulf! The sun was about
half an hour high, and covering the waves with gold and
orange, while the heavens in the west, where he was going down, were gorgeous with green, purple, and crimson,
beyond painter's pencil or poet's pen. No wonder the
Indian, in his fresh imagination, believed the western
heavens to be the gate to his celestial hunting grounds!
A little child once gazing on such a sky of glory, said
to me :—

"Aunt Kate, heaven is so full of light and pretty

colors, that when God opens its gate at sun down to let
the sun go in, they burst out, don't they?"

Is not that pretty, Mr. —— ? Children's sayings are
so fresh and original, often so wonderful, that if parents
would preserve all their speeches in writing, a lovely book
could be made up of them, of the greatest interest.
What mammas will recollect and send to you for a corner
of your paper, all the pretty thoughts out-spoken by
their little ones? A little girl of five years, whose attending ears had heard talking at home about High and
Low Church, was taken to a church where the pulpit
was unusually lofty. While they were singing she
whispered to her ma, "*That* minister, ma, must be very
high church, as *high* as the Communion of Saints!"

But while I am chattering about little people, our
yacht begins to

"rock lightly on the tide,"

and curvets and rears like a cantering pony to the undulating waves, which ever and forever roll and unroll
themselves in the deep sea. The motion is, however, by
no means unpleasant; but we have to look after move-
ables, and whoever tries to walk, goes toddling about not
half so gracefully as my little Harry, whose natural gait
being a roll, is quite at home as he moves about the
cabin, *his* roll, meeting the yacht's roll, counteracts it,
and he goes about straight as an Indian. The weather
is always delightful at this season, and never was a
lovelier evening than that, amid the roseate and golden
beauties of which we sailed across the channel to the
island, which lay like a huge emerald upon a sea of silver
rosée, to gallicise a word.

Wher. about a mile from the island, and just as the sun descended into the deep, all the gentlemen together fired off a *feu de joie*. At this loud fusilade, ten thousand ducks that were reposing upon the surface of the water near the island, rose like a black cloud into the sky, and flew round and round in a wild vortex, about a hundred feet in the air; while herons, pelicans, and gulls, that were in the covert of the island-shore, startled from their propriety, scattered in all ways and in the utmost alarm. With the spy-glass, an alligator, a rare visitor in salt water, was seen to plunge into the water; and last, yet not least, the sloop which was moored about a mile from us, close under the island, hurriedly slipped her cable, hoisted her mainsail and jib, and fairly ran away from us, no doubt believing our merry and peaceful pic-nic party, a piratical expedition; or at least of such "questionable shape," as not to be waited for! Thereupon the bearded ones of our company set up a wild and loud huzza, and cheered the flying sloop with the greatest good humor imaginable.

"Doubtless," said my quiet husband, "that skipper, when he reaches New Orleans, will report having seen and been fired into, and hotly pursued by a flotilla of seven armed boats, full of men, off the mouth of Bayou La Fourche! and that he and his crew only escaped, by slipping his cable and putting to sea." The result showed that my husband was in the right.

The wind left our canvass as we drew near the island, which the Spaniards call "Isla de Boca," but the old Frenchmen, "Isle des Oiseaux," or Isle of Birds. It is about a league in length and half a mile wide, with clumps of live oaks sprinkled over its surface, which is dry and elevated, but without any variation of its perfect level. The rowers pulled into a little cove, where we moored our fleet; and by the light of the rising moon the gentlemen landed in the small boats, and began to look out a place for the servants to set up the tent.

On board the admiral's vessel—that is in *my* ship— the ladies all assembled to take tea by invitation while the gentlemen superintended and assisted in landing the paraphernalia. We had a pleasant time and a laugh-ringing one, at our supper, which was gracefully handed round by Petit. In less than an hour the great tent or "markee" was erected, and lifted its white pyramidal walls in the soft moonlight like a palace of pearl. In the centre was suspended a swinging lamp, that brightly lighted the interior. Camp-stools, a table, lounges, and all the furniture necessary to make it a handsome draw-ing-room, were placed within. There were five other tents smaller than this, two of which were exclusively for the ladies' abodes; though one or two of them, from fear of horrid alligators, imaginary lions, tigers, wolves, and bears, to say nothing of dreadful elephants, de-termined to keep their quarters in the cabins of the yachts.

Hammocks and iron-framed bedsteads were provided for those who chose to sleep in the tents. The spot where our little snow-white city was thus magically built was very picturesque. A crescent shaped cove of spark-ling sand was in front, where the yachts lay moored, bows outward, in a half-circle, like a fleet protecting a harbor; overhead spread the interlaced branches of three great oaks, and near was a well of pure water, which the buccaneers who had once resorted to this island, had dug; for this island is not far from Barrataria Bay and Isle, where "Lafitte" had his rendezvous before the last war with England; and in the sweet place where we pitched our camp, Theodore and Constanza had doubtless walked and sighed and loved beneath the same golden moon that shone on us.

"Suppose," said one of our romantic young ladies "that there should be buccaneers here now, and that they should suddenly appear in one of their terrible long, low, black schooners opposite our cove, and come in and fight with our defenders, conquer them, and carry us all off to some remote isle, where in some splendid cavern they live like kings and lords!"

The pretty Marié ejaculated, "Not for the world!" The noble Mathilde smiled and said, "How romantic it *would* be!" Grace Lyndall, one of our belles, clapped her beautiful hands and exclaimed,

" Of all things how I *should* like it!"

"Don't speak of such things, I beg of you," said the young and charming Madame Dumont, who with her husband had joined us, the evening before, from their plantation.

" The tents are all pitched and ready for occupation, fair dames all," said Monsieur M. from the shore, "but what are you talking about?—the pirates?"

"Yes, colonel, and we were wishing that a nice, long, low, black, saucy-looking schooner, would pay us a sudden visit, and carry us all off," said Grace; and this girl had the richest voice, that I ever heard from woman's lips; every sound that music knows were mingled with a surfeit of sweetness in the golden alembic of its tones.

We were soon all on shore, and were perfectly charmed with the preparations which the taste and attention of the gentlemen had made for us. The green sward, the bright moon, a violin which Scipio (one of our boatmen) was tuning, and the joyousness of the occasion tempted us to dance; and for an hour we outdid Queen Mab and her fairy ball. Suddenly, while we were in the midst of our gaiety, a long, low, black, ominous-looking vessel poked her sharp nose around the point, and as her tall sails became visible in the broad moonbeams, Grace Lyndall, who first espied it, as she was splendidly schottisching with her cousin Louis, uttered the loudest and most terrified shriek, that I ever heard or ever hope to hear!

It transfixed us all like statues, and Scipio's music froze stiff on the strings of his fiddle bow. Grace ended her scream in total unconsciousness, for she became instantly insensible on Louis' arm. The rest of the ladies, beholding the same dreadful vision, took up the key-note, and screamed "most musically," each clinging to one of the gentlemen.

Marié gasped to my husband, "Save—oh—save me!" As for myself, I was petrified with bewildering astonishment. That it could be a buccaneer, I could not for a moment believe; but reflecting where we were, and what the island had been, I began to wish little Harry and myself and husband and all of us safe at home again.

The younger gentlemen ran for their arms; but before any defensive steps could be taken, the whole hull of the schooner came in open view, not three hundred yards distant, and from her deck came a hoarse hail, that nearly killed out what little courage I had left.

"Ahoy! what boats are those?"

And with the words we could see a lighted fusee in the hand of a man who was standing by a cannon that was pointing towards poor us.

"Pirates without question!" said my husband gravely; "and we must make the best battle we can!"

"Oh, no—no!" cried the ladies; "it cannot be so bad as that!"

"Ahoy, ashore! Give an account of yourselves, or we fire into you!" was again thundered from her deck.

"A pleasure party," answered the colonel; "nothing more! Are you the surveying Revenue Cutter?"

"Yes," answered the officer on deck, laughing so that we could hear him; "beg pardon for disturbing you. But we were informed by the skipper of a sloop, an hour ago, that hailed us on the south side of the island, that he had been chased by a fleet of armed boats. The ladies will please accept my apologies and regrets for alarming them."

We were now all mortification and laughter. The captain of the cutter was hailed, and invited to land, which he did in a four-oared boat. He was a fine-looking young officer, and enjoyed our fright vastly, when the gentlemen—to two of whom he was known —informed him of our table chat about "Lafitte." We invited him to dine with us next day, as he grace-fully took his leave of us, and in a little while we

saw the vessel which had caused us such a terrible fright
gliding slowly and beautifully away until she was lost in
the distant haze of mist and moonbeams.

Yours truly,
KATE.

LETTER LXIV.

DEAR MR. ———— :

IT seems to me very strange that people will not take folks as they are, and not amuse themselves with guessing that somebody is somebody else. Now I hear and see from certain editorial notices of my poor Needles, that I am *not* Kate Conyngham at all, but that this is a *nom de plume*, a mere masque to conceal my true features. Another saucy fellow of an editor asserts that I am not a *Miss* at all, but that I am a *Mister* W., or *Mister* D., or some other *gentleman*. Dear me! What *can* there be so masculine in my poor Needles as to give rise to such a hint? Even those sage persons who believe me to be a lady declare that I am Miss Pardoe, the authoress; some, that I am the fair daughter of the Rev. Mr. ———— of Mobile; and some, that I am a younger sister of ————; and somebody says, I dare say, that I am nobody at all.

Now, Mr. ————, I protest against all this skepticism. Have I not been for five years, or more, your correspondent? Can you not bear testimony to my personality and alleged identity? Have you not seen my letters, and have you not, at this moment, my daguerreotype? I call upon you to bear witness to my having been Miss Katharine Conyngham, and no other lady else, and that, though I am now a married dame, I am entitled to that former name, if I choose to retain it as an authoress. Because the talented Fanny Fern, Grace Greenwood, and other brilliant autorial ladies, have noms de plume, is no reason that every one should have !

Please say to these naughty editors that I am myself, and nobody else, and that I am not a mere shadow, an "*umbra umbrarum*,"—if that is bad Latin recollect it is lady's Latin; and that ladies can decline Bonus better than a certain western member of congress, who once gave, as the relic of schooldom, the following toast :—

"The ladies—*Bonus, bonior, bonissimus!* good, better, best ! The Lord bless 'em !"

But to our pic-nic campaign ! I ended my last letter with an account of our visit from an imaginary buccaneer. That night we slept as safely in our tents as we should have done at home; and as the gentlemen took turns, two at the time, in standing guard to see that we were not intruded upon by mischievous animals from land or water, we felt perfectly secure. I recollect falling asleep, soothed by the sweet melody of a guitar and a fine manly voice. It was the cavalier, Louis, serenading outside her tent the fair Mathilde within.

In the morning we were up bright and early, and, finding breakfast all prepared by the willing servants, we were soon ready for the day's adventures. The order for the day was, that the ladies who chose to do so should accompany the hunters in the largest yacht, as the former rowed around the island, in search of game ; and that they should fish, crochet, read, and amuse themselves as they pleased, while the gentlemen landed and pursued their sport.

We had a delightful row around the point, to the south

of the island, where we again saw the cutter which we had taken for a buccaneer.   It was a beautiful object, all grace and symmetry, her white wings spread, and her taper masts diminishing to mere wands.

With all her lightness and grace, her black hull and warlike guns gave her a battle air that made me think of sea fights, and all the horrors of naval warfare.

Far away to the west we saw two other vessels, one of which was the runaway sloop; but she was now trying to regain the mouth of the Lafourche, no doubt satisfied that, as the revenue cutter did not molest us, we were harmless people, with all our fusilading and huzzaing.

But I will not take up your time, Mr. ——, in making you read a complete journal of our ten days' stay in the islands of the Gulf, for we did not confine ourselves to the Isle of Birds, but on the fifth day, during which we had charming weather, the gentlemen got up an expedition to Barrataria Bay, a few leagues eastward.   They had got weary of killing!   Birds of all wings, alligators, deer, and fish of all fins, had rewarded them and our praiseworthy efforts; and a change, for the sake of variety, was gladly welcomed.   We, therefore, left a guard of two servants with our tents, and, having provisioned our boats for three days, we all embarked in the sunny, bright morning on our coasting expedition.   At this season of the year the weather is all unbrokenly fair, and rain was no more to be feared than an earthquake.

It was a delightful voyage along the curving Gulf shore, from which we did not venture more than four or five miles.   Now and then we could see a distant sail that lay low on the horizon, and looking no bigger than

a lady's finger-nail.   About noon I discovered, with my
"sharp" eyes, a brown smoke, seemingly rising from
the sea.   I pointed it out to Marie, and she exclaimed:

" A volcano at sea !"

Whereupon everybody looked from all the boats.

" It is a steamer, bound from New Orleans to Gal-
veston," said my husband, the admiral of our fleet.

" But we see no vessel, only smoke," remarked Grace,
trying to steady a spy glass, which Louis was holding
with both hands to her eye.

" The boat itself is under the line of the horizon," said
Colonel M.

" The periphery of the earth conceals it beneath the
curved line of the arc of the convex horizon," said one
of the young men who had lately left college, and was
entitled to talk learnedly.

The sight of a column of smoke, actually rising from
beneath the level sea line of the horizon, was a novel
sight.   With the spy-glass we could see the smoke rolling
and rolling skyward, as if not more than a mile apparent
distance, yet no sign of chimney or masts discernible !
There it ascended from its invisible smoke-pipe, for all
the world like a volcano belching itself up out of the
Gulf.   We followed it with our eyes until it gradually
receded westward, and disappeared in an hour far below
the horizon's arc.

It is a very strange sight to see smoke traveling along
the sea in that style, without any apparent cause appended.   What a visible proof of the earth's sphericity
it is !   I recollect when we passed Portsmouth, in
England, the masts only of the British fleet were visible,
looking like a forest in the water, the hulls being below

the curve. The truth is, that there can be no such thing as a perfectly *straight* line on this globulous earth! Even the yardstick is but a curved wand, to be sure the arc it makes is not perceptible; and the floors of our houses if extended far enough, would form an arc of the earth's circle of more or less degrees. The term level is a misnomer—it does not exist. There is nothing level or plain—sphericity possesses all things terrestrial.

One wouldn't suppose that such a big world as ours would betray its roundness, in so short a distance as lay between us and the steamer. I have no doubt, with proper data to start with, that the height of a steamer's chimney being known, and also her exact distance from the eye, a calculation could be made which would reach a figure that would show the earth's circumference in miles.

Last summer, while at the beautiful watering place at Pass Christian, I made a curious and perhaps new calculation of ascertaining the distance of an object. There is a light-ship moored nine miles off the town. I found that by placing a small needle at arm's length horizontally until the needle and ship *appeared* to be exactly the same length, which is when the needle covers the ship's length completely, that I could verify the distance to be nine miles. I did it in this way: I first fixed the needle horizontally by striking it in a post level with my eye. I then stepped back until the needle and ship were blended in one another exactly. I then measured the distance between my eye and the needle in inches. As I knew the length of the needle and of the ship, with these three known terms, I obtained accurately, the fourth unknown one. Perhaps the process is known to mathematicians; if so, I will not take out a patent. I wish some of your "great cypherers" would verify this process.

But I am getting too learned, and must go back to our pic-nic. All that day we coasted along the level green shores of the Gulf, with not a tree visible for two and three leagues inland, and then they looked like round blue clouds. No shores can be more tame!

At length, just as the lovely day was closing, we came into the mouth of "Lafitte's Bay," as it is termed, and on our right saw the island Barrataria, where the bucca-neer had his rendezvous. Now it looked peaceful enough. A few fishermen and a fleet of oyster boats were anchored around it, plying their fishy trade; and we could discover above a group of trees the roof of a mansion where resides, or did reside, a planter, who had a sugar plantation on the island. The gentleman's name I believe is Bennet, and he has fair daughters, whose presence throw a grace over the scenes of ancient buccaneerdom, that disassociates the island of all its former renown, as the home of the pirates. We remained on board our boats all night; and such a star bright night never was! The atmosphere ap-peared to be full of light. The splendor of the fixed stars, and the milder lustre of the planets were unsurpassed. The heavens seemed to come nearer to us. Every star above had a star beneath it on the sea; and when the moon arose about eleven o'clock, there was a pavement of silver across the water from our feet to her very throne.

The next day we wandered over the island, and pic-nic'd on the grassy glacis of the ruined fortress which Lafitte fortified to defend his island home against cruisers.

A large oak stood near, beneath which he had his tent, which, says tradition, was more luxuriously furnished than an Oriental prince's. We were shown by an old French fisherman, who knew Lafitte, a gun that once belonged to his vessel; and as the old man, who could not have been less than seventy, loved to talk of the famous smuggler, we let him relate his stories to which we listened—being on the ground itself of the scenes—with lively interest.

Louis read aloud several pages from one of the romances, and we sought to verify *all* the descriptions; but novelists cannot always make use of placid and level scenery, and they remove mountains and place them where they want them; and gardens, waterfalls, vales and groves, cliffs and rivulets, all obey the waving of their wand, and *presto!* appear when they command. But we found mainly the novel and the scene in gratifying harmony, one with the other; and where there was a difference, was evidently owing to the changes produced by time and circumstances. Our visit was a most satisfactory one, and we re-embarked at evening, delighted with our excursion over the Pirate's Isle.

On the evening of the third day we reached our encampment without mishap, and found all safe. The next morning we struck tents, and, with our boats filled with game and its trophies, we set sail, with a fine landward wind, for the mouth of La Fourche. As you already know the scenery of that bayou, Mr. ——, I will not describe our voyage home, which we reached on the third day, all well, and marvelously sun-browned; looking like so many gipsies. As for my Harry, the little fellow's cheeks are as brown as a chinquapin; but he has gained full four pounds, and is more saucy and handsome than ever.

I was charmed to be once more *at home*. Not all the beautiful cabins and pretty yachts, and fishing and camping out under markees, can compensate for one's own home. Home is home, and nothing else could *be* home! I would rather live in a cabin of logs, and feel that it was my home; that there was a peg for my husband's hat; a place for his chair in one corner, and my work-stand in the other; on my right hand *my* little tea cup-board, and on the other the stand with the large Bible, the cat on the rug, and old Buck, the house-dog, chained in his kennel; my milch-cow and her calf in the neat yard, and nobody to molest or rule over us, as one finds it even in the best of boarding-houses.

There is a wretched and unhappy custom in vogue, for young married couples to go to a hotel or boarding-house! When should husband and wife love to be by themselves in their *own* home, if not the first months and year of marriage? It is a miserable life, garish, hollow, artificial, love-killing, heart-withering life, this boarding, for young couples! Girls, better wait a-wee! better delay than be married and put under the peculiar system of keen-eyed espionage and authority common to boarding-houses. Boarders have no souls of their own —that is, they dare not *say* so! Keep house—if only in one room! You will be happier, and your husband will love you better, and it will be far better for you both. A boarding-house life, for the fresh young hearts of new married folks, is, with all deference and respect for all lady-like, and good, kind landladies, like a killing

frost upon the young buds of spring.   One never *lives*
that boards !   One only *stays* and endures !

But, good-bye, Mr. ——

Your friend,

KATE, AND NOBODY ELSE.

LETTER LXV.

My Dear Mr. ———:

I am, for a few days, sojourning in this lovely shore-side village of villas, Pass Christian. It is, as the map will, or *ought* to show you, on Lake Pontchartrain, where the south border of Mississippi is washed by the waves of the salt sea. The "Pass," as it is familiarly called, is celebrated for its pure and salubrious air, the beauty of its site, the elegance of its private mansions, the refinement and wealth of its citizens, its excellent academy of education for young misses, and its military school; moreover, it is the favorite summer resort of the more opulent New Orleanois, many of whom have built tasteful abodes along the shore facing the lake, where gardens and lawns, porticoes and verandahs, enchant the eye.

There is properly only *one* street comprising the town; but this street is *four* miles long, open one side to the breezes of gulf, and on the other bordered by handsome villas, most of its length.

A little brown Roman Catholic chapel lifts its cross amid these mansions, its front adorned with two statues, one of the Virgin, and another of St. Paul, in a niche high above the entrance. There is appended to the latter, this inscription :—

"DOCTORI GENTIAM;"

So, to the *Teacher of the Nations*, this chapel is dedicated, while "Mary," like the goddess Diana, (for the
blessed Virgin is now made a *goddess* by the Pope,)
stands upon a pedestal above, to receive the homage and
worship of her votaries. Jesus, being always represented only as a little child, is quite cast into the shade
by His mother.   The Romans, in their adorations, never
seem to contemplate Christ as a man, but only as the
"child Jesus" in the mother's arms, and hence transfer
all their worship to the mother, whom, it would seem,
they believe more capable of appreciating it than a babe.
I think this, as I have before remarked, is the secret of
their Mariolatry.

Nevertheless, it is a pretty little chapel, and in keeping with the place; but its worshipers are chiefly of the
humble class of Creole fishermen, and descendants of
the old French families; for the Pass was once wholly
French. Here the Marquis of Ponchartrain once so-
journed, and buried his only daughter, who, report says,
died of love for an Indian Prince. Her grave is beneath
three live oaks that stand on the verge of the beach, not
far from the chapel; but the head-stone has long since
disappeared. It was this nobleman who gave name to
the lake. The residence of the Marquis, who was one
of the most accomplished courtiers of the French court,
and sent by Louis to govern this Province, is now marked
only by the site of the light house, which stands *in a
garden;* a lovely object, peering above the trees, and
singularly contrasting with the usual desolate look of
such edifices, standing alone and treeless upon some

storm-beaten headland. In the same garden with this snow-white tower, which, after sunset sends its brilliant light far out upon the waters, guiding the mariner home, is the village post-office; a snug little cottage nestling under its walls. The post-master is a "lady," and the daughter, if I mistake not, of the famous Captain Hearn, who, in the last war, beat off a British vessel that was coming in to fire the town; or he did some equally brave act, for which, government at this day rewards the daughter by an office, as it did the father. A son of this sea-fighter commanded the superb steamer, Cuba, in which we came over from New Orleans; and, though a large, rough looking man, he has a great and generous heart, and is as true a gentleman as ever took off his hat to a lady; and looks as, if there were any more fighting to do for his country, he would not be found wanting. When I was quite a young girl, I used to think no man could be a gentleman who did not dress in the "fashion," wear kid gloves, a nicely brushed hat, and polished boots, with one ring at least, and a gold watch. But that was the folly and ignorance of girlhood, which thinks all lovers should be knights in helmet and buckler, and that no young knight was fit for a lady's love who had not killed his rival and her *other* lover in a "wager of battle."

Dear me! I have had time to reverse my decision since then; and *much* dressed men I always suspect! I have found in the world that the truest merit is without affectation; and that a right down gentleman thinks but little of fashion; and so I have met with as noble and true gentlemen in rough linsey-woolsey garb, as in broadcloth. In a word, I do not *now* form a preconceived opinion of a man from his dress or appearance.

The most eminent men that one falls in with in traveling, are the plainest and simplest in dress and manner.

The Pass, as I have said, consists in one long street, that winds and bends with the graceful curve of the lake shore. About the centre of this is the landing place, where passengers embark and disembark for Mobile or New Orleans; these cities being about equi-distant (or seven hours' sail) on each side of the Pass.

About half a mile from the pier, westward, is the Lake Institute, at the head of which is the Rector of the church here, Rev. Dr. Savage, the gentleman who was pioneer in the Cape Palmas mission, and who remained nine years in Africa, which owes more to him than to any other man living, for her religious prosperity. The doctor is a scientific man, and is a member of several foreign and cis-Atlantic Academies of Science ; and, as a naturalist, he stands in the front rank. I was charmed with a visit made yesterday to his school, which is a large southern-built mansion house, facing the lake, from which it is separated by a spacious lawn, tastefully ornamented. The trees of a pine grove form a dark, rich background to the house and its dormitories and study hall. This school is the best in the South, and deservedly has a high reputation. It numbers about sixty pupils, which, I believe, is its full limit. It is patronized chiefly by Mobile and New Orleans ; and of the former city I saw at least a dozen fair girls, whose beauty gives one a favorable idea of female loveliness in that city, which we are soon to visit.

So great is the hostility of the northern abolitionists against the South, that southern parents are becoming more and more reluctant to send their sons and daughters there to return with hostile opinions to create discord and confusion at home. For self-protection they are rallying around their own Colleges and Female Institutes; and all that has been wanting was this union of purpose, to raise schools of learning to the highest scholastic rank. Northern teachers are regarded with suspicion, though employed. Lately Professor Silliman has struck a death-blow to the sending southern young men north, by asserting in a public lecture: "We do not want your southern youth! We can get along without them!" It will be a bold Southerner that sends his son to a northern college after this.

Even the school-books published in the North are to be expurgated, ere they will be introduced into Southern schools, for instance, in a geography now before me, printed in New York, occurs a sentence which says "that the negroes will yet one day rise against the Southern planters and destroy them;" and fifty other such things are in Northern school books. The result will be, that unless Abolitionism cease its hostility, the South will separate itself from the North virtually, by having its own teachers, schools, clergy, mechanics, literature, and books of education.

The church, of which the Rev. Dr. Savage is Rector, is near the Institute, in a grove of oaks and pines. It is a picturesque Gothic edifice, and the very beau ideal of a rural church. In the rear is the cemetery, with a handsome arch above the gate-way, and contains several tasteful tombs. A Sabbath holiness and quiet reigned over the spot when I visited it yesterday. I was shown there the grave of a wealthy young South Carolinian, who had been a dissipated man and a sceptic. Just before he died he desired ten acres to be purchased of government in the wild forest beyond the town, and a grave to be dug in the centre, wherein he directed his friends to place his body; and after filling the grave, to smooth it level with the surrounding earth, and removing all signs of sepulture, let the grass and the brush grow up and conceal it from human search; and in order that it might be forgotten, the land was never to be claimed by his heritors, but to revert to the government again as wild land.

This Will—the expression of a soul dark and desolate, without the hopes and promises of the Gospel, which make the grave a hallowed rest, above which Hope ever hovers on golden wings, waiting the resurrection morn— this Will was, of course, not carried out. His body was conveyed to this secluded cemetery, and here interred, with all the respect that the living owe the dead.

Upon leaving this solemn home of the dead of earth, our steps took us in the direction of a mound near the village blacksmith's dingy shop. Already I knew the story of this green mound of earth; but an old negro, "Uncle Tom," at the shop, gravely and politely, with his hat in his hand, informed my husband, "Dat it was de fort General Jackson *fout* the Indjuns from." General Jackson however never "fout" at the Pass.

The mound is now much worn away; but trees grow upon it showing its age. It is an interesting relic of the past. By the French it was called the "Young King's Tomb." The tradition is, that when the Indian chief heard that Eugenie, the daughter of Marquis Pontchartrain, had wilted and died like a blighted flower, he refused to eat, broke his spear in two, buried his arrows, and sat day and night upon her grave singing his death song. At length he was found cold and dead one sunrise, his head laid upon her grave. The warriors bore his body to the place where his father was buried, and entombed him with his arms, beneath a mound which their affection raised to his memory. Not far distant is another mound, not so high, where repose the bones of Tamala, his father. The sound of the forge and the anvil alone break the stillness of the spot.

As we turned away to resume our loitering about the Pass, a man walked slowly by, whom a lady, who was with us, pointed out as the son of a celebrated buccaneer who used to rendezvous here.

Afterwards I saw this man, now a peaceable citizen, part farmer, part fisherman, who not only verified the assertion, but from him I learned that his brother, who dwelt upon the coast, had in his possession a package of papers and a chart of an island in the Gulf, which directed where exactly to find buried a great treasure. This treasure consisted of the spoils, he said, of Spanish ships, and had been buried on one of the Tortugas'; but no man had yet been to search for it. He has promised to get the papers, which he said are written in French, and a copy of the chart. Hear that, Mr. ——! The next I shall hear of you, *may* be, that you are commanding a schooner in search of this hidden treasure!

There is no doubt about this man having "the papers," I am told by a gentleman here; but as such researches have so often proved failures, no attention has been paid to the fact. You shall be duly informed, Mr.——, *when* I discover the hidden gold.

This was once a famous haunt for buccaneers, and after cruisers broke up their "dreadful trade," they settled down here in quiet occupations; and among the humble French citizens, are found their descendants—inoffensive people enough, who subsist by fishing and coasting.

There is a Military Academy here under the command of Ashbel Green, once a lawyer in Philadelphia, and son to a former President of Princeton College. It is, I understand, a very efficient school, with about fifty cadets.

There is an amusing peculiarity of water scenery here at the Pass. Every house on the shore has its private bath-house. The water being shoal, they are erected at the end of a wharf projecting sometimes a thousand feet out into the lake. Thus, when one looks up or down the shore in front of the town, the eye is filled with the spectacle of one or two hundred narrow bridges and bathing-houses, built on the water. At evening and other bathing-hours, these bridges "in the season" are filled with ladies and children and servants, going to and from the baths; the former grotesquely arrayed in long waistless robes of calico or gingham, and their faces concealed by horrid hoods or veils. At such hours, gentlemen are tabooed the baths; but they have their time too. Nothing is thought of, or spoken of in summer, but bathing. "Have you bathed to-day?" takes the place of "How do you do?" in other places. Not to bathe daily is to be voted out of society.

The school-girls go to the bath in merry parties at day-dawn, and frights they look in their awkward, loose bathing gear. I am told these misses swim like ducks, and have been out as far as a buoy in the channel, a quarter of a mile beyond the bath house. But this is now forbidden, as a young lady from Mobile, last summer, being too venturesome, and not yet as skillful a swimmer as her companions, in following them out became wearied and sank. Two of her companions, both a year younger than herself, but good swimmers, bravely dove down and brought her to the surface, and sustained her until they regained footing.

It must be laborious swimming in those heavy saturated robes which the bathers wear. I never had courage to go beyond the latticed fence of the bath house; and then I am afraid that some ugly fish, crab, or "fiddler" will bite my feet! Yet bathing is a luxury; and some of the citizens bathe before every meal, all summer long.

We remain here a week longer, and then proceed to Mobile on our way north to pass the summer.

Yours truly,
KATE.

LETTER LXVI.

MOBILE, ALABAMA, 1855.

MY DEAR MR. ———:

THIS lovely Southern metropolis has been our sojourn for a week past, and has presented so many attractions both to me and my husband, that, were we not desirous of being in New York early in June, we should yield to the solicitation of many kind friends and our own wishes, and enjoy its refined hospitality for some days longer.

The Mobileans are genuine Southerners by birth and feeling; that is, this city is not made up, like New Orleans, of strangers, but mainly of those who are "to the manor born." It reminds me more of Charleston, South Carolina, in this respect; and gives, like that elegant city, a true representation of Southern manners.

We left the delightful watering place, Pass Christian, and by a reverse course towards New Orleans met and boarded another steamer, the Oregon, at the Lake wharf, and so came hither, running across the lakes by moon and star-light. We passed late at night Round Island, celebrated as the rendezvous of the Filibusteros three years ago. It now lay huge and black upon the horizon, a league off, looking like Behemoth asleep. Around us gleamed three or four light-houses, penciling the water's rippling face with slender lines of golden threads. Over us glittered the thousand worlds of glory, which we call stars. In the west, Orion had just sheathed in the wave his bright, star-gemmed sword. The moon walked in brightness high above the horizon, and seemed to glory in her beauty and purity.

My husband and I walked the deck till late, enjoying the sea-wind, for one never takes cold at sea. Such a fresh breeze on land would have chilled me to the heart. But bonnetless and shawlless, I continued on deck till midnight. As we were about to go to our room, a dark object, over which seemed to hover a cloud of snow, was visible ahead. As we came nearer, I made out the shape of a schooner, her white sails shining in the moon, while her black hull was in shadow.

"Helm-a-port!" was the quick order from some one on deck.

The steamer abruptly changed her straightforward course, and steered round the vessel, but so near as to create no little commotion on board of her. We passed so near that I could have tossed my fan upon her quarter deck, where stood a man with a pipe, uttering strange oaths, instead of blessings at his escape. In a few minutes, the little vessel was mingling with the obscurity of night in the distance, and soon disappeared altogether.

At four o'clock in the morning I was aroused by persons talking on the "guard," near our window; and on looking out found we were moving through a narrow pass, and close to us was a dwelling house, built on a small island of sand. The cocks were crowing, (among them a horrid, hoarse, bellowing Shanghai,) dogs barking, men shouting, and the water dashing and splashing against the little island as we slowly shoved our way through. The chambermaid told me that this picturesque place, this

"Half-way House," in the Gulf, was called "Grass Patch." I wondered at the appellation, since blade of grass on this sand-bank there was not one! But the captain the next morning enlightened us, by calling it "Grant's Pass," so named from the proprietor. We had a pleasant laugh, of course, at the transmogrification of the name in the mouth of our kind and very civil chambermaid.

Just at sunrise we came in sight of the shipping in the "Lower bay"—for you must know that Mobile city is thirty-five miles up from the Gulf, on a narrow "Delaware-sort-of-a-bay" of its own. This bay being too shallow for large cotton ships, they anchor below here in the "Roads," and their freight is brought down to them in tug steamers, or Bay boats. This fleet consisted of nearly a hundred ships and barks, and had a fine appearance, extending for a mile or two in length. To and from its anchorage plied the smoking Bay steamers, and among them sailed a graceful cutter, the vigilant watcher of the coast. We subsequently met the captain of the latter, Douglas Ottinger, in the city, where his charming family reside. He is a remarkably "fine appearance of a man," and an accomplished gentleman and sailor. He is well known to the world by his humane invention of the Life Car, commonly called "Francis's," which has saved so many hundreds of the lives of the shipwrecked. To have invented and left this "car of life" to the world is honor enough for any man to achieve. Francis was only its builder. It should be called "The Ottinger Car;" for Congress has formally recognized his right as inventor.

Our trip up the Bay of Mobile was truly delightful.

The morning was cloudless, the wind cool from the south, the shores green, and dotted here and there with villas; the water lively with vessels of all kinds, moving on every possible course, and our steamer fleet, and passing everything with a sort of quiet indifference, that made us feel like conquerors.

These lake boats from Mobile to New Orleans are superior to any I have sailed on, either in Europe or this country. The two I have been on, the Cuba and Oregon, are elegant and commodious, with attentive servants, "excellently good living," that would gratify Mons. Ude. The captain's civil courtesy to us all most favorably impressed me, and led me to reflect how little civility, and smiles, and courtesy cost, and how long they remain upon the memory, and make a boat popular; while the absence of these has a contrary effect.

The captain is a Maine man—one of those enterprising Portland seamen who have carried the star-spangled banner into the farthest corners of the globe. His fine face, his respectable gray hairs, and affable manner, presented as fine a portrait of an experienced captain (sailor and gentleman in one) as we ever encounter.

After breakfast we came in sight of Mobile. The captain, as we sailed up, was kind enough to point out to my husband the several watering places in the shores, such as "Point Clear," the CAPE MAY of the South; kept by Chamberlain, formerly of the Revere House, Boston, and a resort of the ELITE of Mobile; Hollywood, a charming looking retreat, crowded in summer; besides others equally beautiful. I marvel, with such delightful retreats so near their city, that the Mobileans should ever go North! It is an homage the South pays the

North uselessly; and this year few will proceed North, I am told, as hard times have rendered Lilliputian purses indispensable, jingling with gold dollars instead of eagles.

The appearance of Mobile from the steamer did not strike me as interesting. Its approach is disfigured by marshy land, covered with old logs, and the forests crowd close upon the city. But, as we drew nearer, the towers and spires had a pretty effect; though the outward aspect of the city, from its level site, is far from giving a stranger a just idea of its real elegance and many attractions. There was a good display of shipping at the wharves, vessels of light draughts, and a fine view of steamers, taking in and discharging cotton, the great staple—the mighty pivot upon which the business of this city of 30,000 inhabitants revolves.

We took lodgings at the Battle House, which a week's experience assures me equals the favorite "New York" or the Revere House. In a word, it is a first rank American hotel. The only drawback is Irish servants. I can never understand them, nor they me, and this irritates their natural quickness, and they sometimes become exceedingly disagreeable. Southerners do not know exactly how to address servants of their own color; and being unaccustomed to them, prefer hotels where they are not. But here they are better drilled and more civil than I ever knew them to be. The price of the hire of colored servants here is so great that, probably, white servants are employed from motives of economy. The proprietors have been very assiduous and polite to make us comfortable, and we feel as much at home as if we were prince and princess in our own palace.

For the present, au revoir.

LETTER LXVII.

My Dear Mr. ———:

THERE is an indescribable softness in this Southern clime, a delicious indolence in its atmosphere, that, with as bright suns and as soft zephyrs, are unknown in the North. This dreamy air indisposes one to exertion; and even to dress for dinner is an heroic effort.

A dozen times I have approached my escritoire, and taken up my pen, to lay it down again, as if it were too heavy for my fingers. When I do not go to my desk, I sit and look at my paper and pen, that await me, and reproach my idleness. It is so difficult to overcome this inertia. If I could only muster resolution of mind enough to make a beginning, I could go on very nicely to the end; but the first word—the breaking of the ice—*hic labor est.*

I put this Latin in on purpose to take the occasion to inform you that in my last but one "Needle," you printed the inscription over the church door in Pass Christian, all wrong, and make me (if I am a lady) responsible for the barbarous word which your printer substituted for what I wrote. Perhaps the mischievous urchin thought any thing would do for lady's Latin. Please let your readers know that the word should read,

"DOCTORI GENTIUM;"

The word printed in place of the last may be Japanese, but it is not Latin—even feminine Latin.

We leave here to-morrow en route to Montgomery, the elegant capital of Alabama.   This city has been less described than any Southern one, yet possesses attractions few possess.   I am delighted with the society of Mobile. The refined hospitality and cordial attention my husband and myself have received from its citizens have quite won our hearts.   Mobile is peculiar as being a truly Southern city, its principal families being born here; and, also, for being a strictly commercial metropolis.   The "aristocracy" here, as *this* word goes, consists of its merchant princes and their families.   The merchant here is "a lord."   The superb villas, the palatial mansions lining its noble streets, the elegant country seats that adorn the suburbs, are occupied almost exclusively by merchants.

In other Southern cities reside many opulent planters, whose estates lie in the interior.   These gentlemen usually give the tone and take the lead of society in such cases; and this is particularly so in Charleston and Savannah.   But the principal pursuit here being commerce, like the merchants of Genoa, the commercial men of Mobile are the princes of the social empire.   You will, of course expect to find among them intelligence, education, refinement of manners, and all the social *savoir faire* of the higher order of American society.   You will not be disappointed.

We have found the Mobileans among the most elegant people we have ever associated with.   Many families it is my happiness to know are not surpassed in high-breeding and truly elevated character by the best class of English society; and this is saying a great deal; for I look upon the *best* society in England as the best in the world.

The medical profession and the bar and the pulpit have also prominent men, and exert their influence; but these members combined are a fraction compared with the mercantile gentlemen who, of course, give tone to, and lead society.

The maritime position of Mobile, with one foot upon the Gulf, and one hand grasping a quiver of rivers—the Alabama, Bigbee, Warrior, and lesser ones—determines its commercial character. These rivers flow for hundreds of miles, through the richest cotton region of the South, and bear annually to the quay of the city, cotton from five to six millions of dollars in value; while half that sum in amount is returned by her merchants in supplies to the planters and towns along their banks. In the bay, a fleet of from sixty to a hundred cotton ships carrying the flags of Great Britain, Bremen, France, Sweden, Denmark, await to take on board this vast amount of cotton, and convey it to the ports of their respective nations.

Cotton is, therefore, the circulating blood that gives life to the city. All its citizens are interested in this staple, from the princely merchant, to whom the globe with its ports is a chessboard on which he is ever making his intelligent moves, to the poor cobbler, whose round lapstone is *his* world. A failure in a crop of cotton, would cast a cloud over every brow in this city; for the great cotton merchant, lacking his princely gains, could

not build, nor employ, nor pay ; for the merchant is the
fountain of money—the source of dollars and cents,
that flow down from the stream of his own prosperity
through all the lesser channels, as a reservoir upon an
elevation communicates its fulness to a hundred pipes,
and these to a thousand lesser ones, till, at the farthest
extremity, the slave at the hydrant fills his gourd and
quenches his thirst.   The merchants are the reservoirs,
and if they are not full, all suffer below them.

There is one of the finest streets I have ever seen
which intersects this city for two miles.   It is a broad,
smooth, almost imperial avenue, lined chiefly by the
abodes of the "merchant nobles."   In one of these resides Madame Le Vert.   At present she is making the
tour of Southern Europe, and will visit Constantinople,
and, perhaps, "look in" upon the Crimea ere she re-
turns.   This lady is the daughter of a former governor
of Florida, and was celebrated as Miss Octavia Walton,
before her marriage with Dr. Le Vert, an eminent physician of this city, for her rare beauty of mind and
person.   Without question, she is one of the most accomplished women of America, with powers of pleasing
and winning hearts and captivating all who know her,
that is rarely possessed.   Lady Blessington was eminently gifted in this way, and Madame Le Vert is
scarcely less wonderfully endowed, if the half I hear of
her be true ; but, perhaps, I ought not to compare with
such a person as the Countess of Blessington—knowing
her life as we do—a pure and elevated character like
Madame Le Vert.   It is only in their personal fascina-
tions and varied accomplishments, that their names
should be placed on the same page.   Here Madame Le

Vert seems truly to be idolized. This is her *home*, and all know her and speak of her in the most enthusiastic and affectionate manner. Even the ladies seem to be wholly without envy when they mention her, and cheerfully accord to her the high social position she holds. The Mobile gentlemen all seem to speak of her with pride, and a feeling of personal regard, that I was delighted to witness. Truly she must be a happy woman who thus wins all hearts, disarms envy by her sweetness of disposition, and commands homage by her talents. A French gentleman, speaking to me of her, said, with rapture:—

"She can speak five languages well, and I have seen her converse at the same time with a Spanish, German, and French gentleman, around her, answering, questioning, and holding lively conversation with each in his own tongue, and with a precision of pronunciation and elegance of phraseology remarkable."

To the poor, I am told, she is very kind; and stops in the street to speak with the humblest widow, and affectionately inquire after her needs. To end my account of her, I will say that of fifty people I have heard speak of Madame Le Vert, I heard not one syllable of envy, or one word unkind. She seems to have the art of making every body love her. Every body regretted we could not see her; for, not to see Madame Le Vert, they seemed to feel was not seeing Mobile. I am told that an amusing incident occurred here, of which the heroine was a very accomplished person, who came here, representing herself as an English lady of high rank, with letters of introduction to Madame Le Vert, from some of her noble friends in England. The "lady" played her card well for a few days, fairly imposing upon the hospitable frankness of this Southern people, (who are the most deficient in suspicion of any people in the world,) and receiving no little attention. But detected in some peculation of jewelry from a fashionable jeweler's, and borrowing money from half a dozen gentlemen and ladies, her true character was speedily developed, and leaving behind several fashionable calls unreturned, she suddenly disappeared on board of a vessel bound to New York. She was highly accomplished, played wonderfully on the piano, sang like Sontag, and danced in the extreme of fashion. She said she knew Lamartine, Dickens, Bulwer, D'Israeli—every great personage; passed a week at Idlewild with Mr. Willis; three weeks at the house of the millionaire, George Law, as his guest;—indeed, she was traveling through the United States with the intention of writing an impartial book, which would correct the erroneous impressions her *friends*, "the nobility in England" held towards this wonderful empire.

Her letters of introduction proved to be forged, as was apparent, I was told, on comparing her handwriting proper with these epistles. How degrading to our sex to see a woman, evidently highly educated, and capable of conferring honor upon it, descend so low as to go from one fashionable hotel to another through the land as a swindler—a *chevaliere d'industrie!* This woman, who was about thirty-five, spoke French fluently, and played so well, that Gottschalk, who was, at the time, in the same hotel, hearing her in the drawing-room, pronounced her performance on the piano superior to any woman's he ever heard! With such talents, which, rightly used, would command an independent income, how can a woman thus deceive and wickedly act? for I have always associated with education and talents at least the feelings and character of a true lady.

Doubtless this "Countess" Madame Whyte* will yet be heard of in New York, where "distinguished foreigners" are sought after with a perseverance and homage quite in antagonism with the genius of republicans.

The environs of Mobile are charming. Some of the roads for a league west are lined with country houses adorned with parterres; and few houses are without the greatest variety of shade trees. Orange trees abound; but the live oak everywhere rears its majestic Alp of foliage, casting beneath shade broad enough to shelter from the sun a herd of cattle. This tree is always "a picture" in the scenery—a study for the artist. It combines the grandeur of the English oak with the grace of the American elm. There are superb groups of them in and about this city. They shade the lawns and give dignity to the mansions that lift their roofs above them.

The drives to Spring Hill and the Bay Road are the favorite avenues of the Mobileans. The former leads to a fine elevation, two leagues from the city, and commanding a view of it and of the beautiful bay. It is covered with the suburban retreats of the Mobile merchants, whose families generally retire here for the summer, if a northern tour does not tempt them. The Bay Road is a delightful drive for four miles, with the open bay on one side and villas and woodlands on the other. We enjoyed both of these drives very much. We constantly met or passed carriages, containing ladies

* Subsequently appeared as the Authoress of John Halifax.   ED.

without bonnets, and also saw a great number of equestrians; for Southerners are more fond of the saddle than a seat in a carriage. The beauty of the ladies is shown to best advantage on an evening drive; and I must say, that I have never seen so much true "Southern" loveliness, of the sunny dark eye, oval face, golden brown hair, and indescribably rich complexion, (rich without color,) as here.

This city is deservedly celebrated for its beautiful women, and especially the beauty of its girls under sixteen. The men have made a favorable impression upon me for intelligence and frank manner; and they dress well, especially the middle-aged citizens—even better than the young men. The ladies dress with the most lavish expense, and yet with taste, never following a fashion to its excess, but stopping within it; and this good sense and taste is a fine trait in Southern women. Many Northern ladies are apt to keep by the side of Fashion, if not to get a step ahead of her. Wealth without refinement always dresses as far as Fashion dresses her lay-figure; but refined wealth stops this side of the extreme.

I shall write one more letter from this charming city and then we proceed northward.

KATE.

LETTER LXVIII.

AN INN IN VIRGINIA, JUNE, 1855.

MY DEAR MR. ———:

THIS is written in an old fashioned country Inn, in the heart of the Old Dominion, where we are sojourning for a week. It is now ten days since we left the pleasant city of Mobile, which I shall always embalm in my memory with the sweetest spices of affection, for the kindness I received there from so many dear friends. If I were disposed to be personal, I could make my letter brilliant with the names of those esteemed people who extended towards me the hospitable courtesies and graceful amenities of which I was the unworthy object. My husband is charmed with the place, and has half a mind to live there during the winters, which I am told are delightful. In Mobile I had the pleasure of seeing the celebrated Dr. Nott, who, in conjunction with Mr. Cairo Gliddon, has published a work to show that the arithmetic of Moses was not creditable for a school boy. I hear that the work has not overthrown the Bible, although bigger than the Bible, and written almost by as many men. It overshot itself, and from its very bulk and cost will never be read, except by students—and what book ever convinced a student? Learned men read books only to be confirmed in what they previously believed they knew.

Dr. Nott very justly, for he is by no means an infidel, repudiates the infidel portions of this book ("Types of Mankind"); and says he is responsible only for the scientifically anatomical and physiological contributions, and complains that his confrere, Gliddon, surreptitiously inserted, after the MS. had left his hands, into the body of the work his own sceptical theories. But Dr. Nott, like all persons found in suspicious company, unfortunately has to suffer for his companionship. He is at the head of the medical profession here; a South Carolinian, a man of fine intellect, agreeable manners, and with the finished air of a thorough-bred and born gentleman. I liked him very much the few moments I was in his society.

We left Mobile for Montgomery at the close of a lovely day, and in forty-six hours, after a pleasant sail up the romantic Alabama river, reached the stately capital of Alabama, Montgomery. It reminds me somewhat of Albany, in its location and elevated aspect. On board the boat was the venerable Bishop Cobbs, a large, heavy man, and advanced in years, but with a face full of the spirit of benevolence. He has all the simplicity of a pure child, united with the dignity of a Christian minister. He resides in this city, and was on his return to his family, from whom he had been some time absent, on his apostolic mission of "confirming the churches."

After a day agreeably spent in Montgomery, we took the cars for Augusta, Georgia. Our ride was full of interest. I was annoyed, the first hour or two after starting, at having left hanging on a projection of the toilet stand, in our room at the hotel, a valuable ring, which encircled many dearest associations within its golden periphery.

My husband made the fact known to the conductor, who
pledged himself that, on his return to Montgomery, in
the next train, he would go to the hotel and get it, and
forward it to Washington city by mail. As he would be
back to the hotel in three or four hours, I consoled myself with all that was left me, hope, and now hope to find
it in Washington, when we reach there, on Monday!
But I mistrust my hopes; and that the large eyes of the
Ethiopian maid, who waited on me, have discovered the
jewel, and that it last Sunday dazzled the eyes and won
the heart of some sable Cæsar or Pompey! What is
forgotten at hotels falls natural prizes into the hands of
the chambermaids, who begin their foray of discovery
about the room before the lady has reached the last stair
in her descent to the coach.

It is so provoking to leave (and, of course, *lose*) things
traveling. I never yet took a journey without such a
misfortune. It was either a book half read, and I dying
with interest to finish it—or a parasol, or a reticule, or
a glove, (and one can't easily replace *gloves*, traveling,)
or a veil, or a ring! If *all* ladies leave and lose in the
same way, lynx-eyed chambermaids in some hotels on
the great routes of travel can, in a year, obtain stock
enough to set up a *magazin des varieties*. I half-suspect
the minxes of *misplacing*, in order that travelers may
not *see* and so forget; but yet so misplace, that if they
are searched or asked for, they may easily be found, and
all seem to be "accidental."

My husband quietly says:

"Kate, it is your fault! You are careless, and don't
take proper care, I fear, of your things. Literary people are proverbially indifferent [a great scandal] about

mundane matters. If you don't forget and lose Harry
on the way I shall be content. It would not be so easy
to have him mailed on to Washington as your ring, and,
touching said ring, wife, I am very well satisfied you
will never see it again."

"But the conductor pledged his word—and was so desirous of serving me!"

"He may do *his* duty! but the landlord may not take
the trouble to go to the room for it. You know some
landlords care little about guests a hundred miles away
on a railroad. If he ask the servant, she will simply
say, 'Lor', massa, I neber seed no ring in de room!'
and so the matter will end!"

"I hope it will be found!" I said, quite hopelessly;
and I yet hope it will, for it was the *first* ring given to
me by my husband; and a woman values that gift above
all others.

The scenery increased in beauty as we flew on, and I
soon forgot my loss. As we entered Georgia, we saw
finer towns, richer agricultural districts, and more
mountainous scenery. We passed one mountain, like a
mighty pyramid, lifting its great head more than a thousand feet above the level country, and visible for hours
before and after we passed it. The city of Augusta is
a handsome metropolis, with broad streets, a beautiful
river (the Savannah), fine churches, but hotels indifferent. Every city should have a Tremont or Astor. These
hotels have rendered their like, necessities everywhere
else. Most of the hotels South, except in the large
cities, are overgrown inns or large taverns. Why, there
is as much difference between a "hotel" and a "tavern"
as between a "yacht" and a "fishing smack!"

We were pleased with Augusta, but made but a short stay. Columbia is the paradise city of the South. Here resides the distinguished novelist and poet, W. Gilmore Simms, to whom we had letters, but unfortunately he was absent. We regretted we could not pay our respects to a man of genius, who has conferred such distinction on the literature of the South, and of the whole Republic. One has to unpack and repack to stay in a place two or three days, and it is so much trouble to "dress" for a day's sojourn, that one often hurries forward, where it would be agreeable to linger for a few days, as it would have been here. On our way from Augusta we delayed a day to visit a friend's rice plantation, and thence took the cars to Charleston.

This is a city Southerners are very proud of, and with good cause. But it is the people more than the houses and "scenery" that makes Charleston so agreeable to strangers. The Battery is a charming promenade, but there are few handsome streets.

The residences have a respectable, substantial, home-like air about them, and universally are buried in the shade of tropical trees. The finest building is the Military Academy, erected for training South Carolina youth to the chivalrous accomplishment of arms. "Nullification" is a word fast growing into disuse, as it has ceased to have meaning. This State is as true to the Confederacy as the brightest star in our Federal standard.

The proposed superb monument to Mr. Calhoun (the Demosthenes of the New World) is not yet erected! Much as cotemporaries admire a mighty genius rising and culminating within their own horizon, they are never the people who raise the noblest mementoes to him! It is the succeeding generation which is the true echo of a great man's fame. Fifty years hence, Webster, Clay, Calhoun, will be more honored than they now are, and that age will erect to them the colossal plinths which the men of their own day neglect. Centuries after Cromwell and Joan d'Arc lived, even at this day, magnificent statues are erected to their fame.

As the glories that surround the heads of the noble Triumviri, "Calhoun, Webster, and Clay," increase in splendor with time, the higher and grander will rise the monuments that men will build up of stone and marble, to their mighty names! Whatever South Carolina does now in honor of her idol, the whole Republic will later do *more nobly* as a national tribute to his intellectual greatness; and what our mighty Inter-oceanic Republic will do, will later still be done by the whole civilized world! for the glory of the names of these three men, like those of Cicero, Demosthenes, and Caius Cæsar, shall be claimed as the common heritage of the round earth; and in Paris, London, Naples, Vienna, St. Petersburg, and Constantinople, statues and monuments shall likewise be erected to them; for godlike genius like theirs has no country, no other bounds than those of the globe's circumference.

We left Charleston with regret, after a day's sojourn, and part of which was spent in a visit to Sullivan's Island, an hour's sail down the harbor. This is a charming spot for air and bathing and beach-galloping, but its "grass" is sand. Several cultivated families pass the summer here, and the hotel is a fine structure;

it looks like a theatre turned *inside* out, with the galleries running all round its exterior. Commander Ingraham's family reside here. I felt like paying my respects to a man who has contributed abroad so much honor to our national name; but I let propriety subdue curiosity, and only satisfied myself with passing his house, hoping to get a glimpse of the " great man of his day."

The young and rich South Carolinians have a peculiar manner. They move about quietly, are self-possessed, silent or rather taciturn, love to sit and read, are well educated, polished in behavior, dress well, cultivate the moustache, affect small feet and white hands, and are somewhat dilettanti, but yet manly and well-informed; are lovers of the poets, have fine libraries, faultless riding horses and equipage, wear wide-awake hats, and love indolence and ease. Most of them have seen Europe, but prefer South Carolina! They are proud and aristocratic, and do not feel particularly honored to shake hands with a traveling lord, and in England are haughtier than England's nobles.

They are expert fencers, superb billiard-players, splendid riders when their indolence will let them put their blooded horses to their full flight; fond of hunting, unerring with the rifle, have practiced with the duelling pistol, and have knowledge of military matters! Under all their calm and indolent exterior, lies all the fire and energy of their prototype, Calhoun; and to insult them is infinitely perilous, though they never seek a quarrel. I think they are the most *finished* gentlemen (when they reach middle life) in the world! My husband says *he* will write for me (perhaps) a description of the ladies.

We leave this Inn direct for Washington! Shall I find my ring there?

Yours,

KATE.

LETTER LXIX.

MY DEAR MR. ———:

MY last letter was dated from "an old Inn" in Virginia. Since then we have come on to this city of "magnificent edifices;" for the old "magnificent distances" are superbly filled up with noble buildings.

I must say a word about that old Virginia Inn. It was the most comfortable "home," not to be in one's own, I ever dwelt in. It stood in a broad, green valley, many miles long, and from the Inn the country gently sloped to circumenclosing hills, wooded all over with massive masses of green forest. The vale itself was a valley of farms, large, and wealthy-looking, with hospitabl-eappearing farm-houses in the bosom of each, and each with its park of woodland; and the stage road to the Sulphur Springs, (the "Saratoga" of southern aristocracy) of a light brown color, and smooth as a race course, wound meanderingly through its bosom.

The Inn stood in the centre of this agricultural scene. It was a large, rambling, old Virginia mansion house, and once belonged to a family of the old *régime*, one of the proverbial (and in this case truly so) "FIRST FAMILIES" of Virginia. The original proprietor was a cavalier of Charles the Second, and was a large landholder under the crown. But the revolution, which de-

stroyed the stately law of primogeniture, divided and
subdivided among half a dozen equal heirs his regal do-
mains, until within the present generation, the once noble estate, diminished to two hundred acres and a hand-
ful of slaves, and the lands worn out, came into the hands
of the long baronial line of the Bodleys. The gentleman inheriting, finding his harvest would not maintain
the estate, and that money must be realized in some way
from his patrimony, had the good sense (refined and educated a Virginian as he is) to convert his paternal mansion into an "Inn." Situated on the great road of
travel, and offering from its imposing exterior, (ancient
yet respectable,) temptations to the comfort-loving traveler,
it soon became the aristocratic resort of touring Virgin-
ians, and the excellent proprietor (the descendant of a
lord become a land*lord*) has become independent.

Happy would many a Virginia gentleman of the "first
families" be, if he could turn his decaying mansion into
an Inn of profit! Numerous, very, are the old estates
gone to decay, scattered over the Old Dominion, wherein
genteel poverty dwells, with the prideful recollections of
ancestral name and honors. The improvident manner
in which the old Virginia proprietors wasted their lands
with the soil-consuming tobacco, has impoverished half
of their descendants. The present proprietors, unable
to maintain their aristocratic estate, part one after another with their family servants, whose price goes to
maintain what the wretched crops ought to do, or they
leave their barren heritages, and with their servants seek
the West or South, and there buying new land at government price, build up a new, young "Virginia family"
in Texas, Alabama, or Mississippi.

So necessary is the annual decimation of slaves by sale to support these old decayed families, that it has become a settled trade for men whose occupation is to buy slaves, to travel through the " Old Dominion," from estate to estate, to purchase the negroes that the necessities of these genteel families (who have nothing left of their ancestral glory, but the old mansion, half in ruins, and the wide, barren fields scarcely yielding bread) compel them to dispose of, whenever opportunity offers. The slave-buyer is seldom disappointed, however grand the exterior of the baronial looking house to which he rides up. Here he gets one, there another, and in a few weeks he enters Lynchburg, Alexandria, or Richmond with a hundred or more, whom the necessities of the first families have compelled to be sold. Hundreds of such buyers are ever traversing the state, and the markets of the South and West are almost wholly supplied with slaves, through the *res angusta domi*, in the Old Dominion.

From this view of the facts (and facts they certainly are), it would appear that Virginia is gradually coming to *free* farming and the slow abandonment of slave cultivature. As it is, slaves are raised here more as a *marketable* and money-returning commodity than for their productive labor.

It is one of the most beautiful states in the Union. Its citizens, with truth, boast a nobler ancestry from England's halls, than any other! Its character for intelligence, genius, hospitality, and refinement, is not surpassed anywhere. A Virginia gentleman (poor, and living on starved lands though he may be) *is the* gentleman of the age! Washington, her son, has, for ever-

more, ennobled her as the birth-place of heroes. She
has given to the Republic the majority of her presidents!
and to the National Legislative halls, the noblest minds
of our race. The grand scenery of her valleys, mountains, forests, and smiling fields, the diversity of her
climate, the noble character of her citizens, ought to
make her "the Paradise of America," as Sir Walter
Raleigh called it, and therefore named it, in honor of his
worshipful "Eve," (Queen Bess,) Virginia!

Our Inn is worthy of having for its host a descendant
of the chivalrous Borderleighs, (now modernized in spelling to Bodleys,) one of the old North of England nobles.
He loses none of his Virginia stateliness or self-respect
in playing Boniface. He retains his self-respect and is
therefore still a gentleman; and we feel that he is one.
His vast parlor is hung round with old portraits of his
Virginia and British ancestors. The bed-rooms look so
respectable with their black oak and carved furniture,
the panneled wainscotting, old-fashioned testers, and oval
mirrors, that one seems to be carried back into the days
of William and Mary. Some of the furniture is two hundred years old, and was brought over to Jamestown from
England. A beaufet is in the dining room, curiously
shaped and carved, which belonged to Sir Walter Raleigh,
he who sacrificed a cloak, hoping to get a crown. Queen
Bess was a terrible flirt! She had more joy in tyrann-
nizing over the noble hearts of the brave men about her,
than in reigning over her realm of England.

There is a portrait of her all begrimed with smoke, in
the sitting room, which our courteous and high born host
says, once belonged to the ancient Claiborne or Clayborn
family, a race of statesmen and soldiers.

From the Inn one has a delightful prospect of fields, woods, intervales, mountains, and a shining river. A broad lawn is before the house, across which is a smooth, half-moon shaped road, along which the stage-coach dashes up to the door.

Such a table as one has here! Never were travelers so banqueted. At breakfast, coffee and cream like liquid gold; six kinds of bread, each *hot,* as bread always is in the South, and all delicious with butter rich as honey; amber-colored honey also, with a fragrance as if gathered from the flowers that bloom on Hymettus! Then steaks, *so* juicy and flavorable; broiled chickens just delicately crisped and more delicately buttered; fresh fish from a pond, nicely browned to a turn; ham the tint of a blood peach; sliced bread and butter, and I know not what other delicacies. Our dinners are unapproachable by any city "Astor;" and for tea *such* sweetmeats, such blackberries and cream, such delicious bread!—but you will think I am an epicure truly if I go on. Suffice it to say that we remained there a week (for my husband is a quiet epicure in his way), and took stage for a town where we could strike the railroad.

We *flew* through Petersburg, paused to breathe in Richmond, which has flowing at its side a wild, rock-filled river of a hundred rapids, which we crossed at a dizzy height, looking down upon it from the car windows with that thrill of the nerves which gazing from a great height irresistibly causes.

We ascended the Potomac and passed Mount Vernon. I was previously told that when we came opposite to it, the bell of the boat would be struck thirteen times, not only in homage to the Great Deliverer of the "Thirteen

Republics," but also to notify passengers when the boat came near the political Mecca of Americans. But no bell sounded—no notice was taken by the steamer of the spot, which no British war-ship passes without lowering its colors and firing a salute. We Americans seem to be destitute of all suggestive imagination and reverential associations.

We shall remain in the Capital a few days, and thence hasten to New York to hit the steamer; for we reside the next two years abroad. This is the last Needle, therefore, you will receive from me, Mr. ——, and which must terminate forever our correspondence. The request of so many of my friends I feel must be cheerfully complied with; and while in Philadelphia, I shall make (if possible) arrangements with a publisher, to issue my poor writings in one or two volumes under the title of

"THE SUNNY SOUTH:

By Kate Conyngham."

Farewell.